LOVING
WITH
DEMONS

LOVING
WITH
DEMONS

Hana Mahmood

**ЯENE
GADE**

RENEGADE BOOKS

First published in Great Britain in 2024 by Renegade Books

1 3 5 7 9 10 8 6 4 2

Copyright © Hana Mahmood 2024

The moral right of the author has been asserted.

A CIP catalogue record for this book
is available from the British Library.

ISBN 978-0-349-13051-4

Typeset in Berling by M Rules
Printed and bound in Great Britain by Clays Ltd, Elcograf S.p.A

Papers used by Renegade Books are from well-managed forests
and other responsible sources.

Renegade Books
An imprint of Dialogue
Carmelite House
50 Victoria Embankment
London EC4Y 0DZ

www.dialoguebooks.co.uk

Dialogue, part of Little, Brown Book Group Limited,
an Hachette UK company.

This is a work of fiction. Although the author has drawn on her own experiences of trauma, this story is a novel, and should not be confused with an autobiography or memoir.

1

Smell fire and they know they smell us

Love, love, love.

All I ever wanted was to fall in love. Nothing more. Not money, not success, not fame. I was just aching for this passionate, indestructible, kill-for-each-other, die-without-each-other, forever-and-ever type love. The way I ached for it was as if I'd been mourning a piece of me that had been missing since birth. Like I was grieving him from a past life. Maybe he was from a past life . . .

Our souls grasped so tightly onto one another, like two lovers reuniting at the airport after years apart, a bouquet of flowers in his hand, while tears of joy roll down her cheek. Or like an army soldier surprising his only child on a visit home at Christmas, the child leaping into the arms where they feel most safe.

It was that same comfort, familiarity and fulfilment that

I felt when our souls first found a home in each other. I'm certain that there was always a space for him in my heart, from the day I was born, just waiting for him to find his way to it. And there was the same space in his, waiting for me. Whatever was created between us, it was *meant* to happen.

So you can imagine how hard it is to understand why fate had to play out the way it did. Why I constantly found myself lying in bed, physically choking with pain, hugging my weak knees into my chest, pillow soaked in tears, slowly rocking from side to side, shoulders painful from tensing, trying so hard to understand why. Why a love that burned so beautifully had also burned too violently, destroying all that we created.

Those flames burned so bright, exposing all the demons hiding in the darkest parts of us. Some had been hiding there for years. So when the light caused the demons to scatter out from the shadows, I loved him so much that I had no choice but to fight the demons with my fire, burn them, burn brighter and burn them again. If I let the demons win, I'd lose him. I refused to lose him.

But while I wasn't looking, he gave up fighting … His demons were too big, too strong, he even liked some of them. They were all he knew for so long; how could he know anything else? He liked feeding them. He'd dance with them and they'd hold him close. In their eyes he'd see a reflection of himself, fragile and unwilling to let go, a former version of the man he knew himself to be. Eventually, they'd take over him, masking him in their darkness, causing his fire to extinguish.

So I fought them for him. He really liked that. But they were too strong for me, and, after a while … he liked that too.

Him and his demons became one.

And oh, he just loved to fuck me with his demons. Leaving me broken, damaged and alone in the burned ashes of everything we fought so hard to create. Sometimes I bathe in those ashes. I grieve as I try to understand what I could've done differently. I try to understand why he couldn't fight for me like I did for him. Why he had to be so *fucking* weak.

But after three long years, 185 weeks, and 1296 days of battle, I had to leave and set out to heal. I had to accept that you can't love demons.

All I've got left are the memories, the lessons and a love story that could be felt by anybody who meets it.

Even if you've never even loved before.

Even if you've never felt love.

You'll feel love when you read this book.

You'll feel my love. A love that is pain.

2

How I became me

Immigrant parents.

Muslim family.

Pakistani culture.

In a very white part of Britain – Edinburgh, Scotland.

A mediaeval and grey little town home to extinct volcanoes, castles and over-priced townhouses built over the Old Town, which was abandoned due to the plague.

Expectations were always set high.

Angelic mother.

Noble father.

It was the least they deserved.

I was glad my sisters could meet those expectations to some degree. The versions of fulfilment my parents needed from us – based on the way they were wired to believe we should be – came from the conditioning of their own somewhat blessed but oppressed upbringings.

Their love was conditional, the condition being whether or

not I was a good Muslim girl. I understood from an early age that *love was conditional*, and that's why when I sought love, I searched for what felt most like home. It was all I'd known.

If only we could all understand just how much of our childhood manifests into our adult relationships. I'm sure then our parents would have loved us differently. One would at least hope.

I stand around five foot two inches in height, with long, dark brown hair down to my bum, warm brown skin, thick eyebrows. Growing up, I had a slim body that had some curves in flattering places, and was prepubescent-looking in others. I always wore a curious look on my face, though at the same time you could tell I was never really paying attention. I saw the world for what it was: a cruel place, so I daydreamed to escape those harsh realities.

I was probably rather odd. But fuck it, I wanted to be. I was hypersensitive to people's feelings around me, so much so that it almost felt like I could read their thoughts and I could feel everything that they felt. That same hypersensitivity led to me feeling constantly invalidated and rejected by my family and culture. I only felt happy expressing myself creatively, which isn't the most commendable of career choices in South Asian culture – the doctor, lawyer or housewife hustle would have been preferred, but all I was good at was creating.

I created stories in my mind like fine art, the picture so vivid, the dialogue so precise, all six of my senses being teased by a mere thought. I spent most of my pre-teen years day-dreaming about the things I wanted to experience. I found myself especially drawn to the things I wasn't allowed to do.

Anything that seemed taboo (but, quite frankly, *anything* was taboo).

I'd spend hours floating around my room, acting out scenes I wanted to manifest in life, having endless conversations in the mirror. Fantasising about the things I'd do if I had the freedom I craved so badly. If I could make those dreams come true.

I was shaped too differently – too 'weird', too bright to fit into the small, dark box my parents so lovingly built for me. Constantly being told to lower my tone, that my jokes were inappropriate or that I wasn't as timid as a Pakistani girl should be.

'You're just too much, Livia Dalia!'

My lust for life wasn't always a good thing ... My curiosity eventually became desperation and that desperation eventually led to depression. I ended up doing what every child under strict and uncompromising rules does – I rebelled three times as hard. Then the lack of guidance when I did manage to lie or sneak my way into a taste of freedom drove me to lengths that even my friends with carefree parents didn't go.

But I wasn't wild ... I was alive! I wanted so badly to feel, to live all the shit I saw on TV and in films, all the stuff I heard my friends do, or didn't do, everything I'd acted out in my mirror, the things I'd impregnated my mind with. I wanted to birth it all.

I couldn't live in this cage and watch everyone *else* have fun, watch everyone else feel it. I had felt those things in my mind already, I *had* to make them real. So I did, and no matter how far my imagination took me, I returned unharmed each time – well, physically anyway ...

But even with all the partying and bad decisions carrying me through my teens, I still found myself lusting over the simple things my friends had, things I had to accept I'd never have. They were all white and, specifically, rich.

My parents didn't want me to suffer the racism they were subjected to by going to state school as immigrants. My mum had been left with a scar next to her left eye after a racially motivated attack – a stone was thrown at her face while hanging out the washing as a child. So we were sent to private school instead, even though we couldn't afford it, where, ironically, the microaggressions and passive aggressive discrimination felt even worse than taking a rock to the eye.

But it wasn't their big homes and fancy clothes I envied (at least not entirely), it was the simple things, like being able to tell my mum when I had a crush on a boy, or even better, when I got hurt by one. I remember telling all my friends how lucky they were . . . how much I wished I had what they had. I longed for a relationship with my mother where I could talk about what seemed like the most important thing in the world to me. *Love*.

To be quite honest, I spent the last of my teenage years being subjected to racial abuse by pretty much all my peers – whether they said it behind my back, to my face, or simply watched it happen and didn't stick up for me. They were all just as bad to me. I guess the white kids of Edinburgh just really didn't like a brown girl hanging around their scene. Some made jokes about my father being a terrorist, or told me to go back to 'my country'. Some thought I was different, 'weird' and not narrow-minded enough for that little city.

Most of them never even gave me a chance. I was simply too brown for them.

At twenty years old, I finally left.

It was spring when I claimed liberation, moving out of my parents' house and into the great, colourful mixing pot of opportunity: London. I had no idea where my dreams were taking me this time, but I guess they were taking me *exactly* where I had hoped.

3

A beautiful, filthy Judas named fate

Freedom felt like taking that first ecstasy pill back when I was sixteen. Thousands of shiny orbs landing on the surface of your skin, absorbing into your bloodstream and causing you to vibrate pure love through each and every vein in your body. Seeing everything in full colour for the first time, with gratitude for every shade, every hue. It was euphoric.

I rented a few rooms in different parts of London and worked at Fallgirl Casino. Fallgirl promised a glamorous first step into working in the nightlife scene. In reality, it was the opposite. As soon as you stepped through the luxuriously decorated doors of the world's most exclusive members-only casino and into the staff area, you were faced with cheaply painted baby pink walls – that dull sort of paint they use in primary school or in children's hospitals. You were then met with underpaid, overworked and unhappy 'Kittys' (girls in kitty costumes and tights) who wanted nothing more than to take off their uncomfortable heels to relieve last week's blisters and unzip the rib-crushing corsets fitted by the 24/7 onsite seamstress.

I wasn't in costume yet. For four months I'd be in the mandatory, probationary below-the-knee, cheap, Primark-style black dress, which felt like a cross between punishment and a justification for the girls in costume to look down on my amateur status.

I was called into the head office in my black dress around two months into my stint at Fallgirl, and sat next to Ruby, the girl I'd platonically fallen in love with. Ruby wasn't like any of the other girls (cliché, I know).

Our bond first formed at a work night out. We ended up at an afterparty, one that provided an invitation to try a certain white substance. From the roster of beautiful women working at Fallgirl who were offered the white substance, *of course* it was the two northerners who decided to take up the offer.

That night I had no idea I had just met my soulmate. A tall, caramel-skinned, part Mancunian-part Jamaican. An always glowing, usually smiling angel who moved with the most attitude and firmness in her demeanour, whose aura oozed of her stupendously warm and golden heart. She became my rock, the earthy Taurus that kept my slippery Pisces head above deep waters. I still don't think I'd be here without her, telling this story today ... and I really mean that.

There were a number of times we would, as young women new to the big city, be partying three times a week, making some of the best memories of our young adult lives but also meeting bizarre people with strange intentions. We were lucky that we learned and grew together. From men trying to take advantage of drunk women, to girls changing their entire attitude based on how many followers we had on social media, we quickly learned the painful truth of how shitty humans can be in this wild generation.

Sometimes we'd take a pause from our fast London life.

'Do you ever think everyone is just like, weird?' Ruby would ask in her strong Mancunian accent.

'Yeah, no I really do,' I'd respond with complete certainty. *And I did.*

Then we'd fall back to the same happy realisation: 'I'm so glad I've got you,' we'd say, smiling back at each other.

Ruby and I made that big, lonely and unusual city feel as warm and familiar as the smaller cities we ran from. We moved into our own apartment together. We were so close we even shared a bed, even though we had our own rooms. But this love stayed platonic. Nope, she's not the one who injured my soul.

I still remember the nights I'd pray to God in bed and thank Him for Ruby. I really couldn't believe the luck I'd struck in a friendship as beautiful and safe as ours. Growing up, I hadn't developed a great judge of character or much self-esteem, so I was often trapped in friendships with toxic girls who treated me like a doormat. You know, the girls your mum would tell you not to hang out with. Ruby was the opposite of those – and my mum loves her. Everyone loves Ruby.

But, in that office back at Fallgirl Casino, next to Ruby, our boss declared, 'One of you is going to be fired today. You can't work together – the constant laughing and distracting does not align with the Fallgirl code of conduct . . .'

Even that shitty casino couldn't handle the spark between us.

I left almost straight away; shit, I might have even skipped out ... I hated that miserable place. I started working freelance to make the most of the boring degree I'd studied to keep my parents happy – Marketing.

Somewhere between teaching my local nail salon how to post on Instagram, creating the best memories with my Ruby, almost having spiritual orgasms in being emancipated from my childhood, and consuming more alcohol than I'd ever had, I met him.

It was by mistake, almost.

Lost in a blur of drunken nights, I ended up in a taxi I quite frankly shouldn't have been in with some rougher-than-they-needed-to-look boys eyeing up the brown skin I had learned to love again since being in the much more diverse city of London.

And while I was chatting away to one of them, there *you* were ...

Enter Nero.

Sitting in the middle row of the seven-seater, looking back at me, hood up, dark, smooth skin and with a peculiar look on his curious-ass face. With those big, black-as-hell, intense eyes on a sharp, structured face, his strong London accent matched his croaky voice that sounded like he had chain-smoked forty cigarettes in just as many minutes (which, I later learned, he sometimes had).

He turned around to me and asked, almost offended, 'Where the fuck is that accent from?'

We spent the rest of the night at some party in a high-rise council estate in East London, him staring at me from across the room like I was an undiscovered species that had fallen right in front of him at the very moment he was searching for his prey.

I remember exactly what I wore that night. Red Mac lipstick in the shade Ruby Woo. Gold Nike Air Max 97 trainers. White lace-trim cycling shorts and a white lace bralette, with an oversized Levi denim jacket thrown on top to justify my revealing outfit choice in the cold and wet British weather.

I was an uber-friendly, fearless and charismatic ball of energy at this time. I rolled around the room, my confidence and energy renewed after moving to London. I was always so ... excited by fucking everything, down to try fucking everything. I could feel people's attraction towards that and towards me. But the way he pursued me was fatal.

He began to rap, trying to impress me in front of the room.

He was *an Alpha male.* Or at least, he would have died on that hill to make it look like he was.

After intense stares and some painful small talk, we drank more liquor and quickly progressed to speaking about the meaning of life and alien conspiracy theories until the sun rose. I loved that I could impress him with my knowledge, and he loved that I loved that too.

Before I made my exit around a summery and bright 6 a.m., he handed me his phone.

It was like he just expected me to put my number in.

And I did.

The confidence was refreshing.

He knew what he wanted, I could feel it.

And once he'd envisioned it in his head, he knew he had to have it too.

So just like you, there was me.

4

How he became him

Somewhere in the dull, run-down parts of busy Clapham Junction, south west London, where grey skies loom in every shade of grey, where high-rise estates tower over the busy, gentrified high street filled with niche coffee shops, lived a boy. Too mischievous for his own spirit, addicted to rebelling; therefore, addicted to drugs . . . quite frankly, addicted to anything that was prohibited at all. London-born, Monaco-raised, and of Senegalese descent, there was Nero.

He stood at almost six-foot tall, slim with a skinny pack, usually balancing a cigarette in the corner of his lips. He was covered in random, accidental tattoos like daggers, guns, skulls and even Jesus smoking a blunt on the cross; scars from picking his chicken pox as a child, gaps in between his huge, taunting smile.

He was a typical *bad boy*. Growing up, Nero loved to rob people, steal from shops and even got himself a blade to carry around in an all-black, grey or uniform blue Nike tracksuit.

Nero never saw eye-to-eye with his mother. She didn't like his drug use nor his sporadic selling of weed for a few extra quid here and there, so she often chucked him out, locked the door and gave him that tough-love parenting. A conditional love just like my upbringing, but he simply didn't like being told what to do, by anyone.

This made Nero's behaviour even worse. He resorted to sofa surfing, and maybe even slept rough once or twice, but he almost always charmed his way into having food to eat and a roof over his head . . . just about.

But he wasn't always the typical bad boy either, because unlike his other bad-minded, drugged-up, shitty, scatty, good-for-nothing friends, Nero was loud, brave, flamboyant and unique. His creativity was beyond measure. He wasn't like anyone else you'd ever met. The way he carried himself around a room, you'd think he was the main character at a number one, award-winning Broadway show. *The Nero Show*.

He was incredibly switched on – something about the way he looked at you told you he was more intelligent than you. He had an intense glare that was so confident it could force vulnerability on anyone whose eyes he looked into. He made you feel nervous: lying-to-border-police-while-smuggling-drugs-in-your-suitcase type of nervous.

He made you feel like you were lying, like he had just *caught you in a lie*. Sometimes the lie he was uncovering was who you *wished* to be perceived as. That was never going to work with Nero; he had a talent for seeing everyone for who they really were, way beneath the façade.

He loved to draw. Growing up, he drew all over his bed-room walls: pirate ships and skulls, just like a true villain. He learned all the instruments he could, from the guitar to piano, and his handwriting was immaculate.

Nero truly loved art, and every form of it … that boy fucking loved to create.

He began training as a street dancer, until someone commented on how *uncool* they thought that was (everything Nero did just *had* to be cool, it was the true Aquarius in him). Shortly after, he dropped dance and turned his sights to being a hip-hop artist and singer – or whatever the hell that emotion-provoking noise he created so naturally with his raspy, croaky voice was.

He never did well at school, not because he was necessarily bad at it, but because he was governed by the one thing I found consistent all the time I knew him: *a God complex*. This meant that he could not and would not take direction, authority or advice from *anyone*. In fact, anything you told him to *not* do, he'd do *EVEN* harder.

Nero was insecure in himself and the unstable and unpromising path he'd taken in life, always feeling sold short since *he* knew he had all this magic inside of him that he felt nobody else could see. His defence mechanism forbade him from being able to listen to people telling him what to do, or even offering mere advice, without it attacking his fragile, blown-the-fuck-up ego. In his mind, he was special and demanded respect for it. How *dare* someone else tell HIM what to do.

Nero's God complex eventually led him to live with so much hate and resentment that it drove him to seek revenge on the world for not giving him the life he felt he so *badly* deserved. Like some sick, spiritual warfare, hate grew from feeling too caged in life, from watching others with money, their happy families, the pussy and the clout, enjoying the heights he so badly wanted to reach.

He would sit in rooms with his 'friends' – who used his desperation when he was broke against him – and they would take the opportunity to belittle him. He watched them live what seemed to him to be such privileged and undeserving lives.

He listened to Drake on repeat, nodding along with the lyrics of a multi-millionaire music legend, as if he resonated with the hardships that came from a life like that. He knew what life he was going to live, and he was coming for revenge on everyone who didn't believe in his power. He had to get there JUST to rub the dirt he grew from in each of their faces.

Revenge on every teacher who doubted his potential.

On every friend who mocked his unfortunate, self-inflicted situations.

On every girl who wasn't interested in him or was out of his league.

On his mother, who mocked his decisions and goals and offered a love so cold and conditional.

Nero used his visual resourcefulness and ability to feel deeply, combined with his narcissistic rage and personal vengeance, to manifest all the things he had acted out in his head. It was almost as though his delusions of grandeur helped him get to where he wanted to be by shifting his reality.

Except, while Nero was out for a fulfilling, artistic and long-standing revenge to fulfil his ego, I was looking to fulfil my dreams and delve into the realms of true love that I also felt I deserved. While I was willing to give everything for that goal, he was so much more than willing to take.

Delusions of grandeur

A psychological term to describe an individual who has a persistent belief in their own grandiosity.

They might believe that they have a special destiny that makes them more special and deserving than others, that they are gifted with the fate of fame, power or success, that God or a chosen entity has chosen them as his favourite, that they are working through them or for them at all times, rather than anyone else around them.

5

New beginnings, old friends and planned hangovers

Not long after I first met Nero, Ruby and I moved in together. I could hardly believe that we'd found an apartment building so perfect for us: bang in the centre of Aldgate East, close to the hustle and bustle of the city's busiest business district – therefore surrounded by loads of cool restaurants and bars – and only a nine-minute tube journey into Central London. A rare find.

We both shrieked when the moody estate agent rushed out the door after handing us the keys, jumping around the room in celebration.

'He was such a vibe kill, like honestly, we were ten minutes late – it's not that deep,' Ruby said, as she stood staring out of my bedroom window. We were on the ground floor, which had a view directly onto the lagoon-like pond in the middle of a square, with wooden walkways connecting the flats and fountains providing a peaceful backdrop to the summery day.

'We were like twenty minutes late,' I laughed back at her.

'An extra ten whole minutes – shoot me now why don't you!' she exclaimed as she used two fingers to mime shooting herself dead onto the bed next to me.

Rudy made most things a joke, which was such a beautiful quality to have, especially in stressful situations. 'It's not that deep' was her go-to phrase, which relieved me since to me it felt like everything was, in fact, really that deep.

Sometimes I would zone out of conversations with Ruby and become focused on how light and witty her nature was, how freeing it was to have a perspective that was so unattached ... I couldn't help but wish I had met her sooner in life; so many times I had been drowning, I knew she would've brought me back to shore.

I quickly realised how everyone was also fascinated by how unique Ruby was, especially when my friend from back home, Juno, came down for our flat-warming party that weekend.

Juno was special to me. We'd grown up together and she was one of the only friends who really made me feel understood in those tough teenage years.

I think it was a mixture of the fact that she was always that little bit more unstable than me ... but also her incredible intelligence and acceptance of people. Her airy but profoundly carefree take on life always reminded me that it was okay to feel absolutely fucking everything as long as you remembered to release it in the end, to go with the flow. Through all her battles, she somehow seemed so unburdened. She wore that freedom so beautifully, in a way that only she could.

She had short, shaggy brown hair, and wore baggy boys' clothes three times too big for her. Everything about Juno was original; the things she pulled off nobody else could – and trust me, many people tried to copy her. She was a muse, a musician, a star, and the coolest bitch in every room she blessed by choosing to be in.

I smiled, watching the two of them bond in fits of laughter. All sounds around me went mute, overtaken by feelings of gratitude. 'Could this finally be my time to be as free as everyone I've observed from inside this cage?' I asked myself.

You know it is, Livia.

Ruby and Juno each took a shot of tequila at the kitchen counter.

Ruby clenched her face. 'Nobody enjoys doing this, you can't convince me anybody enjoys this,' she cried as she ran over to the sink, covering her mouth.

Juno instantly poured another shot, spilling it over the counter and letting it drip down her neck as she tipped it down her throat effortlessly, releasing a deep 'AHH!' with excitement and shaking it off like a cat.

'Where do you think you're going? Get your ass over here, Livia, look at your crib! We dreamed of times like this as babies, we're celebrating! Get this shot down you right now!' Juno shouted over to me as I sat on the sofa, attempting to figure out the sound system before the rest of our guests arrived.

'Yeah, Livia, you're not getting away with this, you have to suffer too,' Ruby said, taking the bottle of Patrón out of Juno's hand and filling the shot glass to the top.

I stared at the shot, hesitating because I knew what was to come.

'You *know* I'm gonna vom,' I said, making a sorry face, taking the shot glass of clear battery acid out of her hand.

'Good! Then you know you're doing it right!' Juno said laughing.

'Here, we'll do another one with you,' Ruby declared as she poured them both another one.

I rolled my eyes and then said a quick cheers – it was time to commit to the hangover that was to come, I figured.

'To two of my favourite people ever finally meeting each other, I love you guys soooo much,' I yelled.

Juno wrapped her arm around Ruby, 'And we love you!'

'Cheers!' said Ruby.

We all downed our shots as I fanned my watery eyes with my hands, attempting not to ruin my eyeliner.

Ruby ran back over to the sink. 'Nah, whoever invented Patrón is sick in the head, mate!'

A few hours later, Ruby was singing her heart out to 'Ride' by Lana Del Rey in the living room with some of the girls from Fallgirl, while Juno was chatting up a girl on the sofa. She'd already kissed her best friend earlier in the night, but in true Juno fashion, she'd somehow got away with it.

I answered the door, expecting it to be the top-up of alcohol we'd ordered at the unintelligent time of 2 a.m., swinging the door open a little too hard from being super tipsy. The face I saw standing in front of me sent a pleasant shock through me.

'Shay!' I let out, leaping into his arms. He stank of after-shave. 'Mmm, is that Tom Ford, you fancy boy?'

'It's the smell of someone who's travelled six hours to see you,' he replied.

'Shut up? What even happened with your train? I didn't even know if you were going to make it!'

But before he could explain, Juno spotted him as she entered the hall, ushering him into the kitchen for a drink.

Shay was one of my oldest friends from back home. We'd been in each other's lives since we were just fourteen. He was one of the only other South Asian kids in our circle, so he always felt like home.

He was tall and muscular with broad shoulders, contrasting with his innocent baby brown and hazel eyes and super thick eyelashes. Everything about Shay was masculine, but not in an intimidating way, more in an emotionally intelligent way, a make-you-feel-safe way. He'd been raised by a single mother, he had five sisters, and you could tell.

Though I had had many bad experiences with friends in Scotland, the people I kept around, I kept around for a reason. At our little soirée to celebrate the new house, I felt so grateful to call this collective of humans my friends, the best pick of the bunch.

I'd somehow managed to jump out of that prison window back home and land on my feet right here in London. I sat on our wooden porch by the lagoon outside, just staring out at the water, reflecting on how lucky I felt.

'Livia, London's a lot better than Scotland, eh?' Shay said, sitting down on the cushion next to me, beer in hand. We hadn't got chairs and a table for our decking yet, but the cushions felt more intimate anyway.

Music from inside blared out onto the square from behind us but our neighbours seemingly didn't mind; each had their own gatherings going on from their balconies above, one of the perks of living in a city that almost never sleeps.

I smiled at Shay. 'I'm so happy you came, thank you for ... coming.' *I should really stop trying to sound meaningful when drunk.*

'It's cool, Livia, anything for you.'

There was a pause, that for some reason felt a little awkward for a sec—

'You're family,' he quickly added.

I swallowed hard before addressing the elephant in the room.

'How is he?'

Shay took a deep sigh. 'I don't know man, sometimes he can seem fine but you just know he's not. He's just different, isn't he ... It's kind of like the new normal though as time goes on.'

My heart sank, capsized.

'Do you guys speak at all?' Shay asked.

'He said he was really proud and sent me a sweet message when I moved here. Not sure if that was just because he knew I'd finally get off his back and stop trying to help ...' I gently laughed, pathetically.

Shay smiled. 'Nah, he really loved you, he always will.'

'I don't know ... Sometimes I feel like he hates me,' I said.

'Nah Livz, he's my best friend, I know he loved you.'

Whether he was just saying that to make me feel better or because it was true, I didn't care. It made me feel closer to him, made him feel real again.

Josh

I'd only ever been in love once before. My only other relationship. My first love.

Joshua Alexander. And let me tell you all about him.

When I think of my first love, all I can feel is the most precious simplicity that life can never offer again. Sitting on the upper deck of a bus, one earphone in each, listening to A Tribe Called Quest, holding hands as we both felt a little disappointed that my stop was coming up, hoping we'd at least get to the best part of the song before it was time to get off. Then Josh would kiss me goodbye at my bus stop and cross over to the other side of the road, where he'd take the bus back for the entirety of the route until it reached the other side of the small city we both lived in.

Josh was tall, with skin so pale his cheeks would get that beautiful natural blush when he was flustered or nervous, which was all the time. He had thick dark hair he wore swept back, with these big, deep chocolate sanpaku eyes and a huge Adam's apple that gave him a voice so deep I used to joke that it made the ground rumble. He genuinely looked like an angel.

We spent most days lying in his single bed together, legs tangled and foreheads almost touching. He didn't have a smartphone or a TV in his bedroom, so we'd just lie there and talk; sometimes we stared into each other. I can't quite describe that stare; it was like an exchange of souls. If you weren't in love, you might laugh or look away, but if you were in love, you'd stay hooked, lost in this electric current binding you closer and closer.

Josh wasn't like other boys at eighteen. He was the underdog; his presence didn't beg to be noticed. He was an artist whose paintings resembled real life and people adored him for his wit and blunt jokes. His energy was so hesitant and delicate – he thought a lot before he spoke, before he acted, even before he breathed.

That was Josh's problem: he thought too much. Too, too much.

At the time, I resembled a pretty trainwreck. I was seventeen and had practically based my entire personality on Effy from *Skins*. I was depressed and reckless. Josh was my escape and my sanctuary; Josh was my *home*. He was the only person who understood me, and the first boy to make me feel beautiful.

I remember the first time I cried in front of Josh. I was crying because I'd had enough of living with my parents. As I poured my heart out to him about my pain, I turned to him, only to see a single teardrop rolling down his cheek.

I'll never forget the thought that crossed my mind then and every day since. *How could somebody love me so much?* And he did, oh he did so very much.

I remember our very first date; we went to the cinema to see *Fast & Furious 7*. I noticed how his bottom lip would tremble a little in between his responses in the queue for popcorn, as he was so anxious. In the cinema I contemplated the entire time if I should take his hand. A voice in my head was telling me to just do it as I kept side-eying his hands resting there by the drink holder. When I finally got the courage and did, he glanced at me as we both locked eyes. He winked to kill the awkwardness and thank God he did, because we both burst out laughing, while he stayed holding my hand tightly.

Josh and I loved to dance, so in our one year of being together, we'd attend raves almost every weekend. We had a good mixed friend group that featured Shay. All of us high on molly, we'd dance under the strobes as Josh's long arms would wrap around me and spin me round. The way he looked at me was so tender, like he would make the world stop if I just told him I needed more time.

In 2015, we attended one of the largest music festivals in the world towards the end of summer. Josh had taken some dodgy pills that sent him to the medical tent where I sat by him, trying to calm him down. Then he disappeared.

He experienced drug-induced psychosis and never quite recovered.

Once I returned to Edinburgh the day after Josh had made the journey back all by himself, running away from us all and tripping for 20 hours straight, he wasn't Josh anymore.

He looked like Josh, he sounded like Josh, but he wasn't Josh.

Just like that.

My home vanished.

6

Brain sex

Circa 2017 I remember lying on the sofa with Ruby, watching *The Apprentice.* We'd ordered the perfect Chinese takeaway: salt and pepper chips, curry sauce, egg fried rice, chicken chow mein, Szechuan chilli chicken, prawn crackers and sesame prawn toast. For some reason, when it comes to the delicacy that is English (inauthentic) Chinese food, British people go overboard with their selections. But it was just so hard not to, the intensity of each flavour complemented the others so well. Everything shovelled onto a cracker, laying that cracker onto your moist tongue as it softens and the sauces land on your taste buds, releasing the same orgasmic hormones in your brain as from— My phone rang.

It was Nero calling for the fourth time that week, interrupting my Beijing banquet to ask if I wanted to hang out with him. At this point we were ... friends. I liked his energy. I liked him. A lot.

We spoke on the phone for hours and he was always so interested in everything I had to say.

I wish I knew at this point that he wasn't listening; he was micro-analysing everything about me.

I gave him yet another excuse about why I didn't want to hang out one-on-one. I knew what his intentions were and the truth is, I just wanted to party! I wasn't interested in pursuing him romantically. But by this point, he was persistent, ruthless and had already got me in his sights.

That was the last straw for him. He spat out his dummy and began throwing a tantrum. 'I don't even like Insta girls', he told me, then proceeded to block me. I didn't feel much – did having more Instagram followers than him make me an 'Insta girl'? I didn't really care. I hypothetically shrugged my shoulders, told Ruby, who also shrugged hers, and then turned my attention back to Lord Alan Sugar.

A few weeks later, he unblocked me and invited me to his Halloween party as if nothing had ever happened.

'I still haven't heard your apology?' I remember asking, which he eventually gave in the most insincere and somehow condescending way. So I declined the invitation.

A few days later, I went out with a group of girls I'd met in London to some singer's book launch party in Mayfair. I invited him this time as well. The girls were annoying and I felt left out from their synchronised dance moves, so I needed some company.

I spent the time before he arrived flirting with the cocktails at a free bar and was most definitely shit-faced by the time he arrived. I walked right up to him and kissed him. Maybe he had been negotiating with dark forces to grant him his wish when my spirit was most vulnerable. Maybe I was desperate for attention after feeling deprived of it, or maybe it was just fate.

Whatever it was, it worked out in his favour. We snuck out from the event and Nero's moody friend drove us halfway towards his house across town, leaving us in the streets because he wanted to sleep off his sorrows. He was in a bad mood because he didn't have a girl to go home with.

I remember thinking *what a loser. My* Ruby could never.

Nero looked embarrassed, scrambling for his phone and calling his flatmate to book us an Uber. I remember kissing him in the middle of the road to ease his nerves and let him know that he shouldn't find it embarrassing that I was still with him. It wasn't his fault that his friend sucked.

Straight out of the Uber and into the lift to the twenty-second floor, Nero kissed my neck as I heard the lift ding and we headed towards his apartment. We had sex on the sofa. We had sex in the bed. We had sex on the floor. We had sex in the bathroom, over the sink and in the shower.

The next morning, I woke up feeling doubtful over my drunk actions. Nero made sure to ease my nerves, with lots of 'You okay?'s and reassuring smiles.

He put some food in the oven and we lay on the sofa. His place was empty. His flatmates had both gone to visit their parents. I sat on top of him so that we were facing each other, fingers interlocked. I would describe this as the moment he fell in love with me. I think this is when I fell in love with him, too.

We returned to our conversation about conspiracy theories from the party on the night we'd met. I have this tendency to visualise and feel everything I'm saying so I become super animated, hands waving in the air, eyes lit up with belief and passion, slightly bordering on mad scientist. He watched me, smiling a little, like he was in awe of my knowledge, my quirky perception of life. I realise now that it was rather a look of love. There was an invasion going on in his heart, and the uncertainty on his face was the unfamiliarity of this new feeling. His heart was yearning to surrender.

We spoke for hours, back and forth, laughing, touching, debating and smiling, kissing and cuddling, meshing, connecting. I could feel everything he could.

'I feel like our minds just got married,' Nero said. 'It's like playing a match of badminton with our brains ... We need a word for it.'

So we gave that marriage of the minds a name, a meaning: brain sex.

We bounced off each other, sharing all our dreams, getting lost in our wildest fantasies and philosophies while floating on clouds that lifted us higher and higher. Eyes locked, souls touching, it was like a bright white cord of static energy connected our foreheads, encouraging each other to delve deeper and deeper into our imaginations. So far from reality, so present in the now.

We spoke about everything. He told me about his insecurities, the time where he approached a huge hip-hop artist who had been his idol as a child, after all his friends egged him on. How he'd finally plucked up the courage to walk over and ask if he wanted to hear his tape, and how the artist had just bluntly said no. We laughed but he embraced how that moment gave him more drive, more motivation.

I told him about the racism I'd experienced growing up. The bad decisions I'd made. The bad friends before Ruby. We spoke about our darkest nights, deepest secrets, our traumas and our families. Our greatest desire – to be free, to be great. In each session of brain sex, the realisations we had seemed incomprehensible to the average mind. Our minds and souls were attracted like magnets. This was more than a regular connection. This was love, even if neither of us knew it yet.

We had brain sex every night after that until the early hours, when we'd hear the 7 a.m.-start builders begin maintenance outside. Later, we'd wake up stupidly sleep deprived and instantly start having brain sex again. We just had so much to fucking talk about. Or at least I did, but he so loved to listen. I hadn't even left and gone home yet – I stayed for five whole days after that first night – even if he'd hide it behind telling me I 'might as well stay' or 'it's long to go all the way East now'.

You wanted me to.

Every visit after that was a minimum of three days to a week, with a five day or so break between.

You really wanted me to.

We didn't just have brain sex excessively. The amount of physical attraction between us was plausible and laughable at the same time.

Any opportunity we got, you were inside me, whether we ran into each other in the toilet during one of his house parties, or when there were a bunch of people hungover watching a movie on the sofa, and we felt like being sneaky, secretly fucking under the blanket beside them.

We didn't care what anyone thought about us; we were

wild and we were free, but trust me, they thought a lot. His friends thought a lot.

Nero's house was like a party penthouse in west London, a free for all. Every day we were surrounded by his friends, and every night there were gatherings or parties. The concierge hated us. His friends watched us as we ran around the house, in our own childish utopia, play-fighting on the bean bags. They watched us kissing, hugging, holding one another, dancing, singing lyrics passionately to each other, finishing each other's sentences during drinking games, times where I'd say something witty and he'd let out 'this is why I love her'. *I loved those moments.*

When a tattoo artist came round to the house, they watched him choose my suggestion for his neck tattoo: 'strange'. His gang watched him invite me everywhere, over and over again. They watched him run into me at events and take me home, completely forgetting about the girl he came with. There were times when his boys purposefully invited other girls around, ones he may have shown interest in in the past. To their disbelief, he'd proudly hold me in his lap, kissing my cheek, never entertaining the gestures.

They watched him pour me a drink whenever he got himself one, me writing lyrics by his side as he recorded, him using them, us sharing cigarettes, the way I cooked his food, me plating his food, us sharing that plate of food, him saving me the last chicken wing ...

They watched us fall in love.

They fucking hated it.

7

Gang shit

Nero hadn't long signed a record deal and things were really changing for him. His music was starting to blow. Really blow.

This meant things were changing for his friends too. They were allowed VIP tables in places they'd never even dreamed of getting into, given free clothes from brands they'd never been able to afford, and, after Nero got his own apartment courtesy of his label and moved in his two closest friends, Kai and Ziggy, they had a bachelor pad to invite over women they'd never dreamed they'd meet. The game of clout was taking off. Every young boy's dream.

So of course they didn't like me. What was I besides a cock-block to this lifestyle they were hard for? Nero was the star and that meant that if he wasn't single and on some fuck-boy shit, there would be limitations to the lifestyle. Limitations to the girls they could bring to the parties. Limitations to the free weed they could smoke all day, baking off on his sofa because it simply had a nicer view than the bedrooms in their mothers' homes they never planned on moving out of.

I remember when Mika, the one who didn't give us a lift all the way home because he was butthurt from the lack of vagina in his life, showed up at Nero's house and tried to fight him, saying Nero owed him money. How his gang sat around in a circle with a whiteboard, debating whether to chuck him out of the group for his behaviour.

Everyone wanted Mika out, every single person.

No one managed to show that he had any value as a friend. Even I agreed. I mean, I just believed in true friendship and loyalty and Mika, well, he hadn't been acting as a friend.

Listening to the debate around the whiteboard, it was very clear to me that Mika was a lousy friend. It was a battle of toxic masculinity in the House of Commons of west London, each shouting over the other, waiting to be validated by the majority.

But Nero didn't want to kick him out. He explained his theory to the room, how he'd rather make him his bitch for a 'long revenge'. Since Mika wanted to be a hip-hop artist too, Nero knew it was in his best interests to fold, and my Lord he did. Just as he wanted, Mika became his bitch.

Nero did that a lot. He put his friends in positions, on a payroll, and then passive aggressively threatened to take them away if they upset him. Eventually, after his ego, bank, body count and following grew, anything could upset Nero. In his opinion, he deserved even more respect than ever before.

Some of the boys found it hard to make the switch from friend to follower. The gang had a hell of a lot of pride. Lord knows where the fuck it came from. Especially one of the boys, Blake. He'd housed Nero when he was homeless and felt that he owed him something, everything. He challenged Nero's every idea, every notion. It was a battle of egos with an audience. A fiery Aries neck-to-neck with a cold-as-ice Aquarius. He didn't feel insecure in his position as Nero's DJ and producer, and he refused to submit to him.

Blake couldn't stand to see Nero's stalk grow from beneath him to the skies above, Nero's petals shadowing over him. Maybe that's why Blake disliked me so much too. He was the only one who made it obvious. Any time I so much as spoke, Blake would challenge me too, throw shade, make me feel uncomfortable or intimidate me. Blake was intimidated *by me*. We were a mirror of his insecurities. Watching the boy he thought he owned change and truly love someone made Blake feel small. Maybe he wanted that real love too, but he was too caught up in his own self-hating, pessimistic rage to see why nothing was working out for his angry, stubborn ass.

It was beyond me that while I was appreciating Ruby and our wonderful friendship, one that I treasured and protected with all my being, why Nero would want to have such fake friends around him. Why did he seek such hateful and opportunistic energy? Was he really keeping them all around for control, for revenge? To prove them all wrong? An eye for all their necks?

The only friends that Nero seemed to genuinely value and love were Kai and Ziggy, the boys who he chose to move into his new home. Kai was a tall, lanky, friendly, classic class-clown type guy who, also ironically, could be super moody at times. Ziggy, also tall, large and suspicious-looking, was Nero's partner-in-crime. Like the manifestation of Satan in his ear, he fed him stupid and immoral ideas and, in turn, Nero loved to roll with them. Ziggy only fed Nero ideas that benefited himself in some way. He could stretch a lie over years if he had to – Ziggy was a full time finesser. He adored Nero but he loved himself way, way more. Nero gave them roles too: Kai became his videographer and, quite naively, Ziggy his manager, 50/50 with the manager the label had assigned him.

The only woman around us was Ziggy's girlfriend, Chiara: pretty, baby-faced, Greek and loud. She didn't like me either. She had no reason not to, but she joined in with making me feel unwelcome too. She was so head-over-heels in love with Ziggy, I mostly believe she just echoed his desires, and those were not in favour of Nero and me.

As Nero's profile grew, with A-list artists co-signing his music, eventually every single boy in the gang switched up, injecting the clout into their veins as their eyes rolled back into their skulls like casino slot machines. Little did I know they were each being reborn as flying monkeys.

Flying monkeys

'Flying monkeys' is a psychological term, mostly used when referring to narcissistic abuse. It is used to describe the people a narcissist recruits as his followers to use as weapons in order to abuse his victim.

Other synonyms include useful idiot, yes man.

8

Lucky Livi

'You know Nero's never taken a girl on a date ... like ever?'

'How do you know that?' Ruby replied, making a sceptical face as she sifted through the rails of T-shirts in the vintage shop we'd found ourselves in on Brick Lane, close to our apartment.

'Well, the other night while I was over there, Nero was on some work call in the other room with his label so it was just me, Chiara and Ziggy—' I started.

'Oh my God, I couldn't think of anything worse.' She laughed, pulling a vintage Dior T-shirt to her chest and turning it to show me.

'I just feel like it doesn't even look like Dior,' I told her, carefully scanning the top.

'Yeah, like it's not worth £200, right?' she agreed. 'Sorry, continue, you were with the world's most judgemental couple ...'

I chuckled. 'Yeah, so I just asked, has Nero ever taken a girl on a date and they ... fucking laughed in my face, bro.'

'Stop ... What did you say?' she asked.

'Nothing, I just smiled and fake laughed but took a mental note in my head, like *challenge accepted*.

Ruby giggled and turned to me, grabbing both of my shoulders, 'Listen, that stupid boy Nero would be *lucky* for you to be his first ever date.'

I smiled back at her. 'You do not like him at all, do you?'

She let go of my shoulder and turned away to look through the stacked boxes of shoes, hiding her true expression. 'Nooo ... it's not that I don't like him ...'

'Oh, stop chatting shit, Ruby,' I said, still grinning.

'Okay, fine, obviously I think he's a bit weird, but if he makes you happy, then cool. I just think a date should be the bare minimum at this point, it's been over a month.'

I paused for a second, looking at the dresses on the mannequins in front of me.

'You're right, and I've got the *perfect* outfit,' I told her, revealing the sick-coloured granny frock on display.

'Yeah ... maybe lucky isn't the right word,' she said.

That evening on the phone, I finally plucked up the courage to bring forth the topic to Nero.

'Winter Wonderland looks sooo cool, have you ever been?' I asked.

'Nah, I haven't you know, you tryna go?' he replied back in his cool, raspy tone.

Wow, it's that easy? 'Yeah, I'd love to!' I replied.

'Sick,' he said, 'go with Ruby and then bring Ruby round and we can have a drink up.'

I paused.

'A date, Nero.'

'Huh?' he replied.

'I want to go there on a date ... with you ...'

He paused.

'You know I ain't ever taken no girl on a date before, right? In my life ...'

'Yeah but I'm not just anyyyy girl,' I replied sarcastically.

'You're right, you're Livi ...' He sighed. 'Fine, I'll do the date ting – but *only* because you're *Livi*.'

I smiled bashfully.

'But for real though, bring Ruby, I think Kai fancies her.'

We both started laughing.

'Fine, I'll ask her.'

That weekend he showed up with the most random group – Kai, and some guy with his baby and girlfriend. Like an actual baby, maybe just a few months old. Oh, and a bottle in his hand. Classic Nero, making the simplest situations *bizarre*.

We all entered Winter Wonderland under the thousands of lights decorating the archways, as the sounds of joy and Christmas songs danced in the air. It was a cold night with pitch black skies. Light snow fell throughout Hyde Park, so I wore a big red fur jacket with red furry earmuffs to match. Nero took my hand as we headed towards the mulled wine shack.

Kai and Ruby almost instantly disappeared together. Though they were both tall as anything, they were suddenly nowhere to be seen, and the random friend with the baby sped to the toilets when they realised they had to change his nappy.

'Well – they hit it off quickly, didn't they?' I turned to Nero.

He nodded, before shaking his head and chuckling gently. His smile lingered as he peered down at me while we waited for our cups, still holding my hand.

I looked right back at him with a winning smile, and he knew exactly why.

He nodded his head in disbelief. 'You're lucky you're Livi you know! I'd never do this for no other girl.'

I smirked in triumph.

I leaned in for a peck on my tiptoes, but he placed his hands tightly on either side of my earmuffs, holding me in place to keep me from pulling away. So I stayed right there and let him, and as I closed my eyes everything suddenly went slo-mo around us. The Christmas carols echoed softly in the background and the cold, crisp air pirouetted around us as I could feel nothing but his tongue stroking mine and the wetness of the snowflakes as they melted into my hairline. It felt like we were in our very own snow globe.

He moved his hands inside my coat and squeezed my body close to his, before finally letting go, slipping his arms back out. Both of us very hot and a little flustered, we paid for the cups of mulled wine and, as we walked away, I saw that the snow in the spot where we stood had melted.

We walked around the park hand-in-hand, the neon lights from the rides reflecting hues of purple and red across our faces as the fading screams filled the atmosphere, passing enormous teddy bears at the game stands, both knowing it was too cliché for him to try and win me one.

'You look beautiful, by the way,' he said, glancing at me.

'Why thank you, Nero sir!' I couldn't stop grinning from

ear to ear. 'Why do you say that? That I'm lucky I'm Livi?' I asked as we took shelter and sat down on a bench under an igloo bar, 'Baby, It's Cold Outside' playing on the speakers above us.

'Hah,' he laughed. 'I don't know . . . I guess . . . um, it's hard to explain.'

Then he went silent.

For the first time ever, Nero Kouassi, Nero fucking Kouassi, felt nervous.

I gave him a moment to speak, and it felt like he took that moment to realise I actually wanted him to go on.

And then there was another moment, where I saw him intensely debate whether or not he should let down his armour, as his eyes flickered back and forth between mine.

'It's okay . . .' I said with a soft smile, trying to speak to whatever part of his inner child just needed someone to hold his hand.

'You're just Livi, innit. I've never really done the girlfriend ting or anything before but, I don't know, there's something inside you that I just know I really love.'

. . . *Love? It's way too soon for me to take that seriously, right?*

I saw his gaze turn a little colder as he registered the confusion in mine.

'I mean,' he said, 'I love you as a person, I love who you are, you're genuine and that's rare.'

'So you're saying you love me?' I joked, attempting to nervously de-intensify the situation.

'Yes,' he replied bluntly, combating my attempt, staring right into my soul.

I knew he was trying to play a mind game with me, cutting a small incision into my heart and peeling it back to peek inside and see what was in there . . .

And for some reason, I wanted to rip the entire shit open and invite him in.

'Winter Wonderland' by Bing Crosby started chiming through the speaker.

Nero stood up, pulling me up by my hand. He slipped his hand onto my waist and locked his fingers in mine. I tried to resist ballroom dancing with him because I have zero fucking rhythm, but he had enough for the both of us. I laughed into his Stone Island jacket as he led us around in circles of joy. I would usually feel so stupid, but the freedom he wore wrapped around both of us like an invisible cloak. He made me feel invincible.

'. . . in a winter . . . wonderlaaaaand,' the song came to an end as a group nearby began clapping.

A teenage boy approached Nero out of nowhere.

'A– Are you Nero?!' he asked excitedly with his phone in his hand.

'Nah, who's Nero?' Nero replied, signalling me to make a sharp exit out of the igloo.

We finally found Kai and Ruby eating by the shawarma shack (not surprising for two Tauruses) and, after much persisting, Nero and Kai finally agreed to ride the Bomber with us. The Bomber is a huge, fast-spinning ride, consisting of just a large rod holding carriages that simultaneously spin on either side of it. Just the sight of the massive tower is enough to send shivers down your already freezing spine.

We sat in a row of four, strapped in as our legs dangled a few feet up from the ground, rave music and flashing lights sending our senses into overload.

'Are you ready!?' Ruby screamed along our row.

'No!' Kai and Nero let out at the exact same time.

'Aww, babe, do you want me to hold your hand?' Ruby teased Kai.

He replied 'yes' before she even finished the sentence and gripped on to it tightly.

Nero had his eyes shut tight. 'Is it too late to get off?!' he screamed.

'Yes! We're gonna die bro but it's been good knowing you!' Kai yelled back to him.

The ride began to elevate us into the air and in what felt like no time it ascended to full speed. We were spiralling in the sky, the chaotic winds sending a huge rush of adrenaline through us.

The ride came to a halt as it let people onto the carriage below, leaving us dangling at the top of the opposite end, 120 feet in the air.

'Nahhhh, open your eyes, Nero! This view is sick!' I shouted over at him.

'My hat!!! My fucking hat fell off,' Kai cried.

Nero eventually opened his eyes to see the entirety of central London glistening below us, covered by the white blanket of snowfall.

I poked my head out to him, 'You good?'

He smiled at me, long and warm, stared back out at the view and began to shake his head from side to side.

'You're lucky you're Livi!!'

As we got off the ride, the boys shrieked like kids at their experience, in disbelief that they'd survived.

We headed towards some benches to find their missing friend, girlfriend and baby shouting us over. Their friend was waving a blue cap in the air excitedly.

'It was so mad,' he said, 'we were just sitting here and this literally fell right into my lap!'

9

Fingers

One snowy night at Nero's big, modern penthouse, I sat by his side at the computer, Logic Pro on the screen, my legs draped over his lap. Nero was learning to produce a beautiful beat. Usually it was Blake who produced his tracks, but Nero wanted to work on his own idea, so he created his own sound, and he sure created something amazing.

I watched the snowdrops transform to liquid as they landed on the windows next to us, streaming downwards while he played the beat over and over, euphoric, gentle instruments complemented by the soft layers of 'humms' he had recorded into the mic like a sort of robotic acappella. I'd recorded some too. I attempted to give some suggestions to add to the still very premature beat and we joked that if I were his producer, my name would be 'Fingers', so he bounced the file, and saved it as just that.

Later, the house was empty – a rare event. I had noticed a few days ago that Mika added me on Snapchat and tried to initiate a conversation, which I ignored, obviously. Of course, I told Nero, as I would have wanted the same loyalty.

For some reason that had bothered him, and he blurted out, 'WELL *you* shouldn't trust your friends either!'

And then, after what felt like an eternity of demanding the truth behind such a paranoia-inducing statement, he confessed how a mutual friend I had been out with on the night of the book launch had come to one of his afterparties. They had kissed, almost fucked.

I felt my heart sink. I felt disappointed and embarrassed. She was supposed to be my *friend*. True, we weren't the closest friends in the world, but she knew about my feelings towards Nero; everyone in my life did. These kinds of things would always get to me, simply because '*I wouldn't do that to you*' echoed in my mind from past friendships.

'You will never, ever touch me again,' I exclaimed as he hung off my jacket sleeve, begging me not to leave.

'I was drunk and it was stupid, Livia. I just, I don't know how this shit works, I've never had a girl before,' he pleaded.

'So *NOW* I'm your girl, Nero!?'

It annoyed me even more that he decided to claim me in the heat of betrayal, especially since I'd never brought up labels because I was considerate of where we both were in our lives – him being a new hip-hop artist and me, a newborn in the world of freedom. I liked that we didn't put pressure on anything, that we could just *be*. Though we didn't ask each other about other people, we had had plenty of conversations about loyalty and respect. Conversations that *clearly* meant nothing now.

He begged me, quite literally on his knees, endlessly, pacing the room back and forth, throwing his head back, hands in the air shouting *why*, why this *couldn't* have been the ultimate betrayal, why I *had* to forgive his actions and give him one more chance.

At one point, he even got his phone and proceeded to send the girl a nasty message, saying he wanted to 'show me whose side he was on'. He began sending snake emojis to her, shifting the blame as if it was her doing an individual tango that night.

'Stop!' I said. 'Messaging her snake emojis doesn't change the fact you both in fact *are* snakes, Nero.'

'FUCK,' he yelled, throwing his phone onto the floor. 'This all can't have been for nothing, all these days together . . . I . . . I'll never like someone again, Livia. It's you, it's only you, you know that? You know this! Livia! Livia, you know this . . .'

I watched him silently. I didn't even need to respond, it was like he was putting on a very dramatic show, talking to his many personalities, or at least the one who kissed the damn girl.

He proceeded to fall flat onto his stomach and use his hands to slide his skinny body and sorry face across the floor towards me. 'Pleaaaaaaaase,' he moaned, staring up at me with the saddest eyes you did ever see . . . all the way from my toes.

Finally, he resorted to declarations, starting with swearing the obvious – to stay away from my friends – and ending with an offer for me to always be by his side.

'I want you at all my shows, right next to me,' he told me. 'Everywhere I go, I just want you there. I love when you're here all the time, all the fucking time Livia. Just move in with me, honestly! I wouldn't even mind that, I wouldn't mind you being around all the time, I'd actually love it.'

And just as he said that, strangely, his unplugged Christmas tree lit up in the corner. As if it was trying to give me a sign.

We both glanced over at it, without saying a word.

I stood with my coat on, bag packed, watching sleet fall outside. His big, glazed eyes stared at me hopelessly, anticipating my next words. It was almost 2 a.m. and I lived in east London, an hour and a half away in a cab. As my period cramps felt like something clawing against the inside of my womb, I used that as a justification to at least stay until the morning.

In actual fact, I probably just loved the idea of everything he said. He was painting those pictures in my head again ... the ones I wanted.

So I forgave him. He genuinely *did* seem deeply sorry.

I finally removed my coat with a great big sigh, and as he hurried over to hug me. I turned to meet him with a face that said, *do not touch me*.

I got in the shower and, feeling drained by the situation, stayed there longer than normal while I could hear Nero outside the door of the en suite scurrying around to change the bedding and clean his room – something he usually hated doing.

When we finally got into bed, he turned the LED light over to purple as we both lay there flat on our backs, in silence. From the corner of my eye I saw him hesitantly turn onto his side to face me while I remained staring ahead at the lilac-hued ceiling.

In the purple haze, he started to divulge a little. 'You know,

I've not told anyone this but I know you want me to be vulnerable, so fuck it ...'

If I was a dog, you'd have seen my ears perk up.

'When I used to sleep on the underground yeah, I'd just wait until the last stop where the warden would tell me to get off ... Then I'd find another train to get on until morning, and then when I saw people I knew the next day, I'd just spud them like nothing, like I'd just come from home ...'

I turned over to face him. 'Your mum, she didn't let you come back home ... at all?'

'Nah, I'd bang on her door for hours begging her to let me in and she would never open. Sometimes I'd sleep on her doorstep in the rain.'

The way he had begged me to stay that night felt as though he was this broken kid who needed a home, who deserved a chance to learn to love.

I moved my feet closer to his and tangled our legs together. He lunged forward, clinging on to me like a child, burying his nose into my chest.

'Ahh, this just feels like home,' he said, groaning with relief.

I looked into his sorry eyes and considered how it would take great patience for him to learn love. Having never really received much himself, how could he know any better?

I guess I felt something special in him. I knew if I wanted to help him, I'd have to be forgiving and believe in him; I'd have to be the one to show him compassion in order for him to heal.

I lifted his chin lightly with my hand, leaned forward and pressed my lips onto his. He let out another groan as the kiss too quickly grew passionate, like he had been starved for a taste of me forever. He wrapped his arm around my waist, effortlessly pulling my body closer into him, closing any distance left between us. As he lifted his leg up to rub pressure in between my thighs, I straddled him back and we breathed heavily into each other's mouths.

The sex felt different. Feelings had been spilled all over the place and they wanted to join in with us. We felt everything from the night, my hurt, my disappointment, his relief and his promise.

We made love for the first time that night and oh my gosh, it felt *spectacular.*

He sat with his back against the headboard, with me on top of him. The way his eyes were locked into mine was as if there were laser guns pointing at us from all directions, ready to go off if either of us broke eye contact. There was a certain urgency and necessity in the way our bodies moved. He had one hand holding my hair up, the other on my ass, controlling the rotation of my hips. The intensity overflowed as the purple hue from the strip lights flooded my face while he was kissing my open mouth in between my moans, instantly returning to deadlocked eyes each time, his head tilted just slightly as he examined my expression, my reactions.

'Do you know where we are?' he whispered.

I faintly shook my head, absorbed by his question.

'We're on our own planet, a purple planet.'

I let out a louder moan as the room around me dissolved into a purple haze.

'And there's nobody else here besides just me and you,' he

went on ... 'Just me and you,' he said again, pulling my hair back tighter in his hand.

'Just me and you,' I cried back to him.

And when we both came, at the exact same time, the sounds we made were like the weight of the world had just been lifted from both of us. The release of endorphins came in abundance. I felt like we were on drugs. Our own drugs. And they were about to become very addictive.

I could give many reasons why I always chose to forgive that boy, but mostly I just felt bad for him. Looking back, I know he *wanted* me to feel bad for him ... He analysed how I'd melt when I heard his childhood horror stories. He'd see how I couldn't stand any kind of human suffering. He'd watch my eyes widen as I'd pause to swallow nervously a few times, then quickly begin racking my brains for solutions to ease his pain. He felt my extreme empathy overtake logic and he quickly learned I was a healer. *His healer.*

Around this time, Ruby would often come to the penthouse too. Kai was practically in love with her since our Winter Wonderland group date and we'd meshed into this group of young, weird kids.

A few nights later at one of Nero's parties, after most people had left, I was drinking dark liquor straight from the bottle ... something I made a rule never to do again from this night forward.

I was too drunk and I rested my head on Nero's friend's shoulder. For some reason, Ziggy and a few others decided to, I guess ... take pictures? I never understood why, but the way they, as a collective, spoke about and treated women not only showed their misogyny, but also their intense, overpowering, in-your-face *insecurity*. They criticised girls who 'showed too much skin', girls who 'spoke too much' or were 'too loud', girls who had a life outside of obeying their 'men'. Of course they didn't like me. And of course Nero loved me, I was everything the girls they kept around their circle weren't. I wasn't a yes girl, I was nobody's bitch.

I was Livia Dalia and I was *free*.

They showed Nero the snaps – anything to sabotage us. I barely remember what happened after, apart from a blur and a few flashbacks. Ruby told me that Nero tried to force me to leave. She defended me and explained how ridiculous this was, all over my resting a head on someone's shoulder. She noted that, given that I was drunk, if I had to leave, she would leave with me. *But of course* that would have been simply unacceptable as Kai wanted her to stay. So Nero changed his mind.

The next thing I remembered was being in Nero's bedroom and hurting my leg . . . I remember falling into the window; I couldn't tell if I'd fallen or was pushed but suddenly there was pain in different parts of my body. After that, I blacked out.

I woke up covered in bruises, confused and embarrassed as if I'd done something wrong. It didn't take me long to gather my senses and realise how fucking petty and disgusting shaming me for tipsily resting my head on his, and my, friend's shoulder was. It's not like I did anything flirty or sexual. In my drunken state there were no brain cells left to aspire to any kind of foul play.

Nero reeked of weakness that night. His boys made him feel emasculated and his 'Alpha male' crown started slipping.

He fell right into their trap. He didn't realise his crown was being stolen in those very moments.

After that, Nero began to act weird. He'd randomly make statements, like that I 'wasn't going to be able to stay as many days as usual'. In turn, I agreed, confused since it had been him who was so enthusiastic for me to stay day after day. I knew people had been whispering in his ear. I could feel their bad intentions falling off each word on his tongue. He would cancel my invitations to his shows occasionally, breaking promises and plans. Then, out of the blue, he begged me to come on his boys' trip to Paris Fashion Week in February, his very first time attending.

We sat in a dessert parlour in central London, waiting for the rain to calm down. I toyed at my milk cake with my fork while he went on at me.

'I need my Princess Jasmine there, dancing with me by my side,' he told me, steadying the fork in my hand with his.

I refused. I knew his boys would complain that I'd be interrupting their 'lads trip'. He insisted further, going into the living room once we got back to his apartment and declaring out loud to the whole room that I would be coming to Paris. It was decided.

Everything was hot and cold until he called me a week later, the day before we were meant to leave. I was out shopping with Ruby at Westfield, trying to carry all my bags filled with outfits for Paris when he called me and said we needed to talk. All the excitement I'd built up, my ideas about how to style a beret with my outfits, suddenly felt so stupid.

'Listen, you can't come to Paris.'

'What . . . ? Why?' I stuttered.

'Ugh, you're so jarring. Why can't you just say "Okay" like other girls?'

I felt my blood boil. All the times I'd been lowering my standards to forgive him, all his pleas, broken promises and weakness for giving into his boys' peer pressure, just to ask me to say '"Okay" like other girls'?

'Yeah, well, I linked Jay anyway,' I said as I hung up.

Jay was another hip-hop artist from London who Nero knew was into in me as a result of peering over my shoulder when I received a Snapchat notification from him.

I wasn't even interested and I most definitely hadn't slept with him – I actually actively ignored him. I didn't even say it to hurt him, I just felt like I'd lost so much pride in these last six months, that I *stupidly* somehow felt like I could get it back.

So, so stupid.

That night I lay in bed remembering a time I asked Nero what he loved about me, as we chatted drunkenly in bed.

'Your fingers,' he had told me.

'My fingers?' I had asked, confused.

'The way you move your hands when you speak, how your fingers pirouette around you, it's like they're so delicate and small. Beautiful,' he said, cupping them inside his. I had smiled, feeling so cosy that I fell into a deep, dreamy sleep.

Days went by without us speaking, and days turned into weeks, until one day, I opened Instagram to see that Nero was releasing a new song.

It was called 'Fingers', the song we had both produced.

10

Addicted to rain that only falls after a drought

Weeks passed and Nero and I had grown too proud to reach out to one another. I was angry at everything: the way he had let me down over and over again, angry at myself that I kept letting him back in. I hated that he had been so weak when I *knew* he was nothing like those pathetic excuses for friends he kept around for validation.

I wanted more for him. I wanted him to have *real* friends, not competitors. I wanted so badly to heal him, to show him love. But he was caught in this web of blindness as a result of his own thirst for power. He needed his supply to feed his ego, and that stopped him from doing anything true, anything real. Instead, he kept feeding, with women and drugs. He wasn't loving himself at all, and those months of beautiful feelings and brain sex dissipated into nothingness. But what else does one do when they don't know what love is?

Nero was still angry at my comment. Later, I found out that he'd put his phone on loudspeaker while speaking to me so that his boys could hear him, in an attempt to regain his 'manhood' by publicly exiling me from the Paris trip. That's why he was being so cruel. They all seemed to have this infatuation with toxic masculinity. It made me feel physically sick, that feeling of being unable to be at ease until you get it all the fuck out.

Toxic masculinity

Toxic masculinity is a term used to describe the harmful behaviours and signifiers of masculinity that are put on men, such as lack of emotion or being dominant and having sexual virility. Such standards have a negative effect on men and society.

On my birthday a week or so later, the thirteenth of March, I went out with a few friends to see a DJ where, lo and behold, Nero was the surprise guest performance.

I remember seeing Mika through the glass, where Nero's gang of idiots stood outside smoking. Having spotted me, Mika turned to them, clearly announcing to the group that Livia was on the premises. This obviously caused outrage: they all turned to look at me at the exact same time.

Nero watched me all night, smirking. It felt as though he was following me along the dance floor. Everywhere I went, his energy followed. I couldn't focus on having a good night. I walked past the boys and the only one who jumped out to give me a hug and greet me was Ziggy. We laughed off the situation as he tried to convince me to come to the afterparty, telling me it was weird that I wasn't around anymore. It was hard to know what was genuine because Ziggy was as Gemini as a Gemini could get. I saw Blake on his way out of the club. He stuck his tongue under his bottom lip and scowled like a child. You couldn't make this shit up. Some one-sided beef. He had been *praying* for our downfall.

By the time I got home, I was awfully drunk. I stumbled into our empty apartment – Ruby had gone home to Manchester to visit her family. I sat on the bed and stared at myself in the mirror. I felt sad. I felt alone. Seeing Nero had made me realise how much it hurt that things had come to such an abrupt and bitter end. It felt like just moments ago we were on our own magical, purple planet.

I stared at his contact on my phone screen for a while. I kept telling myself that no, calling him would just make me look stupid, that I needed to act like I didn't care— *But I do care, and I don't care about not caring anymore*, my brain interrupted.

His phone rang . . .

And rang . . .

And rang . . .

'Sorry, this person isn't available to take your call.'

I sighed. It must have been a sign.

Then, just as I'd accepted defeat and the universe's plans to keep me safe, his name popped up on the screen.

I answered almost immediately.

'Nero,' I said.

'Yo,' he replied. 'Where are you?' he asked.

'Home?'

'With who?' he questioned.

'Alone? Why?'

'I'm coming to get you.' He hung up.

Roughly forty-five minutes later, he was banging on my door.

By the time he turned up, I had removed my skirt so I was just wearing the baggy T-shirt I'd tucked inside it, wearing my long black socks and with half of my make-up removed since I was preparing to get in bed, panda eyes smeared all over my face.

I looked at him, up and down. I could see from his fuelled-up but exhausted gaze that he had taken cocaine. Something that seemed pretty normal for people to take at this time. Something I'd tried just a handful of times but didn't enjoy enough to continue, but something that Nero had started making a habit of.

He finally said something as I stood there speechless, examining him.

'Are you ready?'

No. I'm not ready. Aside from the fact I look crazy, I'm still angry at him. I'm angry he switched up on me after making me feel so connected to him, after making me want to heal him, help him, save him. I'm not ready at all.

'Yeah,' I said, turning around to grab my phone.

'Just come like this quickly, I need to show you something,' he urged me.

'But—'

He grabbed my wrist and pulled me out into the hall, closing the door behind me.

Something was off. Why was he rushing? Why was he here?

'What's going on?' I asked him over and over.

'Just trust me bro, just come with me, otherwise I need to bounce.' He shifted anxiously.

I said, 'Okay, let me just get my phone, Nero.'

I was anxious at the thought of him leaving me even more confused than before. I turned to open my door, but it was locked. *We were locked out.* I was wearing a baggy T-shirt and fucking socks.

He looked a little guilty. 'It's cool, here . . .'

He took off his Supreme puffer jacket and wrapped it around me, before I snatched it from his hand and put it on properly, sighing and rolling my eyes.

I realised my only choice at this point was to give in to him because my concierge with the spare key wouldn't be back until the morning.

'Why are you *so* annoying?' I asked him.

Had he just locked me out on purpose?

We headed towards the building exit, where the 3.30 a.m. rain was pouring down outside.

'You're not fucking serious. Not a chance Nero, no way!' I yelled at him over the sound of heavy rainfall slapping against the windows.

He looked back and forth between me and the rain for a few moments, then proceeded to walk over and fireman's lift me into his arms.

'What the . . .' I continued to shout but the rest of my sentence was inaudible. He charged towards a black Mercedes parked half on the pavement and opened the passenger door, practically throwing me inside and slamming the door shut. He ran around to get in the driver's seat.

The driver's seat. Nero does not drive.

For that split moment, I looked around the empty car I was sat in.

This is not an Uber.

'What are you doing?! Whose car is this!?' I screamed while he quickly started the engine, screeching the tyres as he reversed off the pavement.

He stayed silent as he picked up speed, heading down my road. The rainfall ambushed the windscreen so loudly it sounded more like hail. I quickly strapped myself in, looking left and right hesitantly, terrified at how fast he was going.

He continued staring blankly ahead, pursing his lips as he pressed his foot down on the accelerator.

'Nero! Nero, stop the car. You're literally fucked up right now, this is not cool. You're putting us both in danger, seriously. Stop, Nero!'

He turned to look at me for just a second when the headlights from another car lit up the window. He saw the terror on my face and, instead of braking, he pushed down harder on the accelerator, saving us from impact by what felt like a millimetre.

After we passed the car, he braked hard at the lights ahead of us. The streets were hauntingly empty and we both sat in silence, panting in sync after what just happened. Or almost happened.

I unclipped my belt, opened the car door, stormed out and slammed it shut. I charged back with my arms crossed towards my apartment.

I felt the blistering cold hit my cheeks, the wet and dirty

road beneath my feet. I felt instant regret for getting out of that car.

'Livia!' Nero shouted as he forged a path towards me through the rain.

I was too angry to turn around. If I hadn't been drunk and felt numb to the *almost* collision, I'd probably have had a breakdown.

'Livia, Livia I'm sorry. I would never ever hurt you, you know that,' he cried, chasing me.

'You wouldn't?'

I stopped walking and turned to face him, spitting water from my lips. It felt like it was raining harder and harder the angrier I got.

'Because I feel very fucking hurt right now, Nero. Very hurt. You can't keep doing this. You can't keep being this elusive guy who doesn't take accountability for anything, being so hot and cold with me – and I mean volcanic hot. You act like you're in *love* with me! Then to disrespect me and not even apologise, instead showing up to my house in God knows *whose* car?'

He paused. His white Stüssy T-shirt had turned see-through.

'I just wanted to say happy birthday,' he said softly.

There was another pause . . .

I burst out laughing.

I don't know if it was the adrenaline from the crash, the liquor, or the fact that we were both half-dressed and soaking wet in the street, but I started laughing. An uncontrollable, hectic laugh, from the pit of my stomach.

He smiled that Nero smile of his, with his grill shining,

and walked over to me, lifting the hood of his jacket up to cover my head.

'It's a bit late for that now,' I said, pushing him back playfully.

Nero parked the car carefully on the closest side street. He agreed to abandon it for now and book us an Uber back to his place, only to realise that his phone had died hours ago.

We stood there, both of us, together and alone, on the side of the road. Me shoeless, both dripping wet and shivering as taxis passed us by without a second thought to stop for us.

'FUCKING COME ON!' Nero shouted in rage, running into the middle of the road and holding his finger up at the cars.

After ten minutes or so, one stopped and finally agreed to take us home.

In wet clothes, with my hair dripping and the remaining mascara running down my face, I walked into Nero's house looking like I'd just escaped a mental hospital. But he didn't look much better.

I heard him arguing with Kai about the car before he joined me in his bedroom.

'It's a violation. A fucking violation, bro! Do you know how much the deposit was to rent that for the music video?' I heard Kai yelling.

'Whatever man, I'd have paid for it, chill out,' Nero brushed it off.

'There was no deposit! That's the whole point – the guy trusted me not to do anything stupid. This is your problem: you get fucked up and you leave everyone else to clean up your mess. It's about keeping good relationships with people who do us favours!'

We changed into dry clothes and both sat down on the edge of the bed. I waited for some kind of an apology, but he looked at me like he didn't know how – he never knew how.

It was almost 5 a.m. We got into bed, defeated by all the drama. Nothing that needed to be said was said. We kissed almost straight away. It felt so fucking good to kiss him again.

The high after such a low felt familiar now. A high that cannot exist without the low that creates space before it, like an arrow that can only go so far once it's pulled back enough.

When I left the morning after, my hangover felt extra painful. I felt drained, and most of all confused as to why I'd given in *so* easily.

'I just missed him!' I tried to explain to Ruby, who was furiously pacing her bedroom, listening to my story when she arrived back home from Manchester that day.

'It's not fucking healthy. He treats you like shit, I don't want to see my best friend being treated like shit,' she said. 'He didn't even apologise to you, Livia!'

Over the next few days, after I'd recovered from an extended two-day hangover, I would often revisit my memories of that night, looking for more answers.

Why do I feel so drawn to him?
Why do I want to see him again?
Do I love him?
Why do I love him?

Now I look back and reassure myself. *No Livia, you were just trauma bonding – trauma bonding so fucking hard.*

Trauma bonding

Patrick Carnes created a term to describe how the 'misuse of fear, excitement, and sexual feelings' can be used as a way of entrapping and entangling a victim. In an abusive relationship, the abuser creates a strong emotional attachment and bond via a continuous cycle of devaluing and rewarding. This cycle of abuse results in the victim developing sympathetic feelings and intense affection towards their abuser.

The cycle of being devalued (and then rewarded) over and over can create a strong chemical bond between the abuser and the victim. A cocktail of different hormones like oxytocin (bonding), opioids (pleasure, pain, withdrawal) and dopamine (reward) are responsible for this feeling.

11

Playing games with knives

For the rest of the summer, I tried my best to stay away from Nero – but the universe had other plans. He was no longer the rare and beloved boy I once knew; he had become a vessel of darkness – power-hungry and fuelled by cocaine.

We both attended the same events and we'd spend the night staring each other down. You could feel the tension, like fire, burning everyone and everything around us until it was only us left in the room. To make each other jealous, we'd grab whichever member of the opposite sex was close enough to us, not caring if we burned them in the process.

It was the enemies-to-lovers trope. It was the epitome of toxic, and it went on for months.

We would both go to London's most exclusive underground club regularly, the Pack. A dark, no-phones-allowed club with deep red, velvet, draping curtains, low ceilings and stripper poles. In the middle of the stage there would be extravagant performances, sex shows and all kinds of inarticulable things going on.

Nero would always be flocked by girls. With his career doing better than ever, he was loving every minute of it. Nero was the *it-boy* of the last decade. Anyone who was anyone wanted to be involved with him. The biggest names in fashion, the biggest artists in America, A-list actors all over the globe – they were all fans of Nero, expressing that all over the internet and in front of the cameras. He was becoming stupidly successful, stupidly quick.

When we were out, I'd make sure he'd see me dancing, or at least laughing at another man's joke here and there. I didn't need to do anything else; that was enough. I'd always catch him doing that intense primal animal predator stare, eyes on his prey. Cup in hand, face forward, not even trying to be subtle, before finding a fangirl to whine on, making sure I'd see too.

We didn't initiate any conversation, apart from one night. He tried to humour me, asking bluntly if I'd come home with him when we were in the smoking area outside the club. I impolitely declined and, not long after, he made sure I saw him leave with his second choice, a huge smirk on his face.

On one night that I'll never forget, Kai had invited Ruby and me to the Pack. I made sure that she'd made sure that Kai had made sure that Nero knew I'd be attending, so there weren't any surprises. I wanted some kind of peace treaty because months of war and immature games had got boring.

I even teased the thought that we'd salvage some kind of friendship. At the end of the day, I had a lot of affection for the once-amazing connection we shared, and I hoped we could end our pettiness.

At the venue, we hugged as the music thumped loudly. Nero asked me, almost straight away, who I'd come with, suspiciously looking around.

'I wouldn't do that,' I said. 'I want to be friends.'

He paused for a second and then confessed, 'I invited another girl but I'll tell her to leave.'

My stomach turned, knowing a disaster was on its way.

He pulled out his phone and texted her as I took a gigantic sip of my spicy margarita about a millisecond after the barman placed it on the coaster in front of me.

'I wouldn't do that to you, Livia.' He wrapped his arms around me and hugged me tight.

I wasn't ashamed to admit that it felt nice.

But then I saw him snort a few lines and his whole aura became cold. It was like watching him transform into a vengeful, angry being. Even his shadow had a reddish hue. Nero had left the building, his body now home to a hungry, self-sabotaging demon.

To my disbelief, the girl he'd invited showed up and, just like that, he was over there, entertaining her, touching her.

I tried to leave but he ran over and begged me to stay.

'I'm not going home with her, I'll go with you,' he pleaded. This made me even angrier – as if I was meant to be flattered that I'd be the one he would fuck in the end. As if I even wanted to fuck him at all.

I tried to wash down the nerves with more margaritas, and

when he finally realised that I wasn't going anywhere with him, we ended up arguing outside the club. I screamed in his face at him fucking me over, again.

How did I give this boy another chance to let me down? When would I learn?

In the heat of all the shouting, Nero stood on a bin at the back of the club and raised his leg as if to kick me. Kai quickly picked me up, dragging me into his car with Ruby.

Hours later, I woke up in Kai's guest room at his mother's house. Going back to Nero and Kai's wasn't an option because he'd gone home with the girl, and our house was much further away on the other side of town, so we had crashed here. I remember crying so hard in that bed, I felt so embarrassed and violated.

Why did he want to hurt me so much?

Clearly, we couldn't even be friends.

The very moment I surrendered and turned my back, he struck again with another dagger.

When I got home and called him, he answered within the first ring – he was ready.

'*You were drunk, you don't remember what happened.*'

'*It wasn't like that, you were acting nuts.*'

'*You are crazy.*'

This was the first time I was introduced to Nero's favourite weapon of choice: gaslighting.

Gaslighting

The term gaslighting refers to deceptive and manipulative actions and behaviour used to psychologically impact someone. Within narcissistic abuse, the abuser gaslights the abused in order to make them doubt their own sanity.

12

Inevitably impregnating the fertile mind

By September, I'd pretty much begun to move on with my life. I never returned Nero's calls and I stopped checking his socials. I'd accepted the lessons learned to the point that his name wasn't even allowed to be mentioned in my friendship circle. We called him 'Voldemort'.

Nero was a thing of the past. A kid who got famous too quickly and let it all get to his head, a recurring disappointment who was obviously too young, too impressionable and now, too much of a coke-head to consider his shitty actions towards others.

I had been on a few dates with a guy called Tobias. He was a six-foot-five British-Nigerian with a charming smile and many other great qualities that didn't include being a hip-hop artist. We had a lot of chemistry, and he had a self-proclaimed love for Pisces women (having dated three). Being super into astrology and all things spiritual, or anything that helped me understand myself and other humans better, I loved that he loved Pisces. I loved that he even knew what a Pisces was.

One evening, I was sitting on my bed gazing out at the full moon when my phone pinged with an Instagram notification.

'We need to talk, can I call you?' Nero had written, with an emoji of a finger held out, the same logo he used for the 'Fingers' cover.

We hadn't spoken since the incident in June, and I didn't know what to reply. But then the phone began to ring. It was him, barging in in true Nero style.

He did what he always did, checking the temperature of the water before getting in the tub.

'You good, Livi?' He loved to call me Livi.

'Why are you calling me, Nero?' I replied bluntly, already exhausted, trying to figure out which game he wanted to play this time.

'Look, I just had a mad realisation that I've been treating everyone like a cunt. I let the music and money get to my head and it's wrong, it's bad karma! Even Kai, Ziggy, so many people and I just – I sat here and called everyone to apologise one by one. You were the last person left to call. In this whole time, I think you're the person I imprinted on most . . .'

I remember staring at the moon, longing for some kind of clarification.

'I just need to apologise to you. You're a sick person, Livi. I'm sorry for everything I did, I'm sorry for switching up on you. I really, really am sorry.'

When someone finally apologises, inevitably it feels good. It's a relief to feel seen after all those times you weren't . . .

Heard for all the times you screamed and they just couldn't hear you.

With Nero, I'd given up all hope that he'd ever admit that he was in the wrong in this lifetime. I accepted his apology and hung up.

I took a deep breath, lay down on the bed, closed my eyes, put in my earphones and finally listened to 'Fingers'. The moonlight fell onto my face, replicating the bright computer screen where we recorded the song together. I felt emotional, which surprised me as I'd pretty much convinced myself that I had no emotions left. I'd given up hope that any of the magic was at all real, but in a sudden and strange turn of events, it all felt so valid.

It's such a beautiful song, you know.

After a few weeks of Nero trying to instigate conversations on socials, complimenting me when I posted, replying to my Stories and me avoiding his calls, I finally agreed to come to the studio and meet him.

The last time I had attended a studio session, Nero had gone to some small-ass studio for free, as a favour. But this time he was in one of the most prestigious studios in London, Metropolis Studios, where the likes of Michael Jackson had recorded.

I wore a black T-shirt with white text that read 'I'm not a rapper', a black tennis skirt and fishnet heels, with my hair tied into a tight high ponytail, an outfit I confirmed in the group chat with all my friends (as all girls do before seeing an ex. Or a Nero).

My nerves felt like they were decaying the insides of my lungs as I entered that room.

A quick look to my left and I saw all of the gang. Fake smiles and some unwelcoming-as-a-hug-can-be hugs. Chiara glared at me like she had no idea who I was. Nero came over straight away but was mostly focused on his work, recording a track with another famous hip-hop artist, AK Biggs.

Things felt different now, kind of serious. None of the boys were fooling around like usual and Nero was in his zone.

At 3 a.m., some girls showed up in heels and dresses as the clubs closed. Naturally, I panicked about how he would act now that there were more women in the room. It was like playing Russian roulette: you never knew which Nero you were going to get.

But just as all the girls were doting over him and AK, he came over and put his arms around me, gently kissed my cheek and then went back into the booth. He practically ignored everyone in the room aside from the producer, AK and me as he poured me drinks, and once a few of those had been drunk we were all headed back to the penthouse.

In the back of Nero's friend's car, the liquor had definitely hit. We started to kiss to some PartyNextDoor track playing through the speakers. The bass was so intense it provided its own curtain for us as his friend raced to west London. We arrived at Nero's apartment and got straight into bed. He kissed me all over and I kissed him back, we were just so familiar with each other's bodies. We knew what each type of kiss meant, where each touch led to and what we wanted next from each stroke. Then he went to pull down my knickers, which wasn't any secret body language.

'I'm not having sex with you,' I whispered.

There was no way he was getting back in that easily.

He tried to convince me a little more, kissing my neck and attempting to persuade me by touching some of my favourite spots, but I kept pushing his hands away from anywhere that would entice me too much.

'You didn't miss me?' he whispered back. 'I missed you so much Livi . . .' he pleaded.

Eventually, he accepted defeat and fell asleep.

I knew he was finding it hard to sleep because he had done a little cocaine that night and sex was always his vice for falling asleep once the drugs were in his system. But I wasn't going to give in because I knew why I was there, and it wasn't to have sex, or end up back in his unpredictable cycle.

I wanted answers. Truth is, I felt something special in Nero. I felt like that special thing needed saving, before it was completely sucked dry by the life he was participating in. I just wasn't ready to give up on this connection. It was like nothing I'd felt before, and I wasn't sure I'd ever feel it again.

When we woke up the next evening, we ordered food before he asked me if I wanted to come to the studio again that night. I was in last night's make-up so I tried to pass up his offer.

'You're one of the only girls who doesn't need make-up,' he told me.

'No, I feel gross, Nero,' I replied.

'Pleaaaase,' he began . . . before he looked like he had had a eureka moment. 'I know!' he said, scrambling to the end of the bed and sliding open his dark wooden wardrobe doors.

He dug through a few overloaded shelves of clothes, all scrunched up in piles, before throwing a black and red pair of sweatpants decorated with moons and stars onto the floor. And then, after some more digging, he pulled out an identical pair.

He stood up holding one in each hand, excitedly doing something that looked like it was meant to be a samba.

'We can both style it out. If we make it look purposeful, no one can chat shit. We make the rules!'

He leapt onto the bed, convincing me further. So I rolled my eyes and went to the studio bare-faced with my hair up in an elastic band since I'd lost my hair bobble, wearing his sweatpants and a baggy T-shirt tied into a crop top, fishnet heels still on my feet.

He had also tried to persuade us to wear matching neon balaclavas – that was where I had to draw the line. But his idea was cute, and I appreciated him trying to make me comfortable with his crazy little brain.

As we stepped out into hall of his home, the boys looked us both up and down. I could tell they were desperate to glance at each other and pull a face, but they acted un-phased, even though I felt their eyes burning into the back of my head. As we walked out of the front door, Nero softly reached out to grab my hand.

In true Livi and Nero fashion, one night turned into two, and then two into a few. Each night he dressed me in his clothes and matched me to him as much as possible.

Every night in the studio, his attention was on one of two things: me or the music. I noticed how he consciously made an effort to reassure me and accommodate me as much as possible, as if he was a little nervous I'd leave.

On the fourth night that week, he had a jeweller come to

take some moulds for a full teeth set of gold grills. Once the guy finished, Nero pointed him over to me.

'And take some for her too, please, bro.'

Blake glanced away from his laptop, looking at Nero in shock.

'What, bro? Are you good?' Nero said blankly.

'Yeah . . . All good, bro,' Blake replied, almost taken back.

'Good. Anyone else got an issue?'

Nero looked over at Kai and Mika, who were sprawled across the couches. Mika was rolling a spliff, Kai engrossed in his phone, probably texting Ruby and getting ignored as usual.

'Nah, bro,' Mika said without looking up.

'You're bugging bro,' Blake said.

Nero stared at him silently. Blake stared right back.

You could cut the tension with a knife.

You could hear a pin drop in the soundproofed room. *It was dead silent.*

Ziggy suddenly entered, swinging through the studio doors with a KFC and Chiara trailing behind him, drinks in hand.

'But nobody makes weird looks when I pay for your grills, for your life?' Nero said to Blake, venom dripping from the corners of his mouth.

'Yooooo, chill boys, not again?' Ziggy laughed, attempting to lighten the mood.

I looked puzzled as the grills guy set up on the sofa next to me, preparing to take my moulds. I walked over to Nero, who was sitting by the mixing deck, and awkwardly made wide eyes at him as if to ask him what he was doing.

'I can't afford gold grills,' I whispered in Nero's ear.

'But I can.' He smiled up at me warmly, rubbing the sides of my legs.

I guess I really hadn't realised that he was no longer the Nero I lent money to or ordered food for anymore. He was rich *and* he was famous, so he was very fucking rich.

The guy had a quick turnaround and delivered the grills within a few hours. That evening we both posed in Nero's mirror taking photos. I had a gold bar covering my bottom six teeth while Nero's entire mouth was filled with gold.

'Another one,' Nero said as he crouched down in front of his bedroom mirror next to me. I lay across the floor on my side, lifting one leg in the air, my finger pulling down the side of my lip to reveal the jewellery.

'These are so sick, Nero, thank you!' I said, standing back up and hugging him tight.

'It's nothing. You know you're my friend, you deserve to smile. I've not done that for you as much as I intended to . . . I *am* going to make you smile from now on.' He spoke with firmness.

I grinned with both of my eyebrows raised, took one hand to his face and pinched his cheek in between my fingers. 'You're so cute when you want to be, you idiot.'

'Seriously, Livia, I'm going to give you what you deserve, because you are what I deserve, and I want you, I want you for me.' His face turned serious.

I sat down on the end of his bed as he stood in front of me.

'I want you to be mine, nobody else's. Mine,' he reiterated.

Tobias briefly came to mind. I'd ignored his texts since arriving at Nero's days ago.

'I mean, if *you* want that . . . But I know you do,' Nero said confidently, the corner of his mouth turned up at one side.

I looked away, pretending to be pondering while, internally, I was freaking the fuck out.

'I want you to show me you can be as nice as you've been this week.'

'Not a problem – you can have all the gold grills in the world, I can give you any—'

I placed my finger over his lips.

'I don't want grills. You broke our trust, you need to fix that. I need consistency, none of that hot and cold shit you did last time. Just be honest and nice and be, be consistent.'

'Consistent,' he said in agreement as I removed my finger.

'Con-sis-tent,' I repeated.

'And we don't need to have sex, Livi,' he said. 'It was never about that for me. It was always about you. I forgot that for a while, but now I remember again – it's only about you. All these other girls just are not you, it's always going to be about you, because you're you! . . . You're Livi.' His voice softened at the end of his sentence.

That night I finally gave in and had sex with him. He punched the wall as he came.

'I've wanted to do that for so long.'

Love bombing

Love bombing is a technique to control a person with sudden and extreme phases of attention and affection. It is used to keep a person from leaving by giving them everything they want. Psychologists have stated that

love bombing is part of an addictive cycle that keeps
the victim hooked and longing for the love bombing
stage to return.

Nero

He was like something from another planet. From the noises he made, to his facial expressions and his body movements to top it off, I used to call him a noodle. He even had the body of a Martian: so slim and tight, with significant shoulders and head shape. I'd watch him, head tilted to one side, eyes big and full of wonder, mesmerised by his eccentric nature as he'd bounce around the room giving an over-the-top passionate speech to everyone in it. Even the way he held his cigarette was obscure with his fucking bony-ass fingers.

I loved him, I loved everything about him.

His energy was electric and fresh. When Nero spoke, people wanted to listen. He was a logic-based being, except he was always fourteen steps ahead of the curve, so when he told people about his revelations and theories, they'd look at him like the alien he was. But I understood him, so I'd always agree.

There even came a point when he'd finish a risky sentence,

his poor choice of vocabulary making it sound even more far off and nonsensical than it actually was. He'd look to me automatically to articulate it better for him. That was our thing: he'd plant the seed and I'd develop it, as I felt out the room to explain. Then they'd look at us like we were geniuses.

He always had a crazy look in his eyes. Most people thought he was on drugs, even when he wasn't. You couldn't blame them; Nero always seemed the furthest thing from sober. But he was just strange, he was so fucking unique. That's why when it came to music, he was such a visionary. He thought outside of the box, and any box he found himself in, he made sure to break down the walls aggressively until everyone could see him standing proud and free.

I was an emotion-based being, and his detachment and emotional control was what made my heart fall for him the most. Nero could do things in life faster – think faster, live faster because he didn't need to feel.

So he made your life faster too.

I thought that was amazing.

It was deadly.

13

False flag attack

And as the rest of September rolled on, the entire month was just perfection.

We spent almost every day and every night together. He treated me with way more respect and love than before, not to mention constantly *apologising* for the past (yes, Nero Kouassi learned the word 'sorry'). I quickly cut off my situation with Tobias because ... I could give you excuses, but I simply loved Nero, and getting what I finally longed for felt so good, even if we weren't exclusive yet.

I remember going to a party with Nero and that same girl he'd taken home that night from the Pack was there. She tried over and over again to approach him. Even with him harshly shouting in her face to leave him alone, she still tried to get on to our table. He eventually got security to chuck her out of the event. I want to say I felt bad, but I remember how she laughed at me the summer before. Looking back, I don't understand how the hell girls were so enchanted by him that they'd fight a security guard just to get on his table. He really had a hold over women.

One night, Ziggy walked into Nero's bedroom while we lay in bed watching *Trainspotting*.

'Chiara wants to talk to you,' he said to me nervously, to which I *just* as nervously got up and walked into Ziggy's room.

'You don't like me,' I said. It flew out of my mouth as I walked in. By this point, I just really hated the fake shit.

'It's not that, Livia. My friend just really liked Nero and you guys were sleeping together and ...' She went on with her excuse. But I knew; she just didn't like me.

I saw her eyes were teary and naturally, I felt for her.

Stepping inside Ziggy's bedroom door, I sat down at the edge of the bed.

'I'm pregnant,' she suddenly, but quietly, announced.

So I sat with her for a while, reassuring her that she was in a solid relationship and whatever she chose to do, she would be supported.

The following morning, the boys debated about the future of this baby as if it was a song feature. Nero gave Ziggy the ultimatum that if he didn't abort the baby, he couldn't be his manager anymore.

'I'm doing it for their future. They are kids themselves; they can't have a kid!' he defended himself to me.

The other boys agreed (as they always did with Nero) and all seemed to blame Chiara. They even came to the solution that they'd have to break them up 'for Ziggy's sake'. They thought of ways, like setting him up to look like he had been cheating. It was so wicked. They had been together for four years.

Ziggy followed Nero's orders, thus breaking Chiara's heart. She was 'banned' from being around the gang.

In the following months, the pain of losing both the woman he loved and the chance to have a family with her ate away at Ziggy. He grew increasingly addicted to cocaine, watching Nero, the man who forced him to take the ultimatum, fall in love and have what he'd lost. Deep down inside, a parasitic type of hate had infected Ziggy's body and it was growing in size, quite viciously.

A few nights later we were staying at Kai's mother's home. The boys were in between apartments after once again being evicted for partying too much. I woke up in the middle of the night, having had a bad dream. Unsettled, I nestled my head into Nero's chest. He squeezed me tight and kissed my forehead. In my sleepy state I let out a soft, 'I love you.'

'I love you too,' he replied.

I fell back into sleep like it was a warm hug. So safe and secure.

It's crazy to think that I had laid in that exact spot, crying, just last June. I never imagined then that we'd say 'I love you' for the first time in the same bed just a few months later. But it was just like that with Nero: you never knew what would happen tomorrow, next week, or even in the next few minutes.

The next morning, as I lay on the sofa with my head in his lap, I asked if he remembered saying it. He gently pressed his head into my stomach, and smiled.

Nero and the boys were set to go to LA for a few weeks.

The night before Nero left, he took me to my favourite

Indian restaurant for dinner. I remember walking back in from the bathroom in a cotton, off-the-shoulder long dress.

'Sorry but have you seen the bathrooms here?!' I said as I sat back down in front of him. 'They're literally gorgeous and there are mirrors on the ceiling. Is it totally inappropriate to take a picture on the toilet?'

I caught Nero staring at me with a gentle smile.

'I love you, you know that?' He grinned harder.

He was really saying this to me. Sober, awake, saying this to me in real life. *Pinch me.*

I rolled my eyes. 'Oh my God, Nero,' I let out with a huge smile and nervous laugh.

Nero got up out his seat and slid into the booth next to me. The orange candles matched his jumper, autumnal vibes decorating the space.

He kissed my shoulder and looked up at me. 'I love you, Livia.'

Fuck, fuck, fuck.

I smiled, grinding my teeth, my leg slightly shaking.

He placed his hand on my cheek, turning me to face him, until we were nose to nose. He nodded his head with encouragement.

'I love you too!!!' I cried out in a nervous whisper, joining in with his head nod.

We both burst out laughing as we hugged tight.

'I can't wait to get back from LA and just continue falling in love with you,' he said. 'You've changed me as a man. You make me so much better, I just know I can be myself with you!'

After he arrived in LA, we spoke every day. On Nero's

socials, I noticed he was posting an unfamiliar face. He'd befriended another British boy while out there called Jude.

All of his snaps were the same: the boys looked totally out of it. At parties, studio sessions, clubs and incredible mansions overlooking the hills, the glittering lights of the LA skyline in the distance.

On the night before Nero returned home, he messaged me saying, 'I love you more than anything. I'm scared and something really bad has happened.' So I Facetimed him, concerned. He was crying and saying he'd taken a lot of drugs. Ziggy grabbed the phone and made him hang up before he could say anything else.

My heart was pounding. I felt completely helpless.

When Nero got home, he told me he'd been arrested for rape.

He told me that there had been a terrible ordeal where they'd all taken a lot of magic mushrooms. He admitted that he was about to get with some girl but then Jude came into the room and sort of joined in. Because Jude and the girl had already slept together in the past, Nero felt weird about it and figured they'd planned a threesome. The shrooms made it feel even weirder, and he'd left the room.

Not long later, the girl ran downstairs crying, saying that Jude had raped her. The police came and arrested each of the boys, but Jude had already left and got on a flight to New York. Nero told me that he was released because the girl admitted to the officer that *he* hadn't done anything non-consensual.

I could hardly believe what I was hearing. After my initial shock and disgust, my protective nature took over as I thought of the right thing to do for both him and the poor girl ... I was adamant that he should call her and ask if she wanted to talk. I told him to make sure that she was okay, that she had everything she needed and might need moving forward. I told him to support her in any way he could and to make sure she knew he had no affiliation with this Jude guy before this trip. He needed to clear his name. But if she didn't want to speak to him, to respect that. I believed he was innocent.

The seriousness of the situation over-rode my emotions about the fact that he had almost slept with a different girl. I'd made it clear that Nero could do whatever he wanted, until we were official. I didn't want to get fully attached like I did last time – so even though it hurt, I stayed mostly quiet about it.

I stuck by him through that crisis as the record label paid £10k to the Airbnb owner to cover any damages and to stay quiet about the police visit. Nero continued to check on the girl who said it was appreciated and who was doing okay – and just like that, life moved on. Jude became a new enemy of Nero's, who seemed to have run off and got away with it. It was so awfully unfair.

Nero began to take me as his date to his label parties and music business events (rich white people, cocaine and a lot of people causing slippery floors by drooling over Nero). He introduced me to everyone as '*his girl*'.

'Yo everyone, this is my girl, Livi.'

He posted a picture of us on his Instagram from one of those parties, letting the world know about me. About us.

I knew then that Nero was serious, that he was ready to drop his playboy image by proudly stating that he had someone in his life. All that was left was to ask me to be his girlfriend.

Around this time, we would take a lot of intimate pictures and videos together. One night, he was about to post on Instagram, when a video of me performing oral sex on him showed in his camera roll. He selected it, joking around. I laughed along, grabbing the phone, him grabbing it back – and just like that, it posted. I remember feeling so confused. But he deleted it before anyone could have seen.

Did he do it on purpose?

What better way to claim someone than a video of them sucking your dick? And Nero was most definitely on a mission to claim my ass. He posted me every day on his Story, taking me everywhere that there would be publicity – but that just wasn't enough. He didn't just need to piss on my leg, but my whole fucking reputation.

One of his friends came running to the door ten minutes later . . .

It had been posted on Twitter.

Nero ran back in and I already knew what had happened.

Dramatically as ever, in true Nero fashion, he knelt down on one knee and held his fist to his heart.

'First of all . . . you're my girlfriend now,' he said, out of breath from the scandal *he* was facing.

My eyes began to well up.

'Are you asking me or telling me?' I let out, my voice trembling.

'I've never done this before, so I'm just telling you. You're my girlfriend now so it's okay. I won't let you go through this alone, I'll protect you so nobody can chat shit.'

I pulled the blanket over my head, and began to sob.

'All the girls in the industry have sex tapes. Kim K!' he protested.

I sobbed even harder.

The tape was removed from Twitter within minutes and we never heard of it again. We were protected. I was protected.

And just like that, I was his girlfriend.

Just like when he wanted to give me his number, he simply gave it.

Now when he wanted me to be his, he made sure I was.

When I needed his protection most from a shot *he* had in fact fired, he struck for his prey.

It was a false flag attack.

14

Fire and desire

Things had changed between the boys. Well, between Nero and the boys. We no longer spent much time with them – Nero didn't even like us being in the same room as them. Instead, we'd stay in his bedroom and only set foot outside to collect food deliveries from the door.

We sat in bed discussing the music video treatment for a song he'd asked me to write, which he'd recorded in LA – 'Dream It'. At that time, he was relying on my vision a lot when it came to his music, his image and the marketing around it.

One Sunday evening, I watched his sad eyes wandering as he lay in bed staring at the ceiling. He spoke before I had the chance to say anything, knowing what I was going to ask.

'I just feel like nobody gets me,' he said. I stroked the side of his face to comfort him, moving in closer, encouraging him to open up to me.

'They never understand what I'm saying. I feel like I've outgrown them; I don't like being around them. I feel so alone and weird – I want to take this music shit seriously but they just want to get fucked up every night. Like right now I just walked in the living room and Mika is in there taking pills. He's been taking them for three days straight. It's fucked! . . . I'm alone,' he sighed.

'You have me,' I told him firmly.

He turned his head and rested his eyes on me. 'You're right.' He smiled. 'I have you.' He went back to staring at the ceiling again, his smile still lingering.

The following week, Nero asked me to prepare a presentation for a party he was throwing. I themed it as a 'white' party to represent a blank page and new beginnings as the new year was not far away.

On a cold December night, we were all dressed in white as we turned up to the Lightsvale, a venue in Hackney, east London. I wore a white silk mini dress and white strappy heels with my signature red lips, and my hair in long, bouncy curls.

The venue looked sick; the ceiling was entirely covered with white balloons.

After Nero performed, I noticed a girl wearing a T-shirt with his face on it standing by the barriers near where we were all sitting. She was shouting his name, repeatedly.

When Nero noticed the girl, he looked awfully uncomfortable.

'Seriously?' I asked him. 'Even her?'

She was the fourth girl we'd seen that night that Nero had slept with.

Nero grew frustrated. 'I don't know who's invited these girls,' he told me, scanning his surroundings. We'd been there for just under two hours but Nero was too agitated by this point to stay.

'Let's bounce,' he said, ushering me out with him.

We left through the back door. I felt kind of vulnerable leaving everyone else behind and walking the streets when most people were here to see him. As soon as one person noticed Nero and started asking for photos, the rest flocked towards him, creating an even bigger scene.

He was forced to acknowledge a few of them as we waited around for our Uber.

'Yo Nero, Nero, I'm such a big fan, can I get your autograph?' a guy said mockingly, walking over. He had his hood up, wearing an all-black tracksuit.

Nero let go of my hand and turned to face him. The man walked right up to him, until they were both uncomfortably close – face to face, chests puffed out.

I examined the man's face, trying to understand why I recognised him, but I couldn't see much with his hood pulled so far over his head . . .

Then I realised that it was Jude.

'So you've been telling people I'm a rapist, yeah?' Jude said, a taunting smile on his face.

'You tried to set me up, you could've ruined my life,' Nero replied, not smiling at all.

I looked around at all the random people walking by on the busy streets of east London on a Saturday night. Surely nothing bad could happen. *Please don't let anything bad happen.*

'I can still ruin your life,' Jude said, his chin raised high.

Nero glanced at me from the corner of his eye ever so slightly – enough for Jude to acknowledge me.

'You all right, sweetheart?' Jude turned to face me, taking a step closer. Nero moved his arm out in front of him, jerking him backwards, and Jude staggered a little. He was clearly intoxicated.

I pulled a disgusted face at Jude, but before I could say anything, Nero began to shout, 'Let's go, let's fucking do this right now,' as he pumped up his chest.

'Nero,' I said.

Nero proceeded to step towards Jude as Jude chuckled loudly, clenching both his fists.

'Nero, our Uber is here!' I let out, pulling him by his hoodie sleeve. 'Come on,' I urged, 'You can't be doing this in the streets.'

Nero let me usher him towards the cab, while his stance remained very much intimidating, prepared to lunge forward.

'You're fucking lucky, you know!' Nero shouted as he got in the cab beside me.

'Nah, *you're* fucking lucky!' Jude yelled back at him.

Just as we took off, I spotted a black van park right by Jude. The door opened, revealing four or five men, and Jude jumped right in. Then they reversed and took off in the opposite direction. That's when I realised that we really were lucky.

As we arrived back at Nero's, there was already an after-party taking off. We heard the music blasting as we got out of the lift and Nero kicked the wall with a huge grunt, shouting 'FUCK', in frustration.

Inside, we separated as I poured us drinks before I searched the apartment for Nero. I found him in Kai's bedroom, sitting on the edge of the bed, arguing with a girl. She wasn't dressed in white, indicating that she probably *wasn't* a fan.

'Nobody gives a fuck who you are anyway!' she yelled at him – to which I quickly interrupted, 'So why are you here in his home?'

She retorted, 'Fuck off with your ugly face and fake tits.' It was an accidental compliment since I didn't have fake boobs; my dress was just doing me justice.

The girl stood up and shoved me with both hands, so I lifted my hand and slapped her. She was at least twice as big as me and could have taken me out in a second, but the four vodka and Cokes had clearly given me confidence. She proceeded to raise her foot to kick me, but just as her foot touched my beautiful white dress, Nero jumped in between us and began to *strangle the girl*.

A flood of people poured in, separating them. Different boys yelled, 'Nero, chill!', *'Nero you've got too much to lose!'* as he fought them off, shouting the same things over and over.

'How fucking dare she? She touched MY GIRL!'

'She fucking touched Livia!'

'NOBODY TOUCHES Livia!'

I stood still in shock; I could not believe what I was seeing. I tried to stop him by grabbing his hands, I tried to yell his name, but it was like he just wasn't there. He completely lost himself for a few moments before he finally stormed out onto the balcony for a cigarette.

The next morning we woke up in his bed, still wearing our clothes from the night before. The night had been a complete mess. And we were feeling it today.

I unzipped my white dress and showered with him and then we lay in bed, staring at each other.

We did this quite often. Locking into what felt like the most electrifying moment in time, saying nothing with words, but *so* much with silence.

'I realised how much I love you last night … It's like you're … precious to me,' he told me.

My heart was beating so fast.

This was the moment I'd waited for all my life. The last year and a half had felt twice as long with everything we'd gone through, but it was all worth it just to get to this place. I believed he would always protect me after that. My heart let down its hundreds of walls, replaced with gateways of loyalty for his love towards me. It felt so real. It took exhaustingly long, but it was finally here.

I told myself that last night's behaviour was only because he was protecting me. It just showed how much he loved me, right?

We lay in bed and watched the second *Trainspotting* movie, which he needed both subtitles and translation for as he complained the Scottish accents were so thick.

We were interrupted a few times by partygoers – his friends had decided to keep going. They came in and told him the singer Doctor Blue had pulled up to see him. I saw him grow agitated, suffering from a combined hangover and comedown.

'How can they keep throwing parties and invite people to see me when I'm not even on that vibe?' he said to me when we were alone. He refused to leave the bedroom.

Ziggy came back in hours later, coked up, talking to us

about his childhood problems which he had concluded led to his compulsive lying.

'Like yesterday,' he said, 'it was me who invited those girls, that one girl, what's her name? Jourdann? She's mentaaaal – d-d-did you see her T-shirt?' he laughed.

It made sense that Ziggy would do something petty like that. He was still grieving the loss of Chiara and the family they could've had. He seemed broken – broken and filled with resent. It was scary to think of the lengths Nero could drive him to.

At this stage, I'd practically moved into Nero's bedroom. Another night I'll *never* forget while living in that room was when Kai mentioned that a boy was coming over. We'd actually kissed that summer, just a peck, while Nero and I were apart.

When I told Nero out of respect, he took a step backwards and bit his lip. Taking a big, deep inhale, he said, 'I'm not mad, I'm not mad, but I need to go and "bazz" someone.'

'Bazz' was a new word I'd learned around his gang – meaning to manipulate someone into thinking that something is true, or to manipulate them to do something for your own personal gain.

'No, Nero,' I said, leaping up from the bed.

Before I could grab him, he'd already run out of the room. He returned twenty minutes later with a beaming smile, panting heavily like he'd just feasted on the *biggest banquet of bazz*.

'I feel so much better. I told them all WHY *they* need girlfriends, and they all believed me!' He laughed as I stared back at him blankly. 'I told them, you know why you need a girlfriend? You need a girlfriend because you need someone to watch your LEGACY, someone who witnesses greatness. I spoke about it for ages and I watched them all look shook. Mika and a couple of the other boys pulled out their phones and started texting and calling their girls; they fully did what I said.'

He was so excited that he'd had a successful bazz.

'Watch, now they'll follow us. They were losing faith in me as their leader for getting in a relationship, but now they'll copy.'

I was taken aback by how fiercely Nero believed in himself, but in some ways, I'd spent so much of my life being insecure that I couldn't help but admire his confidence.

He bounced onto the bed, landing on top of me. He started kissing me everywhere, wrapping his arms around me as he rested his head in between my boobs – his favourite position.

He sighed deeply and let out an, 'Ahh, this is just great,' calming down like a child wearing off from a sugar rush in their mother's lap.

To my surprise, Nero turned out to be right.

The boys starting to move respectfully around us, each scoring a girlfriend who they regularly brought round rather than random different women each night.

Seeing Nero get high off the 'bazz' was the first time I saw in black and white how *supply* affected him. How it nourished him. Empowered him. Energised him. I had no idea how ravenous he would become for that supply.

Narcissistic supply

Narcissistic supply is a pathological need for excessive attention, validation and admiration, regardless of how it may negatively affect other people, their feelings, preferences or opinions. A narcissist will constantly need supply, and they are never full, constantly seeking more, it's the only way for them to cope with the world and thrive in life.

15

A trippy home planetarium Christmas

As much as he denied them, Nero did have a family. He was super close to his older sister Layla growing up; she had practically raised him by letting him sleep on her sofa when he'd been kicked out by his mother.

Layla had asked Nero to come over for Christmas, which was difficult as his mother would be there. Their relationship was tough growing up, but since he'd begun to make something of himself, she was genuinely proud of her son. They'd started to rekindle a relationship, especially since she had fallen ill with a pretty serious heart condition.

I encouraged him to go and make the effort with his family that Christmas, and he did, returning refreshed, revived and excited, showing me pictures and videos of his beautiful family.

For his Christmas present, I had bought Nero a home planetarium star projector that illuminated thousands of stars all over the room. I was so excited to give it to him as there couldn't have been a more perfect present for that boy. I had thought about it hard since I wanted something that'd inspire him and give him his own space when he needed it. Nero loved space. Sometimes it was the only way he could calm down or return to a solid state of mind. I also gave him a Louis Theroux T-shirt because he was infatuated with his documentaries. He forced me to watch every single one. I could name each working girl in the brothel episode if needed.

When I arrived at the door that day, he looked at the wrapped presents in my hands like they were explosives.

'You don't like the old-school red Christmas wrapping?' I joked as I removed my jacket, throwing it onto his bed.

He sat with the two parcels in his lap.

'You look like you've seen a ghost, Nero!'

'Oh, nah ... I just didn't know you were getting me gifts. I didn't get you anything ... This is really nice, Livia, thank you.'

I paused for a second before sitting down next to him.

'I don't care, I didn't buy them for something in return. Your reaction will be a gift enough!'

'They're just wrapped so nicely; I don't even want to ruin them.' His expression grew sadder as he examined the gold bow.

I realised then that he wasn't sad – rather, this act of kindness was foreign to him.

'Anyway,' I carried on. 'My family doesn't celebrate Christmas so I'm living my childhood dreams right now.' I started ripping apart the wrapping paper and Nero finally opened them.

Nero took off his woolly jumper instantly and slipped on the Louis Theroux T-shirt.

'This is legendary!' He laughed, lifting me up in his arms and spinning me around. He planted a kiss on my cheek before running into the living room, closing all the curtains and showing the boys the planetarium.

'She's fucking lit! She's the best person I've ever met, what the fuck!' I heard him yell from the living room as I smiled, knowing that he was living his childhood dreams right now too. His inner child finally felt a little Christmas magic.

We ate Christmas dinner out at some fancy Mayfair restaurant as a group, and then decided to go home and celebrate the rest of the night by taking some magic mushrooms. Most of the gang were with their families, besides those who didn't celebrate Christmas or didn't have families – Nero, Blake, Mika and me.

Nero and I were the only ones who hadn't taken them *properly* before (Nero had dabbled in LA but they were some mild chocolate kind, these were the real deal) so we were reluctant and started off slow, one fungus at a time. We moved a load of plants that were in Kai's room from a recent video shoot into the living room, creating a jungle-like shelter around the sofas. We switched the lights off and had the star projector on above us, the speaker playing music in the background as the psychedelics kicked in. I was assigned DJ that evening so I made sure to do a conscious job of playing classic bangers that nobody could complain about – aware of my biggest critics in the space among us.

After twenty to thirty minutes, overwhelming sensations of elation and a shift in intense focus took over me. The beauty of everything was right in front of me, which for someone with social anxiety was heaven. Even Blake, who I still didn't see eye to eye with, didn't bother me. I just felt so warm in the present moment. I didn't feel conscious of how I was being perceived, I didn't care – instead, there was so much to feel grateful for, all around me.

We ate eleven or twelve more and it began to feel like time didn't exist outside of that night. Gratitude overtook all ego as we danced to 'Dancing in the Moonlight', spinning beneath the stars. I can only describe the feeling as when people say, 'Dance like nobody's watching' – that's exactly what we were doing, not a worry in our minds.

Nero watched me twirling around in the centre of the living room, smiling softly, before he grabbed my waist. Then we ballroom danced together, beaming, our lips touching in between kisses.

We headed into the bedroom, tripping hard and feeling everything intensely in our mind, body and spirit. We took the projector with us, of course. We weren't even interested in sex. Nero played me the new Bon Iver album. If you've ever listened to Bon Iver sober, you can only imagine my experience on mushrooms.

We spoke about everything in that room, especially our fears. It was like we could talk about them without the attachment of anxiety and triggers from each word. Instead, we felt encouraged and safe. All the things that had ever been lost in translation between us emerged as the smallest, most solvable of problems. It was like we were shooting down each of them, as shooting stars fell down around us.

This had to be one of the most beautiful moments I've

experienced. I was floating on a whole other frequency. We had left Earth but we hadn't landed anywhere quite yet. We just remained content in space, among the cosmos.

I sat on top of Nero, fingers entangled, as I told him how much I loved him and the human being he was. How I was so glad that I finally felt love. I looked up at the stars around us as I smiled and swayed from side to side, letting the vibrations and the Milky Way and galaxies rush through my hair.

He stopped me for a second as he put his hand on my chest. On my heart. Placing his finger over my lips, asking me to be still and quiet, he looked like he was having some kind of epiphany.

'But what if . . . we were forever?' he whispered, eyes wide and eyebrows raised, observing the windows to my soul.

My imagination felt like it was bursting into flames, millions of intricate images, decades and centuries flooding my mind. For the first time, I imagined us old together, grinning, cuddling each other with our frail bones, after getting married . . . having kids . . .

He smiled a big delicate smile and gently teased, 'You'd never thought of that before, had you, Livi?'

16

Waterlight

To no surprise to anyone, Nero was being evicted from his third apartment. He'd reached the end of his tether with the boys, so after celebrating New Year's Eve together, he asked me if I wanted to get a place together instead.

I will never forget waiting for Ruby to get back from work that day as my broken heart lay pumping on the floor. How was I supposed to tell my best friend, who I had taken the city by storm with, that our journey was taking an unexpected turn? She was and will always be my soulmate. It was the hardest thing I had to do – I felt like I was betraying our friendship. But it turned out to be divine-like timing. She told me she was missing her family and that she was ready to move back home to Manchester. I cried because I cry at everything, but in this moment I cried because it was almost painful imagining not living with her.

'Stop it, I'm only two hours away on a train. We're going to see each other all the time,' she said as we cuddled on her bed.

Nero's label manager had sent his assistant, Karina, to help me look at properties. Nero trusted me – he didn't even want to view the place. By this stage, I was doing a lot of work for Nero: marketing, writing lyrics, music video treatments, presentations, whatever he needed. Eventually, he offered for me to come on board and work for him officially.

'Everyone in my crew works for me, you're a part of the crew – I don't want you working for anyone else,' he'd said. And I guess it just made sense. What could be wrong with living with and working for my boyfriend? My partner? My protector? He knew what was best for me, better than most, and so I trusted him.

Karina was odd; she was like a fan and an assistant at the same time. She would get drunk at events and call Nero at 3 a.m., asking for a number for coke. In the mornings, she was a messy scatterbrain hurrying him to rehearsals. It seemed like everyone did coke around him now, even his label manager, George, a tall, lanky white man who had no idea how to manage a young hip-hop artist at the best of times, especially as most of his clients were techno or house artists.

We viewed a property in Canary Wharf that was surrounded by buildings and traffic. Karina's choice. All of her choices were in congested and busy areas with towering building blocks closing us in. In the end, I went by myself to view a property I'd found online in Waterlight Quay, a new development in south-west London, overlooking the River Thames and the London Eye.

As soon as I walked in and saw the view from the eleventh floor, I knew it was the one. And I knew Nero would think it was too. The calm of the river met the London skyline, rocketing around the floor-to-ceiling glass windows wrapping all around the living room. Different-shaped buildings wrapped around the Thames as it trailed into the distance, bright red spotlights decorating the London skies. This flat was inspiring, the kind of view that made your problems feel so small – a breath of emotion, a breath of imagination, a breath of tranquillity. And so, we made it our home.

I'll never forget Nero's first time seeing it, on the day we got the keys. It was night-time and the whole of London twinkled over the dark river as he walked onto the balcony, grinning and laughing, pointing out at the view.

'Do you see that, Livi? That's the fucking Thames!'

Waking up with Nero was perfection. In our peaceful haven, there was no stench of weed, no unwashed red plastic party cups lying about. This was a clean, private little abode floating on the river. We were hyper-meshed by this point, as if someone had dislocated our hips and joined them together, intertwined and interlocked. We woke up early and sleepily rode together to meetings, interviews, studio sessions or radio interviews. I'd sleep with my head in his lap or vice versa, and I'd grab us lunch, our regular from Joe and the Juice – spicy tuna sandwich with extra avocado and an Iron Man smoothie.

He was my best friend. It was so comfortable and authentic, it always felt warm. We puzzled everyone with our synchronicity and seemingly telepathic communication. When we got home, we would order our favourite takeaways, watch a movie, go to bed, turn the projector on, have sex, read our prayers out loud to each other and pass out. We'd ask God for things for each other.

We went to Paris Fashion Week together that year, *finally*. Oh my God, I was so, so excited.

Nero had made a big brother-type friend called Axel Dupont, a French thirty-something-year-old who did styling and networking for him. Axel was a social butterfly; he knew *everyone*. He saw a big future for Nero, and he was connecting the dots to make that happen. It was odd because he wasn't getting paid, but the fruits of Axel's labour were just too sweet to be suspicious.

The boys came to Paris too, although it seemed that Nero did everything in his power to avoid them. There, Axel introduced Nero to Lumi Bjork, a famous A-list Swedish actress. Nero told me that he was convinced she had an infatuation with him. It was then when I noticed that he thought *every* woman he met had an infatuation with him, that they were 'telling him with their eyes' that they wanted him – deeply, obsessively wanted him, ready-to-rip-off-their-clothes, get-down-on-both-knees-and-suck-his-manhood wanted him. He was convinced he had this hypnotic effect over women; even over his friends' girlfriends. It was, of course, easy to believe at the time, given that I was utterly hypnotised by him. Why wouldn't everyone be?

After Fashion Week I even got a tattoo of his name on my arm. I know that most people would find that shit utterly deranged, but hear me out ...

It was his birthday soon, his mother was ill and he felt totally cast out by his boys. What better way to show him solidarity and loyalty through those uncertain times? I knew this was the perfect present for him. Nero needed *permanence* in his life.

I'd told myself I'd wait three more days until his birthday and hide the love heart with his name in it on the back of my right arm, but as soon as I got home I couldn't hold it in any longer.

Seeing the tattoo, he fell to the floor and kissed both my knees before lifting me up. He threw me onto the bed behind us, crawling on top of me, panting as his eyes shifted back and forth between mine. As if he was trying to believe what he was seeing. As if I was just too good to be true.

'I promise from this day on, I will do *anything* to be the greatest man I can for YOU.' He began to cry tears from happiness as he kissed every inch of my face.

I felt warm and fuzzy inside. I felt complete. I felt *whole*. You know that feeling when you know you are exactly where you are supposed to be in life, right here, right now?

'I just wanted you to know that I'm not going anywhere, I've got you,' I told him as he smiled and sighed, stroking my head in disbelief, teardrops rolling down his cheeks.

He took a picture of me sitting in his lap and showing my arm. He posted it on Instagram, captioned 'mine'.

17

Holocene

I lay in Nero's lap, watching the grey February clouds through the Viano window as we drove through Marylebone. Nero was on the phone with George, discussing his European tour the following week.

'Yeah, I'm gonna let Ziggy know this week ... It's time.'

Nero was preparing to fire Ziggy from being his manager because, well, Ziggy wasn't really doing anything ... He wanted to offer Ziggy some kind of creative direction role, so things wouldn't turn sour between them.

But it didn't just turn sour: it turned stale. Ziggy practically told Nero he hated him. He wouldn't even let Nero explain; the pain in his voice was pain built up from over the last six months – from hundreds of unspoken things.

Nero seemed defeated; I knew he missed his friends. We were spending too much time together. I knew it and he knew it – but neither of us wanted to say anything in case it stopped.

'I'm not going to come on tour with you,' I finally told

him, hoping to avoid the obvious having to come from him. After all, why would I want to go on a congested tour bus with seven or eight boys (and Karina, but she was never great company, drooling over my boyfriend)? Nero agreed but assured me that there were some layovers in cities where they'd stay in hotels.

'I'll fly you out then,' he told me.

The night he was leaving, I joined him on the bus as the rest of the boys loaded their cases. We sat opposite each other holding hands in the tiny lounge, which was fitted with an on-board studio, an intense red LED lamp flooding the space between us. We stared at each other awkwardly, unaware of how to say goodbye.

'You're going to make some of the best memories of your life, Nero. You're going to be back with your gang, proper bonding time. It'll feel just like old times,' I reassured him.

It was everything I had hoped for him. I knew that this was every young boy's dream – travelling the world, getting fucked up with their boys, performing at shows in new countries. Nero had been nervous that he didn't have friends anymore, but it was nothing that a few drunken nights on this bus fitted with ten bunk beds wouldn't solve. I also knew tours were not girlfriend-friendly. Tours meant shows; shows meant fans; fans meant what they refer to as 'bitches'.

'Please just . . . don't cheat on me, Nero.' I looked into his eyes, desperately searching for any kind of doubtful energy in response.

'I'm not going to,' he reassured me confidently.

We'd already spoken about my concerns. I was terrified

of being cheated on. Absolutely terrified. It's no secret what music artists' lives are set up to invite; it's no secret what hip-hop artists sing about. Dating an up-and-coming musician can give anyone an anxiety disorder. Anyone. But I trusted him: he wasn't a musician, Nero was my best friend. My partner. It was me and him, just us and our eccentric telepathy against the world.

'I'll never cheat on you, Livi,' he said. 'I swear on my mum's life, I'd never ever, ever do that. I swear to you I'm not a liar.' He pulled out his phone. 'Watch, I wanna make a video reminding all the bitches before this bus leaves.' I tried to stop him a few times, feeling shy and unsure but he insisted. He kissed my forehead repeatedly and then we both stuck our tongues out at the same time. He put a love heart emoji above my head and posted it on his Instagram Story.

On day four of the tour I flew out to Amsterdam to meet him. I remember walking down to a café close to where the tour bus was parked and jumping on him in the middle of the street as he spun me round and round with my legs in the air singing, 'Liviiiiiiii.' We were so happy to be reunited.

We went to our hotel room and he placed his hands around my waist, pulling me in closer to sit on his lap.

'Ugh, it feels so good to touch something so feminine,' he said, resting his head on my boobs.

I began to lecture him as he revealed the fact that he hadn't showered or really slept this *whole* time.

'Have you even brushed your teeth?!' I asked.

He was silent for a moment. 'My mum only has a week left to live,' he told me, his big, tired eyes staring up at me vulnerably.

My heart felt tight. I took a deep breath to compose myself. I remembered who needed who at this moment.

'When did you find out?' I asked.

'Layla called me just as the bus took off. I didn't know what to do, I just took bare drugs for days.'

'Okay ... I'm going to run you a bath and you just chill. I'll text Karina and George about what's going on, so you don't need to do any interviews before performing tonight – that's if you even want to perform?' I asked, to which he replied that he did want to.

'We need to go home and be with your family,' I told him, holding his hand.

'I can't leave the tour, Livi.' He looked down and then around hopelessly.

'This is more important,' I said, but he already knew, because for once he didn't argue back.

I did as I said and informed his management, who responded by reassuring me that the interview wasn't longer than an hour.

'He's not doing any interviews,' I replied bluntly.

Nero had been performing every night, hadn't really eaten, slept or showered *and* had been avoiding the fact that he was about to lose his mother. He had dealt with it by taking cocaine and ecstasy every night, but management still chose to treat him like nothing but a money machine, what the music labels were best for.

We flew back to London late the next night. It was around 1 a.m. when we reached home and we didn't want to disturb his mother's sleep so we headed back to the flat. At 7 a.m. we woke up to a frantic call from Layla and rushed to the hospital.

I'd never met any of Nero's family; this was the first time. I remember walking into the hospital room to find everyone crying. His mother had passed just moments ago as his siblings and family all surrounded her. I watched Nero walk over and sob on top of her. 'I'm sorry,' he cried, over and over. I felt my eyes stream uncontrollably as I tried to remain in the background and out of the way, feeling guilty for being upset. This wasn't even happening to me.

Nero introduced me to his family one by one. They were amazing, humble and beautiful people. They loved him so much. He even made amends with his other sister who he hadn't spoken to in years. They all made a promise to rebuild the broken bonds in honour of their mother.

When we walked out of that room, Nero held my hand and looked over to his mother. He kissed his index and middle finger and blew the kiss to her, smiling sorrowfully through his tears. 'Bye, Mum,' he whispered.

We left the hospital and took his older brother Oliver, who'd come from Paris, back to our home where Nero gave him trainers and some other pieces he loved. Oliver was one of the nicest guys you could ever meet, so light-hearted and gentle. I watched them reminisce about Nero's first Traza collab as they both laughed in disbelief because it was Oliver who had introduced him to Traza in the first place. It made me so happy that Nero could feel connected with his own blood on such a tough day. I leaned against the kitchen counter, watching them from a distance. It was as if his mother's energy had brought everyone back together that day. It was as if it had fixed her family.

Later, Oliver took me into the studio room for a word. He

thanked me, telling me, 'I'm really glad my brother has you. You seem really, really great for him, Livia.'

Nobody had ever even noticed me like that before. I told him I was honoured; it meant the world coming from him.

'I really mean that,' he replied.

After Oliver left, there was no convincing Nero not to go on tour. The way he dealt with his grief was to get straight back on the road.

'I need you to come with me,' he said, and of course, I agreed. I made him promise to stay sober with me though. I knew he would need to be clear-headed to navigate his grief.

We rode in an Addison Lee to Gatwick Airport, an hour's drive away. 'Holocene' by Bon Iver was on repeat the entire way, while Nero lay in my chest in the back of the cab, crying into his mother's cardigan that was curled up in his hands. I kissed and rubbed his head the whole way. I asked God to take away some of his pain and give it to me. I knew, with all of my being in that moment, that I'd do everything I could to be there for him and love him back to health. I loved him more than ever on that day. I knew what I needed to do; I knew what my mission was.

Protect and love Nero, always.

When we got out of the car at the airport, he said, 'The way you just held me that whole car ride, I know you're going to make a sick mother to my kids one day.'

18

What does grieving look like?

We were sitting in some shit Italian restaurant in Berlin, with the tour bus parked a hundred yards away. It was a miserable day. Everything in Berlin was just so grey and ... miserable.

'Can I please get some chilli flakes?' I asked the waiter.

'Just shut the fuck up and be grateful with what you have,' Nero scowled at me.

I could feel Mika's second-hand embarrassment while he sat next to us. I began to feel hot.

'Don't speak to me like that, Nero ...' I answered quietly.

As the tour progressed, I found that I spent most of my time attempting to keep him sober – explaining to him repeatedly why cocaine was the worst thing he could launch himself into – and the rest allowing him to take out each minor frustration on me, constantly reminding me that I didn't know what it felt like to lose my mother. I told myself that it was okay if he was moody and erratic, even if he was constantly embarrassing me in front of others.

I reminded him that it was okay if he needed to cry, but Nero, almost like a robot, had switched off all emotion. Apart from dedicating a performance to his mother, he acted as though nothing had happened. But I guess that's how some people grieve; it comes in all shapes and sizes.

On tour, the boys also ignored the fact that his mum had died. Nobody mentioned it; they simply continued on.

We slept together in a tiny single bunk bed surrounded by nine other bunks, all tightly slotted into the bus walls. I lay on his chest and listened to his heartbeat, trying to sense if he was okay, but he didn't give anything away. He was well and truly numb. The only time I felt anything from him was when he started taking my clothes off. Yes, even inside that tiny bunk with nothing but a curtain to cover us. Around this time, I started to wonder if Nero was some form of sex addict.

By the day of Nero's big finale show in London, I felt like I didn't exist. From the moment I entered backstage to when we got home and had sex that night, he was numb. Nero would be inside me and on top of me without acknowledging the fact I was even there. I would be longing for a connection in our most intimate moments but it was like there was a brick wall in between us.

The months after the tour were difficult, especially the funeral. We went to his mother's home prior, where he made a big point of keeping his designer sunglasses on and looking his best. He told me there would be some family members there that he didn't like, specifically an uncle he briefly lived with when he was back in Monaco. Nero wanted to show him that he was wrong for doubting him.

The rest of the family and friends were all lovely,

particularly his nieces and nephews from his eldest sister, Layla. Layla was someone every human could only be in awe of. She singlehandedly ran the funeral, completely holding it together and taking care of four grieving grandkids in the process. She didn't shed a single tear, I guess to protect their fragile hearts.

Only one of the boys showed up to the funeral to pay their respects.

Once we approached the casket, Nero broke down. I quite literally had to carry him out of that chapel. I could feel each and every ounce of his pain rushing through my veins, but my love for him gave me so much strength in that moment. I chewed all the pain up and spat it out like venom, continuing to hold his spirit up as high as I could. After the short display of emotion, he quickly retreated back to being cold, desperate for normal life to resume. Back to pretending nothing had changed, even though quite possibly, everything had.

My twenty-second birthday fell a few weeks after the funeral, and I woke up feeling awfully excited. I realised that Nero wasn't lying next to me, and I got out of bed as I heard Frank Ocean's *Blonde* playing in the living room. I knew he was arranging something special – that was my favourite album at the time.

'I need ten more minutes!' he yelled down the corridor, so I showered and got ready before seeing what he had waiting for me.

I walked into the living room to see a trail of rose petals leading to a table of gifts, cake, flowers, champagne and all my favourite foods. He had placed biryani on a plate, a whole avocado next to it and sweet potato fries in a bowl, regardless of the fact they could not and should not be eaten together. It was too cute.

And a card, a wonderful card, saying that he couldn't wait to marry me.

Signed *Nocto Procto*. A nickname I'd given him.

I felt so happy that I began to tear up. Together we lay on our sofa in our apartment high up in the clouds. The view always made it seem like we were floating during the day, making my birthday all that dreamier.

I didn't imagine then, my face glazed from tears of happiness, that I'd be crying for another reason later that same night.

We headed to the Pack with our closest friends, returning to our place to continue the festivities. Suddenly, mid-celebration, with a full bag of coke up his nose, Nero announced the name of another man I'd slept with to the room. Someone who was hardly even an acquaintance to him, someone who he'd known about since we first met. I stood in the doorway as everyone just stared at us.

'How am I meant to be okay knowing he's beat my girl? Do you see what I have to deal with?' he proclaimed loudly, his cocaine-infused eyes bulging out of his head, racking up another line with one hand.

'I didn't even know you then!!!' I let out as I felt tears welling up behind the angry mask I had quickly developed to hide from the embarrassment.

I began to wonder why I'd even opened up to him about my history with other men, but I knew exactly why I had done so:

he made me feel like I could. Nero was usually so cool about that kind of stuff. He wasn't ever the jealous type. I couldn't understand why it was suddenly a problem now, and as if he hadn't slept with more than half of the city. But that didn't even matter, why would it matter? The past was irrelevant to *us*. It was like he just wanted a reaction – why else would he cause a scene like that, totally unprovoked? Why else would he shame me in front of all his friends?

Not long after my birthday came festival season, and with festivals came even more drugs. The nights we once spent cuddling, giving our unwarranted ultra-critical commentary of *Peaky Blinders* or having brain sex under the planetarium, suddenly became very cold and very lonely. It became routine – he would message me around 1 a.m. requesting that I book him an Uber. This would be followed by two more hours of him either missing the Ubers or giving me a reason as to why he needed to stay at whatever afterparty for another 'twenty minutes'.

I would lie there, anxiously trying not to nod off in case he was too messed up to make it home all right. Nero's drug use had become a problem by this point. I couldn't count the number of times I'd had to brush his teeth for him, clean his sick or practically carry him into bed. Before he'd get in the cab home, I'd set alarms in case I fell asleep waiting on him. Once I knew he was in the Uber, I'd unlock the door, knowing I could finally doze off.

Nero's compromised spirit would eventually enter the room. Possessed by one of his horniest demons, he would demand sex as soon as he got in the bed. The taste of cocaine under his nose would always somehow end up numbing my tongue and the stench of liquor became a familiar scent inside my mouth. I don't know why I allowed him to use my body as a vice to nut just so he could fall asleep, but it was the only way he could sleep while high. Sometimes it became so routine I felt like I was there to provide a service and nothing more. The sex demon needed to be satisfied in order to stop pestering him. Quickly and vacantly, it was my only way of giving him peace. And of course, when he did cum, he would cum inside me. Even if I told him not to, even if I tried to stop him. Stopping him somehow made him more excited.

He actually told me that.

Sometimes he wouldn't want sex. Instead, he would stumble into the house and undress himself, crawl into bed and tightly clench his cold body into a ball against my naked, warm and sober body. He would let out sighs of relief, clinging on to me from behind in the foetal position. He'd tremble, his aura so vulnerable and broken.

In these moments, it was like the coke demons wanted to punish him. They couldn't possess him so instead they'd leave him defeated, left alone to deal with his own tormented soul.

He'd eventually fall into a deep sleep, sweating puddles of alcohol and drugs, gasping and flinching throughout the night. In the morning, his demons weren't there anymore. What was left was the lack of dopamine and happy chemicals, preventing him from being able to show happiness, or even an ounce of empathy or compassion.

The thing about comedowns is, they don't just last a day or two. Your dopamine levels become permanently damaged when you're a frequent drug abuser. This leads to a short temper, constant irritation and frustration, paranoia and terminal emptiness just to name a few symptoms. *All of these fantastic qualities were obviously compatible with a relationship.*

All of a sudden, we were arguing daily. Each argument stemmed from me attempting to express how I felt about ... anything. In return, he would present me with the harsh reality that he *could not* and *would not* empathise.

Can you imagine how exhausting that would be? Loving someone who lacked the *ability* to empathise?

It's like someone walking up to you and punching you in the face, and when you say, 'Ouch! That hurt!', they stare blankly back at you with no idea why you would say that. Or even worse, they get defensive about it. Now what if that inability to empathise wasn't just because of a drug-induced chemical imbalance? What if, instead, the part of their brain where they empathise just wasn't developed? What if it was a personality trait? Or rather, a personality disorder?

What if the times they did empathise were all an act because there was something to gain?

But what if there was nothing more to gain?

They've already got you.

And they made sure of it.

Wouldn't that be scary?

19

Feeling it

Nero left for Los Angeles to film his music video for his new song, 'Feelings'. I sent him a motivating text message as I always did on his big days. He knew I had a way with words and I showcased those ways often (words of affirmation *has* to be my love language).

While he was gone, I wanted to make him something special. Something to celebrate him and our friendship. Our love. I wanted to put an end to the arguments and put a smile on his face. I ordered an enormous piece of canvas and began making a vision board – I'm talking like seventy-three inches big. I took all of our dreams and put them on there for us to wake up to every day, to inspire us every day.

I pasted his head over Travis Scott's, performing to a huge crowd, and over Adele's while she held all six of her Grammys. I printed out a picture of the mansion from *Scarface* (his dream home) and added silhouettes of a family with kids. Pets. Dogs. I added art I found online that was symbolic of the Aquarius zodiac sign and some fish to represent Pisces. I added his favourite car. Different chakras, aligned to represent the inner peace and happiness we should strive for before all these materialistic things. The ocean, stars and the clouds. Erotic art paintings of figures with both our skin tones. Our photos and memories. In the middle, in the largest size I could print, I stuck my favourite photo of us, Nero smiling, looking down as I had my arms draped around him, kissing him on his cheek. I stayed up till 6 a.m. every single night for weeks, listening to Frank Ocean's *Blonde* until the sun rose over the Thames, as I excitedly pieced it all together.

A few days later, Nero landed back in London but he wasn't responding to my calls. I knew something had happened.

Earlier that week, he had posted one of the models from the video shoot on his Story. Out of curiosity, I clicked on her profile and saw her posting him on hers too. They looked kind of ... close. But when I asked him about her, he casually told me, 'She's just some video bitch.'

That night, I woke up sweating. It felt like there was a weight on my chest, or a bad energy conspiring against me. Almost as if there was some sort of ... impending doom.

What do we call it? Women's intuition, perhaps?

Nero's Instagram account was logged in on my phone – entirely of his own will because I used to plan his Instagram posts for him and he had told me to keep it logged in. My paranoia (gut, women's intuition, psychic abilities, whatever you believe in) led me to read through his messages. There was nothing. But then, it was almost like divine timing.

There she was. This 'video girl', Sabrina, had messaged him, in French. Right in front of my eyes, I saw the message pop up. There and then I saw him respond with the @ to his private page and then delete the message thread. I felt my heart fall out of my ass and splatter blood all over the shiny white stone tiles. In my head, the blood on the floor slowly formed into the shape of a clown.

I called Ruby. I was struggling to get my words out, almost laughing from disbelief.

'I'm being cheated on, I fucking *know* it, I know he fucked her the other night! I COULD FEEL IT.' I spoke like a madwoman. I had no real evidence but I didn't need any, I could just *feel it*.

'Just calm down and call him, be upfront about it,' Ruby told me.

So I called Nero right away. He unsurprisingly gaslit the living daylights out of my soul.

'You're crazy,' he shouted down the phone over and over. 'I told her to message me *there JUST* so *THIS* wouldn't happen, SO YOU wouldn't bug out! I already knew you would. She was just messaging me 'cos I needed her to get me some yay. Sabrina ... She's like a little boy. She's just one of us. Trust me, it's not like that, I'm not attracted to her, I just use her for yay. I don't care about Sabrina, everyone clearly knows that I have a girl.'

I tried to stay firm on the phone to him. I persisted by telling him that I wasn't stupid, but all the passion in the world wouldn't change the fact that I had little evidence. His version of events may well have existed in some reality – in a very, very different dimension maybe, but it could have.

'So show me the messages then? The ones on your other account,' I asked.

Of course he couldn't. Not before threatening to break up with me for being 'too nuts', conveniently buying himself a few hours. When he eventually showed me, the messages were just about sourcing cocaine. Deep down, I knew that the time bought had allowed him to unsend his messages, and he must have directed her to do the same on her end.

When Nero returned to London three weeks later, I had cut my hair short and was in the process of dying it blonde. Looking back, this was when I started impulsively changing the way I looked. He told me it looked nice, hugged me and then walked into the house. I watched his every move, trying to magically gauge from his energy if he'd cheated on me. No luck. So instead, I just tried to mentally move on.

Then, so excited that I could barely contain myself, I took his hand, guiding him to the living room and unveiling my masterpiece vision board . . .

His reaction was debilitating. He barely even took it in before looking away, telling me it was 'cool'. I nervously tried to bring his attention back to it, pointing out his favourite things.

'Wait but did you see the *Scarface* mansion? Like, can you believe that only costs four million? Didn't you think—'

But he just didn't care.

Nero loved art, he loved depth, he loved *his dreams and visions most of all*. I was so sure he'd be more excited by it, just like I was so sure he'd be more excited by seeing me. He travelled a lot, and usually, when he got home, he found it impossible to take his hands off me from the very moment he walked through the door. And I mean, he would begin undressing me from the moment he put his bags down. Why was he so distant? Wait, why was he standing all the way across the other side of the room?

I asked him, 'Why aren't you roasting?'

He responded, 'I've just been wanking bare.'

That evening he wanted to get away, so planned a few nights away at the Four Seasons at Ten Trinity Square for a spa weekend. That hotel became our regular spot after that – it was private, luxurious and somewhat still undiscovered.

That weekend, he was nice – aloof, detached ... but nice.

Or was the bare minimum just starting to feel nice?

After those two or three days, he returned to his usual routine.

Back to the studio.

Taking more cocaine.

Unavailable for love.

20

Don't do drugs, kids

Every time I woke up, I felt sad. Depressed, if you will. Like there was a longing in my heart. Like I'd woken up in the wrong dimension, in the wrong body, at the wrong time. I had a yearning inside me that was everlasting; a yearning that cried and ached, just wishing to be fulfilled.

Where did my love go?

I got into the routine of quietly leaving the bed to make Nero food, although most times he wouldn't join me and would instead heat it up later.

One evening we were watching a Louis Theroux documentary on drug addiction together on the sofa – Nero's choice. When he suddenly began sobbing, I turned to him, confused. He nestled his head in the middle of my chest, the place where he said he felt a 'healing, motherly golden energy'.

'I'm an addict,' he let out.

I paused for a second, before telling him it was okay.

'Now we know,' I said, 'we can do something about it.

You're young and you have an amazing life ahead of you. Isn't it great that you can deal with this now? Look how strong you are! This ain't nothing for you, Nocto Procto!'

'Please help me, Livi.' He looked up at me, his eyes watery.

It felt like a huge step towards getting him back to himself. Back to being my best friend.

'I'll always help you, do you understand that? I'm right here with you every step of the way, I promise. We'll do this together. We got this. I got you,' I reassured him as he hugged me tighter.

And I meant it.

Nero sent messages to everyone saying that nobody should visit him for three weeks; that he was locking himself in the house to get sober.

'I only need to be around Livi right now,' he told them.

For those three weeks, I made us a schedule and coached him through it every day. We woke up early, went on a walk or did yoga in the living room. I called my mother every day and asked her to help me with her recipes over the phone. I learned to cook – and well too, might I add. I made him healthy home meals: that shit's good for your heart. We watched inspiring YouTube videos together about sobriety. About life. We prayed together. We meditated. We ordered a PlayStation and played together, completing the whole of *Grand Theft Auto V*. He cried a lot and we grieved together. He made the most beautiful music in the home studio, with a spring in his step – a healthy mind and spirit. We worked out during the day and at the end of the night, when we lay together, he kissed my forehead and thanked me. Each time I'd tell him not to thank me, that this was what I was here for, and he'd snuggle right into that special spot on my chest.

One night, I bathed him. The bathroom was full of steam, and lots of glimmering tealight candles surrounded us.

Nero sat in the bath as I knelt on the heated floor next to it. I rolled up my pyjama sleeves, squeezed some body wash into my hand, and rubbed it into his knees and down his legs, then dunked my hands into water and washed the bubbles away.

'With these legs, you're going to walk. You're going to walk until you get to where you need to go, and you're going to keep going,' I told him as I kneaded love into his bones.

I lifted his hands out of the water and looked at both of them, then up at his face. 'With these hands, you're going to create the best music that's known to man. You're going to hold that microphone and you're going to sing into it.'

I washed his face and told him to visualise washing off any shame he'd grown to wear on it. I cleansed his eyes and told him to see clearer because there's so much beauty in everything around him, that he had so much to be grateful for.

'Once, you couldn't even imagine that your life would be like this ... Now, your imagination is limitless, because you know you're capable of anything, anything you imagine ...' I told him, rubbing water into his temples, washing his forehead and the back of his neck.

I kissed his forehead long and slow, before finally letting go.

I'll never forget how in love Nero was with me in that moment.

'You're actually a G, you know ...' he said delicately, his eyes switching back and forth between my eyes, filled with tears and what looked like disbelief.

'You've helped me beat this addiction. I finally feel myself again ... I couldn't have done it without you. I'll love you forever. You are the one,' he said, kissing me back on the forehead, long and slow.

Everything felt so pure – we were so pure. And all the effort I'd put into helping him get off the coke was worth it. Every damn moment, just to see that look of true relief on his face.

He wasn't the problem, the drugs were.

And the next morning when I woke up, I knew I was waking up next to my partner, my love, my amazing, unique and wonderful Nero. But the longing in my heart, the loneliness, it never went away ...

I wish I could tell you that these times lasted. I helped him get clean around four or five times over the course of our relationship, with the same home rehab remedy. But it never lasted. I'll never truly be able to describe how hard it was each time he got sober and then abandoned me when he relapsed.

Every time I got my best friend back, I was so relieved that I felt like I was high off the love I'd waited so patiently for. The love I'd so desperately worked for. I poured everything into him, using every fibre of my being to get him better, but he'd always go back to his demons. It's like the lighter he was, the bigger the demons he'd attract. Like a moth to a flame.

Everything I poured into him, he poured into them.

The more I tried, the more I loved, the more I was pouring straight into *them*, and each time he relapsed, it was worse than the last.

What hurt most about it all was the gaslighting. One drink would turn into two, three drinks would turn into five, and then we'd be arguing in public over whether it was acceptable to take 'one line' or not.

To make things even worse, Axel Dupont was even more addicted than him. I'd have him breathing down my neck with his arm around me, telling me in his thick French accent that this was all just 'okay'.

'Chill, Livia, relax!' he'd laugh, reassuring me that it wasn't a 'big deal'.

But that was the problem. Nobody believed that it was a big deal. They never saw him cry, they weren't the ones to get the brunt of it when we got home. They didn't have to live with the demons the coke brought to bed with us. They didn't have to turn their emotions or basic needs off and suffer in silence. They weren't losing the man they loved over and over again.

As the woman who loved him, how could I watch him deteriorate? How could I watch him self-destruct? What kind of girlfriend would that make me?

Nobody believed me. Nobody cared until it started affecting the money, until he started walking out of the studio, pulling out of shows, cancelling £90k performances abroad the day of flying, having breakdowns in hotel rooms, accusing everyone of disrespecting, disobeying and underrating him. His friends, Axel, even his fans. Constantly complaining about his success, bashing on any other hip-hop artist who was achieving anything.

'I'm better than him, I'm the BEST IN THE UK,' he'd shout down the phone at Axel, at his label bosses, hanging up when they tried to remind him that he was doing amazingly, that he was going to get there too. He grew to obsess over other rappers who were thriving, creating imaginary beef with them, vendettas even. Throwing tantrums in private after they'd spud him, demanding that everyone reassure him that he was *better* – better dressed, better at making music. Walking out of venues in a rage if they had a better audience than him. He was impossible to disagree with, impossible to work with. When people tried to give him constructive criticism, he'd storm out. He'd threaten to take away their roles for simply having an opinion. All of a sudden, everyone wanted to take the drug problem seriously. Axel started calling my phone, asking for my advice, but he was addicted himself. He couldn't help but fall into temptation with him over and over again.

He was the one helping Nero dig his own grave – and mine too.

21

Police, ambulance and a fire engine

Nero's addiction got so bad that I had begun waking up to the sound of him smashing things in the house when he returned home in the early hours.

The second time there was broken glass across the kitchen floor, I got out of bed, sleepily rubbing my eyes as I began shovelling the glass away.

'What the fuck, Nero . . .' I said wearily as I cleaned up.

He sat on the end of the sofa, smoking a cigarette. It must have been around 4 a.m. He didn't even look at me, nor speak a word, so I just turned around and started walking back to the bedroom.

'I'm going to bed,' I said as I left.

I got into the still-warm bed, closed my eyes and dozed off.

I woke up, feeling Nero's hands groping my boobs from behind me. I let out a soft moan.

'I'm too sleepy, Nero,' I whispered.

He pushed up against me harder and wrapped both his hands around my neck from behind me. In my ear he told me, 'I love you so much.'

I realised then that he hadn't said that in so long.

He started kissing my neck. This felt different: it didn't feel cold and vacant. I felt somewhat desired and somewhat desire – it felt just like love.

I turned over to face him, kissing him back as he licked his fingers and moved his hands into my pants. He played with me, rubbing gently until my legs were clenching around his hand, before he got on top, pulling my knickers down.

He pulled his boxers down and stared at me for a second, touching himself.

A second turned into a few . . .

My breathing slowed down as I anticipated his next move. I leaned forward in an attempt to pull him down on top of me, but he told me no.

He continued pleasuring himself, staring at me intensely.

'I want you to sleep,' he said.

I frowned. Confused, I replied, 'Umm, you don't want to have sex?'

'No, I want you to pretend you're asleep.'

I laughed nervously, 'What!?'

Nero and I had what I would call a pretty normal sex life. I mean, outside of the quantity being rather excessive due to his obvious sex addiction, and outside of some unserious neck grabbing, we hadn't experimented much.

'Why do you want that?' I asked him.

'Because I love you. You're mine and I want to feel like I

can have you all the time,' he explained, his voice sounding a little hesitant.

I looked to the side as I thought about it for just a moment, but Nero got back on top of me ...

He began thrusting a few times as I moaned, and then he stopped. While still inside me, he brought his hand up to my mouth and covered it, then brought his other finger up to his lip, as I stared at him wide eyed.

'Shhh,' he whispered.

Then he removed his hand from his lips and brushed it over my eyes. 'Sleep,' he whispered, and my eyes stayed shut.

He continued having sex with me. I couldn't help letting out a moan but that seemed to annoy him and he squeezed his hand over my mouth tighter. He was eventually squeezing so hard that my lips were hurting as they pressed against my teeth.

But my eyes, I kept them shut. I kept them shut tight. For some reason, I almost felt like I had to ... I felt like I needed to lie there, somewhat limp and lifeless ... to make him feel good. I was scared to open my eyes and see him, or see what demon was in place of him.

Nero came faster than he ever had before, then he rolled over and practically fell straight to sleep.

I lay there awake, staring at the ceiling.

The next morning, Nero rang Axel when he woke up. He was hysterical about an advert for his upcoming mixtape release, crying that they had placed him on a banner with 'similar' artists that he felt he was better than, and shouldn't be compared to.

Then he demanded cocaine right in front of me. It felt like a bid to taunt me, doing it so brashly while staring me in the eyes, like he wanted me to react. How couldn't I?

We broke out into an argument and in the heat of the moment, I started to panic. I couldn't stand another night of Nero taking cocaine. I felt insane, I felt delirious. I felt like I *had* to stop him from leaving me again this time. In my blind panic, I ran to the bathroom cabinet, grabbed a packet of painkillers and chucked them down my throat.

I'm not sure if it was a cry for help, or if I was just that desperate for him not to return home possessed that I did something so stupid. I risked my life just to make the vicious tormenting cycle stop. I was fed up. I was *that* desperate.

Before he could even react, I ran to the bathroom and stuck my fingers down my throat. I knew what I did was ridiculous. But he called the ambulance anyway.

In the hospital, while waiting for my test results to make sure the painkillers had not reached my blood, Nero turned to me.

'I don't love you. Imagine you had killed yourself in my house? What would that have done for my career?' he said coldly.

I felt numb just lying there, staring at the dull hospital ceiling above me as he told me he didn't want to be there with me, that he was itching to go out and get high.

He had the nerve to say, 'See, this is why I have to take drugs. How am I meant to deal with my *crazy fucking girlfriend*?'

After my dedication to ending his fucking addiction,

after he'd asked and *begged* for me to take him back, that was enough to tip me over the edge.

I remember trying to run out of that hospital. I got up off the bed and headed towards the exit. I was so over everything. *I could have run in front of a car at this point and not cared. I felt so discombobulated.*

The nurse tried to stop me from leaving and called security while Nero chased after me, shouting. When security tried to grab me, Nero started fighting with them, yelling 'Nobody fucking touches her'.

He began to argue with the nurse, who already disliked him for his attitude during my assessment. She had ended up asking him to leave during it because he kept telling me that I was pathetic, that it was taking too long, that he was a 'rockstar', that this wasn't the type of life he signed up for. He had responded to her dismissing him by asking her if she was 'a bitch' because her job was so 'shit'.

'Do you know who I am?' he asked her. It was how he was with all the waiters, call representatives, Uber drivers ... 'I'm a fucking star'.

It was a mess.

They were eventually so fed up with us that we were allowed to go and wait at home for my test results (not protocol). Before we walked out, I was given the result of my urine sample by a nurse.

'You're pregnant,' she told me.

It was like her words never even entered my mind. I heard her but I stayed completely silent.

Suddenly all the extra hormones and feeling crazy enough to take an overdose made sense. Well ... as much sense as doing something like that ever could. I just didn't feel like myself. I felt like I'd lost all control of who I was. I guess I had been so lost in Nero's addiction that I'd totally neglected any responsibility towards my body.

Who was I becoming?

At home the argument escalated – Nero told me immediately that he couldn't have a baby.

'Can you at least think about it for more than a second? It's a whole baby!' I yelled, standing in our bedroom.

'If I have a kid, it will fuck my whole career,' he shouted.

I could hardly believe what I was hearing. 'Oh my God. IT'S NOT ALL ABOUT YOUR CAREER. IT'S A BABY, A LIFE!' I screamed back.

He got angrier, pointing at the door. 'GET OUT!' he shouted.

I paused. I was so confused.

'What do you mean get out? This is my home too, Nero!'

Somewhere in between all the arguing about the baby and him kicking me out of our home, the police came to the door. They separated us to ask what had been going on before telling us we needed to be physically apart before they could leave. Even that somehow ended in us arguing with *them* about why we should stay together. After some time, we reached a compromise – Nero would take a fifteen-minute walk.

Eventually, they left, giving us the perfect opportunity to continue arguing. Things got more and more heated as we stood by the bed, shouting in each other's faces. That's when Nero told me he couldn't have a child with me because I was too 'crazy'.

'Look how you're screaming right now,' he said, as if he wasn't screaming back. As if he wasn't making me feel like I didn't have any right over our baby. As if he hadn't just taunted me in hospital for hours.

I began to respond with, 'You're the most fucking horrible—'

I can still feel the impact of the slap across my face to this day.

The smack was so fucking hard I completely zoned out of reality and went into shock . . .

. . . When I came to, Nero was holding both my hands that were automatically shielding my face. He was trying to move them, saying, 'Livi! Livi! It's me. It's Nero!'

I felt tears streaming uncontrollably, my left cheek burning as I sobbed into my fists, still protecting my face.

It was over. It was done. We couldn't come back from this. Why did he have to hit me?

This is where it would end. It was done. It was *literally* done.

He really didn't love me . . . You wouldn't hit someone you loved.

He didn't love me. You protect people you love.

He laid me backwards onto the bed as I continued to sob, and climbed on top of me.

'I'm so sorry, I'm so sorry. It was just a reflex when you were shouting at me. I'll never do that again, Livia. Let's keep the baby, Livia, I want to have our baby.' He begged me as he lifted my T-shirt and started kissing my stomach.

He kissed my mouth and then my neck as we both cried. He started pulling my tracksuit bottoms off and took out his dick. He kissed me so hard as he began fucking me, saying over and over, 'I'm so sorry, Livi, let's have the baby.'

I lay there, face soaked in tears, and just let him. I'd re-leased so much cortisol, the stress hormone, that day that the influx of serotonin from the sex felt *so* good. It was like a rush. And that very rush is exactly why everyone wonders why make-up sex feels so good. Instead of going from zero to one hundred during intercourse, you're going from minus one hundred to one hundred. It's like taking drugs and *just* as addictive. The high only feels so good because the low feels so bad. That high is what you become addicted to. *This* is trauma bonding.

A week or so later, Nero's manager George, Axel Dupont and Layla became very involved in the baby situation.

Layla's stance was simple. 'You can't get rid of my niece or nephew. Mum just died and she has given you this baby. Three people have fallen pregnant since she died. This is spiritual,' she said.

Since Ruby wasn't really aware of Nero's behaviour – due to me hiding it so that she wouldn't become concerned – she wasn't totally against it. She just reminded me over and over to take my time and not rush my decision.

George was as emotionless and shallow as you'd expect a label-appointed manager to be, with his, 'If it doesn't make me money I don't *fucking* care' attitude.

But Axel ... Axel had a plan. He had just dropped the bomb on Nero that he would only continue to work with him as his manager, the role George was obviously already con-tracted to do, which revealed just how smart Axel had played the whole thing. He took shiny networking opportunities, cool brand deals and clout-y connections and shoved them in Nero's face (for FREE) until George began to look lame and out of his depth. When Axel demanded the managerial position, Nero just *had* to submit.

So, while Axel was in a legal battle over George's position, why the fuck would he let a *baby* get in the way of all the money he was plotting to make? Instead of giving any real advice, Axel instead told Nero a horror story about someone in his family who'd had a baby really young and it drove his entire family apart. The child went into foster care and the father had to fight for years to see her.

'We chose this life. I would be lying if I didn't wish it was easier sometimes, but we wouldn't trade it for the world. We don't want normal lives, and these are the sacrifices we must take to make it,' Axel texted Nero.

The week progressed. In between Nero regularly changing his mind, our explosive arguments and him constantly breaking up with me and then asking for me back within a few hours, there must have been some kind of evil energy in the air. Not only did the police and ambulance service end up at our door, but even the fire brigade came when I accidentally set some toast alight while cooking breakfast on the grill.

Thankfully, since I switched the grill off and closed the oven door right away, it suffocated the flames. But despite the panic – running down the eleven flights of stairs while the fire engines arrived and having a complete meltdown seeing all the young kids in the lobby – I'll never forget Nero telling me, 'If you burn my house down, I'll never forgive you. You're going back to Scotland.'

The man wanted *me* to burn.

One of those nights in that hellish week, we got into another argument. Nero threw some noodles at me from the

Chinese takeaway we were having. I picked up some water and he ran away as I squirted it on his back. We were laughing but the battle was no joke. I ran into the bathroom as he got some ketchup and squirted it in my hair, to which I got the shower head and totally soaked him with it.

We both sat in the bathtub moments later, facing each other, eyes locked without saying a word. We were letting our eyes do the talking, and even then, there was so much they were too afraid to say. The energy was so damn sensitive.

'I'll never love *anyone* as much as I love you, Livi,' he told me.

'Neither will I, Nero,' I said as I lay my head onto his chest. He wrapped his arms around me.

It was a true Harley Quinn and Joker moment.

And then, another evening, Nero offered me money.

'What if I give you five figures? To sort your life out after the baby, get a place ... We go our separate ways. You've done a lot for me, all the work you've done, you deserve it ...'

I started to cry. I felt so abandoned and confused.

'I don't want money, Nero, I don't want anything. I just want us to stay together.'

By this point, I'd begun to lose all sense of who I was, what I stood for or what I fell for. The pregnancy hormones had me feeling like I could break at any given moment. I couldn't think clearly. I felt fragile. My body felt weird. I'd been ignoring all my friends – not on purpose, I just didn't have the energy. Or more so, I didn't have the energy to tell them what was *really* going on. I'd put so much time, so much effort, so much love into this man, into this home, I just couldn't walk

away. I knew I should. After all, we were both pretending
that he hadn't slapped me the other night. But I also thought
I shouldn't because at the end of the day, he was an addict
who'd just lost his mum. He needed me.

Just like he'd always said, 'I need you Livia, I have no one.'

That was why he had raised his hand to me, I told myself.
He was grieving, and grief makes you act out of character. I
forgave him. He was sorry, he was going through it, so I forgave him. He was damaged: I felt bad for him so I forgave him.
He was suffering: I knew I could help him so I forgave him.

I felt so lost and confused, and I think that was why I
wanted the baby so much. I felt like my only purpose was to
be a mother, and I was already in love with our unborn child.
Some nights Nero and I would lie in bed and imagine our
little baby lying between us.

'It would look half like you and half like me,' he'd tell me.

My heart would stop beating in that moment, as I imagined
that beautiful child. We'd joke about how the baby would be
super creative and just a little crazy. How we'd protect him
or her from the world, making sure they'd have a healthy and
happy loving home to grow up in – unlike ours. Ironically,
unlike the one we were living in right now.

Eventually, as the week ended, Nero gave me an ultimatum.

'If you have this baby, I'm breaking up with you and you'll
have to raise it alone. If you get rid of it, I'll know how much
you care about my career and I'll stay in this relationship with
you.' He followed this up with, 'When we're both ready later,
we can have the baby. I know you'll be the best mother ever,
but just not right now.'

I felt stuck. Like I had no control over what I could do

about this little life making a home somewhere below my stomach.

I agreed to the abortion on the basis that I couldn't raise the baby alone, and nor did I want to. He knew I had no choice, considering I worked and lived with him.

'Your life will be over. You'll have nothing, no home, not a penny for the baby,' he told me.

Later that week, Nero convinced me to create a new Instagram, telling me it was a better look for when he was super famous, just in case there were any messages from other men that could be pulled up.

'No one should have had access to *my* girl,' he said.

To end the week from hell, Nero ripped up the vision board I'd made for him in a fit of rage. The reason? Tobias had sent me a follower request on my new account. I hadn't even accepted it.

Fuck you for that, Nero.

That shit was art.

22

Wear all black

The day of the abortion, Nero arrived home from a festival he'd performed at in northern England. He sat down on the bed next to me. I was lying down, facing the other way and crying into the pillow.

'I've had no sleep, I'm on the maddest comedown. Let's do this, Livi.'

As I got up to get ready, he told me, 'Wear all black.'

Maybe he thought it was going to be some kind of funeral, but one thing was for sure, Nero's energy was very dark and very conniving that day.

Something was in the air. It was so grey outside, a greyer-than-usual London sky. In the Uber to the abortion clinic, I started freaking out. Thinking about how ungodly this was, that God had given us this baby for a reason, that this was my God-given chance to be a mother, I felt trapped by his ultimatum and so bloody alone. I was stuck between a rock and a hard place, scared to make the wrong, irreversible decision.

To make things worse, he had George on speakerphone as some sort of mediator, whose only suggestion was, 'This is the only day Nero can come with you for the abortion, his schedule is really busy.' You couldn't even make this shit up.

How did I have just a week to decide something I could never come back from?

Mid meltdown, there Nero was ... recording me. Seemingly for his own amusement, he had his phone out recording me crying.

What is this place? I thought to myself as I cried harder.

I finally called Ruby and sobbed down the phone. 'I don't know why he's doing this.' All she could do was echo my thoughts. 'Why the fuck is he doing that?'

Nero was truly possessed. It was like he enjoyed pushing me that little bit closer to the edge. My emotional state was so bad in the clinic that the nurses almost refused to do the surgery. They had to take me into a private room to confirm that it was my choice. I pleaded with them to allow it to happen as Nero was losing his patience with me.

'I'm just sad but I know I *need* to do it,' I told them.

After I woke up from being sedated, Nero was there next to me. He kissed my forehead and giggled at the gibberish I was speaking coming off the drugs. Everything felt calm, like it was in slow-motion. I slept in his arms in the cab home and once we got back, he put me in the bed and disappeared.

I woke up from my nap feeling vulnerable. I held my stomach and the energy that I once felt there was gone. I felt awful. Regret began to attack me from every angle, and I found myself searching for Nero's reassurance that this was the right decision. He was on the sofa in the living room, so I walked in and lay down beside him. He shrugged me off.

'Why aren't you hugging me?' I quietly asked, puzzled.

It was like now the baby was gone, so was my value to him. As if he was disgusted by me for having the abortion or something. He was so cold. I felt my heart fill with anger as I grabbed both his hands and sat on top of him.

'NO. You're not doing this today! You're not doing this to me when I need you most. I did this for *you*.'

I saw his eyes light up. As he scrunched up his face, whatever I could feel in the air that day, it looked me right in the eye . . .

He bit his bottom lip in anger and let out a grunting sound. He grabbed my face tight in his hand and threw my head hard, backwards off the sofa and onto the cold, solid floor. He got up off the sofa and stood above me, repeatedly kicking my legs and my sides. When I eventually managed to get up, I looked him right in the eyes again, this time pleading, tears flooding down my face as I tried to catch my breath, struggling to hold myself up. He stared back at me, panting, raised one foot up high and he kicked me in my stomach.

That one killed me the most. In my stomach. Where our baby *just* was.

He grabbed me by my shoulders, pushing me into the balcony's glass door, and then walked out of the room. I lay on the floor, against the glass, for what felt like just a second before he came charging back in.

He had a hammer in his hand.

He waved it around, smashing holes into the living room

walls, laughing psychotically as he brought it right over to me, knelt down on top of me and held the hammer right up to my face. He pressed its cold end hard onto my cheek, breathing heavily as he said, 'I'll fucking kill you.'

I closed my eyes tight, waiting for the impact, sobbing uncontrollably.

I accepted my fate. He was filled with so much rage that the next hit would kill me. But then he stopped and simply walked away into the bedroom.

I grabbed my phone off the sofa and FaceTimed Ruby right away. That was when I first noticed my burst lip. I think I had bitten into it from the impact of being thrown to the floor.

'You need to leave right now, Livia. Go to Juno's,' she told me. Juno had just got her apartment in London that week.

I grabbed my Supreme fleece jacket from the hallway, put on my trainers and ran. I had nothing else on me. Not a penny.

Juno booked me an Uber and I got in. I cried the whole journey, wiping the snot from my nose on my fleece, shaking and whimpering. I noticed the top of my hand was bleeding. It looked like his nail had dug a chunk of my skin out. When did that even happen? My adrenaline levels were so high it all felt like a blur.

The Uber came to a halt, and I began panicking, asking the driver why. It turned out that Juno had accidently booked an Uber Pool because she was drunk. I got out, overwhelmed by the thought of sitting in a car with some stranger while all beaten up and crying. I sat on a step on a street corner. I think I was somewhere in Angel, north London. I didn't feel like life was real. Sensory overload had depleted me. Everything was moving at super speed around me.

I felt like I was on pause, totally numb.

Totally dissociated from reality.

Unable to feel or hear anything.

I felt non-existent.

Unalive.

My phone began ringing. It was Axel.

It snapped me out of my trance, reminded me that I still existed, just for a second.

'We are your family, we're going to figure all this out. Where are you? Please come home. You deserve to be at home going through your abortion, I'll take him to my place.'

There was nothing I wanted more than my bed. And an apology. And an explanation. Actually, a time machine: some way to reverse the irreversible.

Axel booked me a car home. If I only knew then the relief I gave them by not going to the police or a hospital. I fell right into their trap.

Juno insisted that she wanted to come and see me, but I was at my wits' end and just needed to sleep. I didn't even explain to her what had really happened.

The following two nights I was completely alone. I think I almost lost my mind on those evenings, when Nero was no-where to be found. I waited for a call, for a text, any kind of apology. Anything to feel like it was all real, like it had even happened. But there was nothing. All I had were the bruises and cuts.

Axel even stopped responding to me. *They both blocked me.*

I didn't want to call Ruby because she was on holiday in

Spain and I knew her not being here would upset her too much, so I told her I was resting. I told her I was okay.

I sat on the bathroom floor and sobbed as I bled out my abortion, hating him, hating that I was going through this alone. I wondered what I ever did to him to deserve this, thinking over and over again how much I'd never do this to him. How I'd never hurt him or leave him all alone with all his demons in the aftermath of their attack.

I felt like a piece of fucking trash, thrown away, pressed into landfill and buried. I cried at my bruised, naked body in the mirror. I had a scab on my lip. I didn't eat for three days. I didn't have money nor a desire to either. Nero had initially promised me that he'd pay me for working for him, but that had never happened. At night I had dreams about the baby– or nightmares, rather. During the day I just lay in bed, replaying what had happened in my head. Feeling the kicks on my back and my leg. Feeling the hard grip of his fingers pressing into my arms as he threw me around, his hands squeezing my face so tightly. The look on his face, showing zero remorse as I held my stomach and cried after he had just kicked it.

Suddenly the doorbell went. To my fucking shock and horror, to my fucking disbelief and some kind of fucked up relief – it was Nero.

He was alone. He came in and sped straight past me, grabbed one of his duffel bags and began packing. Quickly throwing his things in the bag, I realised that he was packing for Paris – he was going there for his mixtape launch.

'D ... Do you need help with anything?' I asked pathetically.

Why the FUCK did I ask that?

I was too scared to say anything else in case it set him off. I desperately needed some kind of resolution before he left again: I needed him to free me of this pain and torment. I needed him to answer all the *'why*'s in my head. I felt like I was in a mental prison; there must have been *something* he could do to help me escape. I was alone and scared and he was the last thing that felt like home. He was meant to protect me. He was my best friend and that, for some reason, didn't change despite what he'd done to me.

'You should get out of this house as soon as you can, or they're going to get an injunction on you,' he said.

'What's an injunction?' I asked, beginning to sweat.

'A restraining order,' he replied.

I sat on the bed in disbelief, staring blankly ahead. As he headed to leave, I snapped out of my shock and cried out, 'Wait!' I ran to the door and stopped him.

'You're just going to leave? Just like that? Nero, I need some answers. What should I do? Where should I go? You ... you left me, you hit me, you beat me up ... I'm still bleeding from my abortion!'

Tears streamed down my face. He rolled his eyes as he opened the door to leave. I held on to his arm and tried to pull him back.

'I'm scared, Nero, please. I did what you wanted me to do. Now please, please just tell me what to do? Please,' I begged frantically.

He tugged me off his arm and I immediately took a step back. I stood still and stared at him. Becoming aware for the first time that he might actually hit me again. Realising that I was afraid of Nero.

What he said to me as he walked away is impossible to forget.

With one long look, scanning me from my feet up to my face, in disgust, he said:

'I don't even recognise you anymore.'

23

Staying pure

After Nero let it be known that he and his team were only cruel enough to invite me back into my 'home' to try and gather evidence that he needed a restraining order against me, best believe I swiftly packed my things and left for Juno's.

I didn't hear from him *once* during that first week he spent in Paris, but one thing he did do was post Sabrina, the girl from LA, on his Instagram Story, with hearts next to her head.

I wasn't there for the launch of *Seratonin*, the album that I'd named – and helped to write.

He eventually contacted me, offering me money – if I signed an NDA. He offered the same five-figure sum he'd offered a while back, in exchange for my silence – the promise that I would never tell anyone what he did to me.

Was that the best his team could come up with for damage control? Was that even legal?

Seeing the document made me quiver. It just looked so official, so overwhelming.

From
Nero Kouassi.
To
Livia Dalia.

I remember dreaming about seeing our names together on some kind of marriage certificate. I just never thought I'd see them together on a deed of confidentiality.

I spent a few weeks with Juno, and Ruby came to visit. The time spent with my girls was euphoric. It's like I could feel the white blood cells in my body working together to replace all the broken brain cells I'd been left with. Each day they cleansed away the brainwashing and each night they untied the blindfold that love for Nero had left me in.

The energy of being around people who loved me (or not being around someone constantly breaking my boundaries and manipulating me) quickly became enough to remember that *this* was what life was supposed to feel like. Isn't it crazy how quickly we forget?

Us humans, we're creatures of habit. And just like a habit can form, it can break too. But that takes discipline.

The girls and I spoke about the NDA and after much de-liberation and agreeing that I *needed* the money, we concluded that I couldn't take it. The love I'd felt was real and it wasn't going to end with some hush money. It just didn't feel right, after everything we'd been through, to be silenced and paid off. This was the realest shit I'd ever experienced.

My friends persuaded me to go to the hospital to document my injuries, and to the police too. The doctor was so nice. When he asked me what had happened, I cried like I had never cried before. It was such a release. He told me I had whiplash; his face looked so saddened by the whole ordeal.

Next was the police station. I walked out twice midstatement, having a meltdown, before they told me that I could make the report that day, but I didn't need to go ahead and press charges yet. I spent some of those nights feeling lost and scared about my next move in life, but Juno supported me, helping me make a CV to apply for jobs. I was heartbroken, yes, but I could feel myself getting healthier. I had been skin and bone, my face drained and pale, my eyes hollow with puffy bags underneath them. But now, even I could see that I had some of my colour back. I'd got my eyebrows threaded and dyed my roots, all thanks to Ruby lending me some cash. I was doing all the little things that were getting me back to looking like me.

But just as you're probably fearing – we're not even halfway through this novel – Nero came back.

They always do. They always come back.

When your skin returns to its fleshy colour, when your tears no longer soak your pillow, when you finally get your appetite back, when the sky looks noticeably bluer, when the birds sing a little more in tune in the mornings and that joke on the TV actually makes you laugh, that's when they come back – just when they feel you becoming *you* again.

It was 8 a.m. in London and 9 a.m. in Switzerland, where he was at that time. I remember turning to my phone, which was vibrating on the floor, and just staring at his name on the screen.

As I answered, there was a pause before he said my name softly: 'Livi.'

My heart felt too heavy for my chest. Beating so loudly, it felt like it was too large to be held any longer inside my weak rib cage. With each beat, it was like the bones inside my chest were breaking, like my organs were being crushed.

'I love you so much and I miss you so much,' he told me.

The tears began to roll down my cheek instantly, uncontrollably and viciously, and I asked him the one thing I so desperately wanted to understand.

'Why did you do it?'

'Because I was dumb and I was fucked up off the drugs.'

'I was taking out my demons on you.'

'I've been with girls all over the world on tour, none of them are you.'

'I just need my Livi back, I'm so sorry.'

'No girl is you, you're the one.'

'I'll never hurt you again.'

'I thought I wanted to be single but I know now what I want.'

'I only want you, Livi.'

'Please tell me you've stayed pure, that you've not let anybody touch you.'

'You're my wife, please come home.'

'Let's fix everything.'

'I have anger issues, I should never have hurt you.'

'I'll never take my anger out on you again.'

These are just some of the things he said in our four-hour

conversation while I lay in the empty bedroom in Juno's attic. Just hearing his voice again, hearing him affirm our love, felt like it wasn't real life. All my pain just felt so seen, so valid. Yes, I wasn't crazy. He really knew how wrong he was. The man I'd loved this whole time, the man I'd made so many memories with, *did* acknowledge what he'd done to me.

When I finally went to see him, he opened the front door and snuck me in. He hadn't told the boys yet. I wondered what he *had* told them. When I asked him, he said, 'They all just think you're nuts', but I didn't take much notice at the time because I couldn't give a single flying fuck what those boys thought of me.

We lay in bed naked, hugging tightly for a few long minutes, then began having sex. He kept telling me how much he loved me.

'I'll never let you go again,' he said, holding my hands while we fucked.

We kept the door locked and didn't leave. Between the en suite for when we needed the bathroom and food deliveries he collected from the door, the boys didn't suspect a thing for two whole days. It was just like the old days when we used to live in his bedroom.

Eventually, Nero broke the news to everyone. I let the girls know of my decision. Each of them was worried to their core.

The NDA was called off.

I called the police in secret one evening and told them that I was moving to a different country, that I was ready to move on with my life and that a case would be unnecessary to move forward with.

In my mind, everyone made mistakes. He was human, after

all. And he was my friend, I knew him so well. As if after all that he'd even *imagine* physically hurting me again. He left and he saw what life was like without me. Now, he wanted me back. He would surely appreciate what he had.

Right?

I was safe, wasn't I?

Oh, I just loved him so much.

Once we got back together, I was burdened by the pain of losing the baby. Whenever I shared this with Nero, he would shut down the conversation, telling me it was 'negative'.

I also told him that I wanted to get a job. My friend had a position available as an artist's stylist for his new record label. Nero instantly lost his mind, berating me for wanting to work for another man. 'Don't I give you enough?' he yelled.

'You do, of course you do. I don't want you to think I'm being ungrateful, it's not that. I just want my own money, so I'm always good in case something happens,' I said.

'So you're planning on breaking up with me?' he asked, offended.

'No, Nero. I just mean I should have my own money. I don't want to have to ask you for money to get little necessities and stuff.'

When he didn't like that idea, I suggested a role in the Indian restaurant downstairs in our block. Right there where he could see me. Part-time.

To my surprise, he went on to say, 'We're getting a dog. I'll pay you £500 a month to take care of it. I'd need to pay someone anyway so it might as well be you.'

Jefe

Jefe was the name I wanted to give our baby if we had a boy, so we gave it to the dog instead. He was a bid to get me out of my depression.

Jefe looked like a dog from a TV advertisement or some shit. He was fucking perfect. I had been afraid of dogs growing up, so at the dog breeder's house, with all these little blue-silver Frenchie puppies yapping at my feet, I felt a little overwhelmed. Then this tiny baby, the only one with his ears not standing up, came and lunged himself into my lap, adjusted himself to be comfortable and just sat there. His energy was different from the rest, he was so chilled. It was like he *chose* me to be his mummy.

I looked up at Nero as if to say 'he's the one', so we took him home. In the car, he did a poopy (a stinking one) and he couldn't stop shaking, he was so nervous. He was so timid, so precious.

Those early days spent falling in love with Jefe are

memories that'll be engraved into my heart forever. It's the kind of shit I'll tell my kids about. I felt like Nero and I were parents. Jefe's little paws and head were too heavy for his tiny body waddling around the house. We'd run after him, watching his every move. Cleaning his poo, wiping up his piss.

The first night, we didn't even have a bed or a cage for him. We slept in the living room with him because our bed was too high up, and we feared that if he fell off, he'd be done for. We made him a little pillow fort to sleep on on the floor and squeezed together onto the sofa above him. Nero was so in love with that lil baby, I'd wake up during the night and catch him watching him.

I remember we'd go days without having sex, covered in puppy pee, surviving on a few hours' sleep, going crazy in celebration when he finally peed on the pads. When we finally did get some intimate time in, it was a half-dressed, very quick but very satisfying scenario, swiftly interrupted by Jefe's puppy cries from the living room. It was like we were young parents whose lives had been taken over by their new infant.

Jefe filled the hole in my heart that the baby had left. He followed me everywhere, even to the bathroom to pee in the middle of the night. He'd be there, resting on my foot as I sat on the toilet, or sleeping on the heated floors in the bathroom while I showered after he realised that he couldn't get in there with me.

When Nero travelled, Jefe and I had our baby and mummy adventures. We did everything together. He was so adorable and funny; I'm sure my Instagram followers got sick of me snapping his every move, but I didn't care. Our bond grew so strong.

As Jefe grew older, in my darkest moments, I'd be locked in the bathroom, crying on the floor. I'd hear him scratching at the door and let him in, where he'd just lie in my lap.

In the moments when I'd be losing my mind, alone in the house for weeks, I'd talk to Jefe. I'm somehow so sure that he understood everything. When I slept, he'd slide his face under my chin and let out little snores from beneath me. Always warm, always keeping me safe.

I'll never forget the night that I spent sitting on the sofa, crying over some mean texts Nero had sent me. I looked at Jefe. He put his paw on my shoulder, tilted his head and stared at me, like he really was consoling me.

Sometimes, when I saw other dogs, I'd whisper in their ear, assuming dogs have some kind of telepathic connection.

I'd say the same thing every time.

'Tell Jefe I'm sorry.'

24

Can I lie and just pretend it all got better?

Back then, if you asked anyone who watched my Instagram feed what my life looked like, they'd tell you it was a fucking dream. Shit, Nero and I even had fan pages for our relationship.

Travelling the world with my man, he was a star: backstage at every show, fashion week, runways, beautiful locations, flashing lights. But let me tell you what was going on behind closed doors. *Exactly* what was going on.

There was the time we went to Paris. Nero was shooting the video to his single, 'No Strength'. We posed in front of the helicopter he'd used in the video, me on his back. Looking as blessed as ever.

Shooting began at 5 a.m. and lasted all day. I was bored after six or so hours on set and found my way into the make-up room where the models did their glam. I hadn't worn much make-up since being with Nero because he always told me I looked better without it, but I missed that feeling when your make-up looks perfect and you feel super pretty. I thought I'd surprise him. After an hour of carefully creating a subtle pink, glossy make-up look with winged liner and mascara, I headed downstairs.

Nero laughed as soon as he saw me, then he became really, really condescending.

'No, no, no, Livi. Please go and take that off, you look fucking ridiculous. I don't need my girl to look like the bitches at this shoot.'

I went upstairs and took it off because, well, his opinion did matter to me. Deep down, though, I knew I looked good.

Then there was Barcelona. We were in the city for his show, a drunken escapade which looked so appealing to all his fans watching. In reality, before the show in the hotel, he was on Instagram Live. I got out of the shower, totally unaware that he was on camera and very briefly walked past without a top on. Nero got so angry that he ended the Live and threw a chair at me. Right after, we went downstairs and pretended that nothing had happened. I fought back the tears, trying to hold it together so I didn't bother him. I had to do this *all the fucking time.*

Sometimes I'd go to the bathroom and cry, before looking in the mirror and giving myself a pep talk. 'You got this, c'mon,' I'd reassure myself.

Then, when we rolled in drunk at 4 a.m. after the show, he told me that we had to break up. Because he literally couldn't think of any fucking reason why, he resorted to, '*There's just something you're not telling me.*'

Pathetically, I let him go through my whole phone, holding my head and pleading for hours.

'Nero, how can I prove it to you? Please, I swear to God, I swear I've never hidden *anything* from you!'

My abandonment issues had got so bad. I was doing anything not to hit that wall that I did when he left me to go through that abortion alone. I didn't want to regret taking him back.

In the morning after the ordeal, I was drained and depleted. He wrapped his arms around me in the airport on the way home and announced, 'Livi's mad hungover,' to George and Blake. Blake was also his DJ so he'd often travel with us. On the plane home, Nero told me he loved me and didn't want to break up after all.

Then there was Nice. We went there for the creation of a statue of Nero for one of the world's most famous designer labels, an enormous thirty-foot statue they wanted of him in one of the flagship stores. On social media it looked like a beautiful getaway. The night before we arrived, Nero was given some bad news, something to do with his passport not making it in time for his American visa.

He was in a bad mood in bed in our hotel room.

'You okay, Nero?' I asked him.

He lay in silence and ignored me. Then, a few hours later, at around 1 a.m., he stormed out of the hotel room. Later, I woke up to him sitting at the end of the bed in the dark.

'I went out to that ocean . . . and I thought about drowning myself,' he whispered.

I sat up, confused. As I went over to comfort him, I put my head on his shoulder, and he pushed my face away with the back of his hand.

'W-what's wrong . . . Nero?'

Panic filled my chest. I was hoping and praying, always hoping and praying, that the next thing to come out of his mouth didn't take it too far, didn't hurt too much.

It was like lying beneath a dagger tied to the ceiling with rope.

Just waiting for it to fall.

Frozen, unable to move.

He went on to tell me how he was misunderstood, how he wasn't appreciated enough, how we need to break up because I just 'didn't understand him'. As usual, I begged and pleaded. I really believed that he felt that way . . . I wanted to help him, reassure him.

'What have I actually done? What is the reason you feel this way?' I always asked. My brain was reverting back to good old logic, looking for the issue so I could find the solution, so I could change whatever he needed me to change. I'd exhaust myself, running in circles trying to get through to him, guilt running through my veins.

Every time he did these fake break-ups, he got annoyed at me, especially when I started crying. He would squeeze my face hard, coming so close that we were nose-to-nose, or slap me repeatedly with one hand as he shouted, 'SHUT THE FUCK UP AND STOP CRYING.' Other times, he'd physically chuck me out of the room, dragging me by my clothes, my arms or my hair, knowing that there was nowhere for me to go in whatever country we were in.

Every time he'd threaten to leave me, I'd feel so trapped. He wouldn't let me get a job without emotionally blackmailing me, so I'd submit to save our relationship. Without him, I'd be losing my home. I had literally nowhere to go. All I could really think about was losing my family, the only family I really knew and the only place I ever felt like I belonged. I had worked tirelessly to build this home out of love: Me, my baby Jefe and Nero. I couldn't imagine life without him. It seemed impossible. It was like I could feel all the bullets he'd left in me and, as soon as he left, I'd have to remove them myself. The thought of that pain was just too much to cope with. Him staying meant that the wounds remained closed, and that was okay because it bought me time. If I could get him better, then all the bullets, all the hurt would be worth it. We could both take them out, we could heal the wounds together.

At the end of every argument, he'd remind me that *I* was ruining his career, telling me that he needed to sleep. 'Some of us actually have to fucking work tomorrow.' Sometimes I'd try and get to some sort of conclusion so that I could sleep without the mental torment of his demons, but he'd blow up into an even worse rage, smashing the bedside lamp or whatever else was close to him.

Each time I was forced to be silent and shut off my emotions, I'd weep silently into the bedsheets, trying hard not to awaken or trigger him. He'd sleep peacefully, relieved of all the demons he'd just exposed me to. As I lay there crying, I'd feel them dancing around my head, laughing, repeating all the things he'd just spewed onto me.

In the morning, we went to the statue design studio. I was taking photos of his 'fit when I told him to face more towards the camera, before he interrupted and walked towards me. I remember not having the juice left to worry about what was going on now. He put the phone down and kissed my forehead. Sitting me down on the stool behind me, he kissed my chest, before looking me in the eyes and telling me, 'I never want to break up with you, I love you.' I stared up at him with my big, desperate eyes and nodded. He kissed me on the forehead again.

I ran to the bathroom. It was all super modern; grey stone and limewash walls.

I leaned against the wall and slid down to the concrete floor. I began to hug and cry into my knees. I could feel the relief all over my body. I felt so bewildered by the last twenty-four hours. In a state of disbelief. I felt like I was going fucking crazy.

'What the fuck?' I whispered to myself. *Why the fuck did he do all that last night?*

Another time, where we were posted all over the press, I wanted to wear leather trousers instead of cotton tracksuit bottoms to Traza's album party. Axel agreed that the latter made it look like I was wearing pyjamas, given that I was wearing a baggy T-shirt too ... The way Nero went to bite his head off was wild.

'Dupont, I've already told her what to wear. Don't do that again,' he told him. I decided to wear the leather pants anyway and Nero decided to punish me.

It wasn't like he outright told me there would be consequences – he taught me instead.

After he'd realised that I had no choice but to lean on him in social environments, the way he'd enforce his control was simple. He'd withdraw his love. For entire evenings, if I came close to him, he'd run away – actually disappear. Axel would ask me, 'Where did he go?' and I'd have a huge ball of anxiety in my chest knowing that he'd left to get away from me.

Any time I stood beside him he moved swiftly away, as if he was disgusted by me for wearing those damn leather trousers. Sometimes, he'd even go into a section with more girls, just to mess with my head. I'd stand there, alone and powerless. Embarrassed. It was humiliating. From then on, I learned my lesson: whatever Nero told me to do, I did.

So, I carried on doing exactly that. When Nero told me, 'I don't like bitches. When you dress like that, you look like anybody could have you. Why would I want my wife to look like a bitch?' I'd listen. I thought maybe he just knew better than me. Maybe I didn't understand the male perspective. Maybe he had a point.

'I want my wife to be in cool shit, Supreme and shit, tracksuits, no make-up 'cos that's just trying *too* hard. The less you try, the sicker it is!' he said.

So, I did that too. I guess it *sounded* like it could be true, so I started wearing tracksuits with no make-up on. I put my hair in a slick bun. Each time I dressed like that, he'd get so excited, kissing me on the forehead, telling me I looked beautiful. He'd be extra considerate in public, he'd hold my hand, he'd make sure I wasn't alone, he'd invite me to engage in conversions and let me be myself.

By now, you can probably begin to see a pattern. If I submitted to Nero's commands, I'd be rewarded. If I didn't, I'd be punished. Simple enough. It was what had happened the year before when he 'bazzed' the boys into thinking they all needed girlfriends. He had been filled with energy; he was high off it. It was like he was full, like he'd got his supply. Now he was bazzing me, getting high off controlling me.

The thing with narcissists and their appetite for supply is

that it is bottomless. They'll never be full. They'll always be hungry for more. So, after a while, Nero's appetite grew bigger.

I was his quickest and most potent source of supply to fill that void: a sprung young girl, there by his side and totally devoted to him, swimming deep under the waves, trying to save this damaged, poor boy from drowning.

After I'd fed his hunger for a while this way, he needed an even bigger meal. A basic bazz just wasn't enough. Now, he needed validation. What could be more validating than seeing what was once a confident young lady, on her knees, pathetically *begging* for you? That means you must be something special, right? What about making up issues that don't exist, just to watch her sweat? Watching her plead and reason? Oh, that made Nero feel so seen. So important. *Look how badly she needs me. I must be special if someone needs me this much. How much? Show me how much.*

What about … hurting her, physically? Scaring her. Scarring her. Degrading her. Changing her. Making her so unattractive that nobody else wants her. Making her so insecure that she thinks she can't get anyone else.

AND then, the best part: doing that to her and she still *stays*, wouldn't that be the ultimate bazz?

To think how much *power* you must have over someone to break each of their boundaries, to deny even their basic human rights – to turn them into nothing. To make them a slave to fulfil your sexual and egotistical needs, to be nothing but a supply for your narcissistic hunger and a punching bag for your insecurities. To use them as a toy, playing with them, watching them react to each trick and lose their mind over and over again.

That would mean that you would be so in control of their life and emotions that you wouldn't even *need* to focus on the lack of control you have over *your* emotions. Over *your* happiness. Over that emptiness you constantly feel.

Instead you can just control *them*. And when they go 'nuts' and react with emotion, it eases your pain because you think to yourself, 'huh, they're broken *just like me*'. In some fucked up way, it makes you feel less alone in the constant hell you're living in. It sounds crazy – trust me, I know. But this doesn't just happen overnight.

In Nero's case, this shit took time. To do all of that to someone and for them to stay – you can't just punch them in the face the first time you meet them. As the saying goes, you put a frog in boiling water and it'll jump out. You put a frog in warm water and boil it slowly, it'll stay there, slowly cooking to death.

That's what Nero did. He boiled the water slowly, lay breadcrumbs as a trail and, with his carefully crafted plan, he trapped me.

He started by love bombing me, so that I would let down my walls, trust him, fall for him. He wanted me to trust him enough to give up my job and work for him, so that I ultimately became financially dependent on him. Then, he gave me a home. Knowing I had nowhere else to go, I was the perfect prey: someone sensitive who longed to heal people, and someone who had nobody else to fall back on. I had no brothers to protect me and no bond with my parents. I was a girl who left home alone in search of a happier life.

He played with my heartstrings, using his mother's death and his addiction as his excuse. He had sex with me every time I had a breakdown, causing confusion. Each time, I'd associate my submission with being 'rewarded', trauma bonding me further to him. He tore apart my self-esteem, my confidence. He made sure to criticise me, passive aggressively insulting me or giving me back-handed compliments. Every day he drained me, enough to make me push my friends away, knowing that I couldn't tell them the true extent of what was going on. He showed me how bad it was when I left, to teach me to stay. He filled me with false hope and promises to ease the pain he'd left me with in the first place. He bought me a dog and watched me become immensely attached to him. He ensured that guilt was instilled in me in case I ever tried to leave; that I always felt desperation and lived in fear that, at any point, he could leave me.

He kept me in this constant cycle of reward and punishment so I always had *just* enough hope that if I played things differently, I could have the version of him that showed up every once in a while when I acted 'right'. The reality was that I never really did anything wrong; he just adjusted the criteria slightly each time, fooling me. if I believed that it was *me* who had acted wrong, it was *me* who had to recalibrate. Each time, more and more rules were added, and I'd become more carefully crafted, more obedient. Nero loved Jefe but I was the one who was trained like a dog.

When he was certain he had me in the palm of his hand, trapped by all the pictures he'd painted for me in his museum of great illusions, *that's* when he'd strike for the ultimate amount of supply.

The bigger the hit, the more degrading, the more painful and the more it hurt me, the larger and tastier the supply he got. It satisfied him, like a magic potion that could keep him young forever. He was so strong, so happy, so content once he got his supply. The trouble was, it didn't last. Every day, he'd wake up and the emptiness would begin brewing inside him again. His stomach would grumble, in need of that sweet, sweet supply. He began to seek out another hit, a bigger one this time, and more satisfying.

Hungrier than ever, what the fuck could he feed his demons with next?

What in the world would satisfy them more than I already had?

What else could he take from me?

What else could he do to me?

25

The good days

With Nero making sure to reward me *only* for my submission, and giving me *just* enough micro-doses of love after starving me of it, I felt completely lost.

The good moments wouldn't last more than a few days.

I'd wake up and instantly my brain would be on high alert, trying to sense what mood Nero would be in, what version of him I was about to get. I told myself that there was *always* a version available, somewhere, somehow, that *wasn't* abusive; the version I was in love with. I became obsessed with how I could get *that version* to show up, or better yet, to stay.

From the moment I opened my eyes, it would begin – working to serve Nero's happiness. I put my love into cooking. Once I decorated a plate with Nutella French toast, avocado on toast, salmon and cream cheese bagels and fruit, neatly presenting it for him. Around midday, when I woke him up because the food was ready and he had sessions to attend, he told me I was selfish and demanding, kicking me out of the bedroom and locking the door. He headed straight out to his session, the stupid plate of assorted breakfast sitting there all day.

I'd try again and again, adapting and adjusting over and over. I just wanted to have one good day. One. Good. Day.

Wake up.

He wants fruit before breakfast, but only berries.

Don't wake him up.

Go to Waitrose.

Come home.

Plate the berries. Get him a ginger shot because he's recording today and was drinking and doing coke yesterday.

Get him that water he likes.

The glass bottle, not plastic.

Clean the living room so he has mental space for when he walks in.

Take Jefe for a walk and don't let him wake him up.

Success!

If I achieved these things, Nero would be fine. In fact, he would be more than fine, he would be a normal loving boyfriend.

Good days looked like this. Nero would hold my hand and I'd hold Jefe. I'd lie low and take care of him in the studio while Nero worked. Nero always wanted us to come with him, but wherever we went, he'd express the importance of me not speaking unless I was spoken to, and only by him. I was constantly reminded that 'his girl' shouldn't come across as too friendly or approachable, so I'd make sure of that too. Unless I was making lyric suggestions, which he loved, I literally didn't speak to anyone but Jefe.

But, despite my best attempts to be a robot, I just couldn't be.

One time, we went to the studio and I walked over to cuddle Nero from behind as he was sitting in a chair. In response, he pushed my arms off him, spun the seat around and told me, 'Don't ever come and hug me'.

I replied, 'But why? You're my boyfriend – what if I just want a hug?'

He retorted, 'I'll come and hug you – you can't come and hug me.'

I screwed up my face and then remembered that a lot of people were in the room, watching us. It made it so much more embarrassing. I remember thinking, *They must think I'm so fucking dumb.*

I bit down on my tongue, which was already sore from biting it so many times before, and sat back down.

When we got into the car to head home, I already knew what was coming.

That's *all* it would take: me having any kind of emotion or want or need, or questioning his decision in the slightest way regardless of how unreasonable he was being. That face I made when he told me how it was going to be, that was enough for him to need supply. A reaction. It was enough for him to realise that I wasn't well trained enough.

Whenever we got home, always, somehow, he'd find an excuse to argue out of thin air. Whether it was taking my phone and looking through it, each time *finding nothing*, twisting my wrists if I tried to take it back off him, he'd shout, 'What are you hiding?' or ignore me until I couldn't take any more, begging him to tell me what I had done wrong.

'You're just ungrateful,' he'd say, over and over again, every time we fought. If I asked why or how, he'd get angry, saying he needed space, telling me to get out of the room. If I told him that it wasn't fair, that I couldn't live like this anymore, never being able to express how I felt, constantly catering to his emotions only, always receiving the silent treatment for no apparent reason (while he'd purposefully be fine, on the phone or with Jefe), he'd burst into flames.

I'd be dragged by my hair in my nightie, boobs falling out, exposed. I would clutch on to any furniture I could, crying for him to stop, my head hitting the walls and corners. Sometimes he'd leave me half-naked outside our front door until he thought I'd suffered enough. On the nights I would simply leave him alone when he gave me the silent treatment, he'd come and find me and just . . . psychologically fuck with me.

'I used to learn a lot from you, you know? Like when I first met you, you were so sick and intelligent and everything. But now it's like, I've learned everything. I teach you a lot but what do I really gain from you?' he'd randomly proclaim.

'Love isn't about gaining shit, Nero, this isn't one of your business relationships,' I'd try to explain.

He'd get angry, telling me how life was all about gaining things from each other, using people: a game of chess. He'd constantly repeat:

'You're so stupid.'

'See, this is why you'd be nothing without me. Your life would be nothing without me.'

'You don't even really do anything, do you? Besides taking care of Jefe.'

When I tried to reason with him using logic, telling him that it was *him* who prevented me from getting a job in order to stay in this relationship, *him* who told me I was lame and put me down when I suggested doing YouTube videos about astrology, *him* who said I should help *him* blow up first when I said I wanted to be a writer, he'd just antagonise me further. He'd act like what I was saying was categorically untrue, like I was making it all up. LIKE I WASN'T LITERALLY FUCKING LIVING IT. I'd give him dates, relaying the exact scenarios that had happened, memories that were engraved inside my hippocampus, and still he'd deny it. And if I proved it, he'd tell me how it was still my fault. I felt like I was going insane.

Then he would push me just that one step further. He'd throw in one sharp sword.

'You're not even a good girlfriend. You're nothing special.'

'Just because I'm not a yes man like all of your friends and every person around you?' I replied.

'Soon I'll need everyone to be a yes man. I fucking like yes men, I don't want anything else, and soon you'll need to be a yes woman too.'

As if I'd not submitted enough already?

Sometimes I'd just sit in silence, wondering how he could become such a monster, how he could become *this* harsh when unprovoked. Other times, of course, being the human being that I am, after enough tongue biting and submitting, I'd feel like it was all for nothing. I'd feel drained, my heart trodden all over. I'd even feel confused – I thought I'd *finally* managed to crack the code, learned to behave exactly as I should to prevent him from being *so horrible* – so I'd react. I'd cry and scream, telling him he was awful, mean, evil. I'd tell him I was going to leave him, that only *then* would he finally see how much I fucking did for him, how fake everyone was around him, how I was the only one not being a *yes woman*. That his sister and I were the only people left who were real with him.

'Layla is different – she raises four kids alone. What the fuck have you ever done for me?' he'd retort.

I'd quiver in anger. Looking back, I honestly felt like the thing I'd done for him most, more than anything, was allow him to abuse me. I'd let him break my boundaries time after time. More than the constant nurturing and tireless working towards keeping him happy or sober, it was the resentful feeling of realising I'd become a slave for his anger for so long. And then, if I ever implied that I wanted to leave him, that I'd had enough or that I couldn't do it anymore, that's when Nero would really *really* lose his shit.

One evening I'd finally had enough. I figured that even going back home to Scotland would be better than this.

The apartment was silent as he lay in bed, facing away from me. I had just got out of the shower and brushed my teeth. I sat on the end of the bed and took a deep sigh.

'Nero ...' The tears came straight away. 'I just can't do this anymore ... What have we become? I love you and I always will but I think even just going back home to my parents for a while would help. This is unhealthy. Look at us—'

He interrupted me. 'YOU'RE SAYING YOU'RE GOING TO LEAVE ME? AFTER ALL I DO FOR YOU?'

He turned over abruptly and pulled me off the bed by

my wet hair. My naked body hit the floor and I screamed, 'STOP, NERO!' He dragged me into the hallway. I got up and tried to grab my towel from the bedroom behind him as he barricaded the door. He grabbed a glass bottle from the shelf in the hall and pressed it into my chest, using it to prod me backwards. I didn't fall, managing to catch my step. He got angrier and whacked the bottle against the door frame, missing my face by inches, the glass shattering into pieces all over me. He grabbed my hair again, throwing me down hard onto the glass-covered floor before walking away, slamming the bedroom door shut behind him.

I lay there naked, so traumatised I didn't even know what parts of me had been cut, or had glass in them. I was hyperventilating, trying to catch my breath, shaking and crying loudly. Then, just quietly gasping . . .

It felt as if my brain was stuck in a loop. I felt like I couldn't see, that there was glass in my eyes. I could actually *feel* the glass in my eyes.

I don't know how long I lay there before he came out. He picked me up, then I remember ending up on the bathroom floor, him standing over me. I was having a full-blown panic attack. It felt like a heart attack. I just could *not* breathe.

He started crying, trying to calm me down. He was so scared, pleading, 'Livi no, no, no, what have I done?'

He was about to call for help when he squeezed both of my feet while crying into my legs on the floor. I don't know whether the sensation distracted my brain, but I somehow started to calm down. He washed my face with water in an attempt to calm me down further and laid me in the bed. I was covered in cuts.

Nights like this became regular for us. I was constantly stuck in fight-or-flight mode, ready to battle, to be hit, dragged, punched and kicked, slapped and strangled. Put down over and over until I'd react and be punished, or not react and be punished then too. I started every single morning with my calculations, trying to fucking figure out how, *how* I could be good enough for him to stop.

How we could have a good day. Just. One. Good. Day.

Some days I'd actually just look at him, in defeat with all the angst in my heart, and I'd plead with him, 'Please, can we just have one good day?'

In the midst of this chaos, we were still in the public eye. It came as no surprise when people started to make comments that I was off. I was always on edge, reserved and drained.

Once, Nero wanted to throw a party, so I went to visit Juno.

I returned home at around 11 a.m. to find the house completely trashed. There were cigarettes in every cup, ash on the floor. The stench of liquor hung in the air as all the boys sat on the sofa, *still* taking drugs as the new day's sunlight poured into the room. When I walked in, the realisation hit me – not one of these guys liked me. But instead of being nonchalant about it like I used to be, I automatically went into people-pleaser mode, trying to break the tension. I made pizzas, offering them to everyone. The boys mumbled 'thank you', not even looking me in the eyes.

Nero was throwing up into his hand so I took him to clean up in the bathroom before getting him into bed. When we stepped into the bedroom, I noticed that the bed wasn't made. It looked like someone had been in it. The star projector was switched on.

'Was Sabrina here?' I asked bluntly.

I don't even know where that came from. Sabrina lived in France – there was no reason why she'd be in town. Again, call it women's intuition or whatever you like, because it would probably be too crazy to say that I felt like there was something spiritual trying to protect me, something warning me.

He stared at me blankly, taken aback by my remark, and told me no. I continued to put him to bed.

'Why do none of the boys like me? Their energy is so mad,' I then asked.

He responded by telling me I needed to 'earn their respect', knowing that I didn't care to do that and that response would piss me off.

He slept, sweating buckets next to me, while I stared at the lights of the projector on the ceiling. I asked the moon for answers, wishing it could speak back to me.

Just a couple of months after that night, Ziggy came to pick Nero up to go to the studio. Since he'd already got a lift with one of the other boys, I invited Ziggy in for a cup of tea. He was charging his phone when I remembered that some weeks ago, I'd seen that he followed Sabrina on Instagram. Ziggy wasn't in LA when they shot the music video she'd starred in, or in Paris for the mixtape launch, so I asked him how he knew her.

'I met her here!' he told me. In this house. *Our home.* Completely unaware of what he'd just done.

Ziggy quickly realised what he'd done after gauging my

facial expression and made a swift exit. 'Uh, I should go . . .' he laughed nervously.

Later, I confronted Nero, who assured me it was just an afterparty.

'Nothing happened! One of Traza's friends invited her to the studio, I didn't know she'd be there. I couldn't single her out and tell her she couldn't come back to the afterparty . . . I promise, she was on the opposite end of the room to me all night – we did not speak.'

A month or so after that, he told me, while very high on cocaine, that Sabrina had previously tried to 'rape' him.

'Okay,' he said, 'I confess the only thing that ever happened between us was in LA. I was so fucked up. I woke up and she was on top of me, trying to get me hard. I threw up on her. Ask Dupont or ask anyone else, nothing happened. I told her I have a girlfriend.'

When I then tried to message her (since my boyfriend had told me that the girl had supposedly almost taken advantage of him while he was on drugs), he pleaded with me that he never wanted me to embarrass or lower myself to these 'bitches'. He told me that I was way above that, to not even entertain or give that energy because they were obsessed with him, that he didn't care about her.

I didn't message her. Mostly because, deep down, I wasn't ready to hear the truth.

It was paradoxical because, at the same time as abusing me, Nero did a good job of playing a protective role whenever he wanted. At every party, club night or event, he'd make someone escort me to the toilet, making sure nobody could barge into me or get too close.

At one party, I tapped his shoulder and he didn't turn around. A guy said to me, 'Give up babe, he's not interested.' Of course, Nero heard and almost knocked him out.

'APOLOGISE TO HER NOW,' he said, pushing the man into the crowds of partygoers behind him. The guy looked like he might have just shit himself.

A similar incident happened in Paris when someone knocked into me at a club. He was so good at scaring people, making them apologise as soon as he demanded it, eyes dark and popping out of his head. People were intimidated by him.

Something I've only realised now is that he never fought. *Not really.* He never won real physical altercations, never actually lived up to the threats that he spewed out so quickly. The reality was that underneath it all, he was frightened. It was an illusion. A façade.

The only person he could *actually* put his hands on was me.

26

Accusations like confessions

Towards the end of that year, the abuse became so routine that it was normalised. What confused people was how Nero acted towards me in public. Sometimes he could be incredibly rude while remaining protective; other times, he could be loving. Of course, nobody ever uttered a word. That would cut off any benefits they were receiving in the 'yes men' package they had sold their souls to opt into.

Around this time, Ziggy, Kai and Nero had some weird fights that ended up in them calling their friendships quits. The boys had grown very resentful of Nero – maybe because they had got used to the free houses, trips and lifestyle, they felt that little bit more entitled to tell him about himself than the rest of the crew. Ziggy eventually came back, wanting to rekindle a friendship with Nero, but this time he was more business-minded, deciding he would A&R Nero's upcoming debut album.

The morning before they went to Berlin to perform in

November, I heard the front door rattling at 7 a.m., like someone was trying to get in. I woke Nero up and he lay still for a second, listening carefully. He ran into the kitchen and grabbed a knife, telling me to hide in the bathroom with Jefe and call the police.

We could see someone trying to get in. They had stuck a camera through the letterbox and were using pliers, working to twist the door lock. Nero stood by the door, locking it back every time it twisted – it was a double lock. The adrenaline I felt coupled with my nerves was insane.

Funnily, it was just bailiffs. It turned out that since Nero switched management from George to Axel, nobody had remembered to pay the electricity bill. We paid in cash and sent them on their way, but not before Nero cussed them out, telling them that he was a superstar. Those men really did nothing wrong, they were just people's fathers at work, dealing with an addict brat. He hated service workers for some reason. Even when we had people come to do house repairs, he didn't like their 'energy'.

The door had no lock left on it, so Nero checked Jefe and me into the Four Seasons, saying, 'See, this is what I do because I love you.' Our anniversary was coming up that week. He told me to extend our stay so we could celebrate upon his return.

Jefe and I had a ball there together, running around the room, cuddling and napping. We even did a photoshoot; he was a great hype man.

At night, when I sent Nero the photo of Jefe and me, he made it his background, sending me a screenshot. I reminded him to call me after the show, but he didn't. Instead, he texted me at 3 a.m. saying 'I love you', and then I didn't hear from him until the next day. Eventually he *missed* the anniversary surprise I'd arranged for us at the hotel because he was on too bad of a comedown.

Chiara came to visit the hotel the next day. We'd been cool with each other since Nero and Ziggy had got close again but I still felt there was an ulterior motive behind it all. All of a sudden, it was like she wanted to be my friend a little *too much*.

We were sitting on the bed and I'd begun to cry. 'I think I'm being cheated on.'

'Livia,' she replied, 'if you think your boyfriend's cheating on you, I don't know what to tell you.'

I felt so alone.

That same night, I went downstairs to pick up a Deliveroo order. When I came back up, Chiara told me that Nero had FaceTimed her asking where I was and if I'd gone to meet a guy. *Like what?* She'd responded, 'What guy is Livia supposed to go meet? She doesn't have any friends.' She was right – I barely even had female friends at this point. The ones I did try to hang out with, Nero was somehow convinced were 'hoes'. And Ruby was, of course, in Manchester.

Sometimes Nero would come home and pretend he'd 'heard something' about me and other guys. Once, I was on my period and in my pyjamas watching TV when he came in and started *sniffing* the house. He said a man had been there. I thought he was joking. He turned it into a whole argument before telling me I took everything 'too deep'.

One evening, Juno came over while Nero was back over in LA. We picked up a bottle of wine and on the way back, in the apartment lift, we realised it was a cork bottle and I didn't own a corkscrew. We asked a couple in the lift if they could lend us one and they directed us to a party on the sixteenth floor. As we entered the huge penthouse covering the entire top floor, the apartment owner greeted us. I told him that my boyfriend and I lived on the 11th floor, that we had parties all the time and he should come sometime. I asked him if he knew Nero or any of his songs – he recognized one of his tracks – and he opened the bottle for us. We went on our merry way back to our apartment. I FaceTimed Nero, telling him I'd met our neighbour and how cool the apartment was.

'So you basically went to another man's house?' he joked.

The next day, Nero called me from LA. He was high on coke and began to accuse me of sleeping with our neighbour on the sixteenth floor. He told me people were going to come and take Jefe from me. I frantically begged him to stop, going over the exact series of events to try and convince him. I told him I'd never do that.

'Go and ask him now with me on FaceTime,' he responded.

I paused for a second, processing just how crazy I was about to look before Jefe caught my eye. All I could picture was people coming and taking him away. I stormed out of the apartment and into the lift.

'Don't say ANYTHING else, just say "What happened last night? I blacked out," Nero shouted down the phone.

The neighbour opened his door to a sorry state. I was wearing a dirty T-shirt and tracksuit bottoms, my face covered in tears, eyes pink and swollen. I held the phone in one hand as I said, 'Hi, I'm so sorry, there's been a misunderstanding.

Can you please tell me what happened when I came here last night?'

He looked at the camera in my hand and then back at me but didn't hesitate.

'You came here, you told me about you and your boyfriend living downstairs, you said he's a musician, I opened your bottle of wine and you left.'

Nero's signal was bad and I lost him for a moment as I headed back into the lift with the neighbour – he was on his way out – and attempted to avoid eye contact, wiping my tears in the corner.

'Are you okay?' he asked gently.

'No,' I wanted to scream. 'No, I'm not okay. I'm so fucking scared, I'm trapped, I'm being abused, I don't know what to do. I don't want to lose Jefe, he's the only thing I have left. I am in so much pain all the time, I don't know who I am anymore. I need help. Please, please help me, do something.'

But of course, I answered 'yes', and quickly got out on my floor, escaping into the apartment.

I called Nero back, asking if he'd heard the neighbour's response. He replied, 'Yeah, sorry, my bad, need to go. I'm mad tired,' and hung up the phone. *He just hung up the phone.*

I sat on the end of the bed, crying into my knees after surviving another attack. Jefe began to tap my slipper to check if I was okay. I pulled him up next to me as I hugged him tight, crying even harder.

Nero didn't know that I'd spent my time alone decorating the house for Christmas. It was his first without his mother and I'd told Layla we'd host it, so I wanted to make the house special. I put up a classic Christmas tree and, having noticed the Indian restaurant downstairs had bright and beautiful floor-to-ceiling Christmas lights in their windows, I went in and asked the manager to teach me how to do them. He kindly showed me and I made our apartment look fucking amazing. Our windows were completely covered in these magical festive lights, lighting up the entire apartment with a goldish hue.

To my surprise, Nero was staggered by the dazzling display once he returned home.

'This is incredible, you are incredible,' he said as he hugged Jefe and me.

We had just finished eating some lasagne that I made (Nero's favourite dish) and I'd cleaned the puppy piss in the hall. When I came to sit down, Nero turned to me and said, 'We really appreciate you.'

'Why?' I asked, laughing. 'Because I cleaned the piss?'

He told me, 'No, because you really love us and we would be nothing without you.'

I stared at him blankly, the unfamiliarity of the random kindness throwing me off.

'I got you a gift!' he told me.

'A gift ... what gift?' I asked.

He ran into the hall and grabbed something out of his duffel bag as Jefe got excited, following him, then slid back across the floor in his socks and rested on his knees in front of me on the sofa, presenting me with a box.

As I went to open the box, I started crying. He couldn't understand why and neither did I. I felt stupid and didn't want my tears to bother him like they always did, but I couldn't control it. I felt relieved. Desperately relieved.

'Heyyyy, hey, it's okay,' he said as he wrapped his arms around me and rocked me side to side.

'Sorry.' I sniffed hard, wiping my tears.

He removed a diamond ring from the box and attempted to put it on my ring finger, when I jerked away, laughing.

'Okay, okay. God loves a trier,' he giggled as he moved the ring onto my index finger.

The ring was insane. Light and dark crystals creating an oval spiral around a large bright pink diamond in the middle with a gold finish. It was one of the most beautiful pieces of jewellery I'd ever seen; it glistened like the soft ripples of the ocean under moonlight.

We watched a movie as I lay between Nero's legs and he massaged my head and played with my hair.

'You're actually the funniest, kindest, most beautiful girl in the world, and I'm lucky to have you,' Nero said.

I turned to face him, smiling. 'Nero, whaaaat has got into you? Did you miss me this much?'

'Yes! When I'm around other people I honestly can't stand them. Like the girls in America that the boys would invite around, they're so stupid. When they speak, I'm just thinking *shut the fuck up*. At least when you speak you are smart.'

He turned to face me, getting more passionate. 'I've had a realisation that you're the only person who has been there for me since the start, like since before all this fame and money. I should only *actually* listen to you. In all honesty, women are a better species than men. From now on, I'm going to listen to everything you say because only *you* know what's best for me.'

'I don't want you to listen to everything I say, Nero. Just

stop taking coke – that's all I really really want,' I said, looking away.

He turned my face towards him with one hand. As I flinched slightly, he sighed.

He touched his other hand to my cheek, holding my face close to him, 'I'm done with all that. I want to be healthy, I want us to be healthy.'

I looked down because looking into his eyes just felt too intense.

'Seriously, look at me, Livia. I'm done with that shit. I'm doing this for me more than anyone.'

'Okay,' I said.

My spirit had never lost hope. It's hard to lose hope when someone shows you regularly that they *can* be good. It's like you know that they've got it in them. You keep holding out for it.

He let go of my face and I rested my head on his chest.

'Anyway, I'm performing in Manchester this weekend ...' he alluded.

My head swiftly turned to face him.

'I was thinking you could invite Ruby since ...'

I turned my whole body around to sit on him and planted a long hard kiss on his lips. 'Thank you, thank you, thank youuuuuu. Yesssss!' I cried.

We were finally on a good streak at long last.

For that entire week, Nero stayed sober. Every night was movie night, we cuddled and spent quality time together – and I mean, uninterrupted by anyone, any demons, any substances: quality time. We made love, gentle love, passionate love, dedicated love.

We walked Jefe together in the evenings and sat by the river, watching the sun go down. We were enjoying the last sunset of that week, snacking on crisps and hummus, when I asked Nero a question.

'Why can't we always be like this? Things can be so easy!' I shovelled hummus onto another crisp as Jefe glared up at the tub, pleading with his eyes for just a lick.

'No, boy. Not for you!' Nero told him. 'I've just had a mad life, Livi. Being homeless, getting famous, losing the boys, fake people, fake friends, meeting you ... I find it hard to trust people so I guess I create problems instead because it's easier than trusting people ... I know it hasn't been easy for you. Thank you for sticking by me.'

'It's fine ... I love you,' I told him.

'This is what love is ...' he replied. 'It's not always easy but you don't just walk out on people, not if you love them.'

Unfortunately, I really believed that – because that's all that was left to believe in: that I was doing this out of love, not fear.

At the show on Saturday, Juno was performing too. Juno never liked Nero, and Nero never liked Juno. Two Aquarians. Two *stubborn* Aquarians.

Ruby was escorted backstage moments after we arrived. Seeing each other, we both said at the exact same time, 'Ohhhh my God!' and ran over to hug one another.

'You're breaking my neck, Livia,' Ruby joked as I clung on to her.

'I'm sorry,' I said as I released her from my tight grip.

'You don't need to say sorry, silly,' she said, confused at my angst. By that point I was used to apologising for everything and nothing. 'I've missed you so much! Where's my nephew?'

After a short introduction to Jefe before we were ushered onto stage for Nero's performance, Ruby and I stood side by side. It was a forty-minute set and we didn't really say much – it was so unlike us. There was something weird between us. We felt disconnected.

Ruby asked if I wanted to head to the backstage area and get a drink. It was obvious she could feel the weirdness between us too.

She swirled the ice cubes in her drink around with her straw as we sat on a bench outside the dressing room.

'Are you okay, Livi? Nero – has he stopped being such a dick?'

Ruby had no idea what had been going on since the first time Nero and I split. She knew he'd hurt me that one time after my abortion, but she thought that was it. She wanted me to leave then, and she never wanted me to go back.

'I'm sorry, I'm just going to be real,' she said. 'I know people can change and stuff but—'

'He's great!' I replied. 'He's literally been *so* nice, he does genuinely love me and care about me, and he's so nice with Jefe and stuff. Like even this whole week we've been so like, great, like, more than great, really just like yeah ...'

'This week?' she glared at me.

Nero and his posse had returned from the stage and suddenly we were off. Everyone grabbed their bags and jackets from inside the dressing room and we headed towards the exit, but not before we spotted Juno.

As we walked past, she smiled right at Nero, being the savage Aquarius that she happens to be. Out in the car park, in front of Axel and Ruby, Nero lost his shit at *me*. 'HOW

CAN SHE JUST SMILE AT ME LIKE THAT?' he yelled, like even that was my fault.

Just before I got in the car and Ruby got into her Uber, we stared back at each other in silence. She wore a look of regret, like she didn't want me to get in that car with Nero.

'Oh, Livia ... Call me when you get home okay?'

I hugged her tight, and for just a moment while my head rested on her shoulder, I felt a warmth I hadn't in so long.

In the car back to London, Nero and I sat eating McDonald's in silence and Jefe slept in my lap. Aside from that small outburst, the whole weekend had been great. Nero had been reasonable, he'd been level-headed, and I felt brave enough to ask him, 'Nero, why don't you like Juno?' She'd never *actually* done anything wrong.

That spring, he'd asked her to 'take care of me' during the abortion situation. Juno had told him that even though she would a hundred times over, he shouldn't have reached out to my friends for that – that as my boyfriend, he should have taken care of me. I didn't get why that bothered him this much.

Nero responded by throwing the bag of McDonald's, chips flying *everywhere*. The driver stopped and got out, to let us have a moment.

'How fucking dare you ask me that?' He scowled at me. 'Watch,' he said as he picked up his phone and called one of his boys who acted as security, who was still at the venue.

'If you see any of Juno's mates, I need you to bang them out for me,' Nero told him.

I felt like the whole world was caving in on me.

Right before Christmas, when Nero asked me to contact

that same security guy for him, that I saw the text thread on his phone. He'd messaged him almost immediately after the call telling him to forget it and not do anything, but of course Nero never told me that. He was just punishing me, letting me believe it was my fault if someone had got hurt that night. My fault for simply asking a question.

On Christmas Day, we hired a chef and celebrated with Nero's entire family. There was so much joy, dancing, singing and laughing. I had gold charm bracelets made for him and each of his siblings with his mum's face on them. It was so heart-warming to see them share that moment as they put them all on together.

His family told us that we were so good together that Christmas – and so did social media, as we snapped the entire party – totally unaware that he'd slapped me across the face for disagreeing with him while decorating just hours before.

On Boxing Day, we lay in bed, full and hungover. I was on Nero's WhatsApp, looking for something he'd asked me to find, when I saw a message from Chiara:

> Quit this arguing shit with Ziggy or I'll tell Livia
> about what you did in Berlin on your anniversary.

27

Cheating is a choice

'If you have any respect for me, even as a friend, you'll tell me,' I pleaded with Nero over and over, crying into the pillow.

Eventually, he did.

He lay over me and pressed my shoulders into the bed, hesitantly looking into my eyes.

'I had a . . .' he began.

'A threesome?' I guessed.

'A foursome,' he corrected me.

I used all my force to try and push him off me as I shouted, 'Get the fuck off me.'

He grabbed my face and began to squeeze it. He started grunting, holding me down, but then quickly stopped and apologised although he was still gripping me tightly, pinning me on the bed. As if he was about to start hurting me? When he was the one who just got caught cheating?

With Nero admitting to having a foursome in Berlin, is it weird that I just wasn't surprised? I was so numb by this point.

After all, it was our anniversary that night when Chiara had come to the Four Seasons and I'd told her I felt like he was cheating. That's why her response had been so cold: she knew what had happened because Ziggy had been with him.

A foursome.

Him and three girls.

How was that even possible?

What positions do you even do to make that work?

Can you imagine the type of women these were?

He'd just posted me on his Instagram Story celebrating three years together, so the women knew that he was in a relationship. And after he fucked them, after he put his penis inside three different women, then he came home and ... fucked me.

I screamed and I cried. I tried with all my might to get out from under him, but he used his full body weight to hold me down. I wanted to leave so badly. With every attempt to move him off me, I felt weaker and weaker. The hangover was already dehydrating enough. I felt so small, like Alice trapped under that little teacup. What rights did I even have left? I couldn't even move my body when I wanted to.

I cried until I couldn't cry anymore. Then, he finally let go. He made me promise not to leave. If I tried to get up, he'd barricade the bedroom door. I sat in bed, staring vacantly ahead at the wall, and then he put the new season of *You* on Netflix on his laptop. We watched an entire season in silence, in just one sitting. I didn't say one word. It felt so good to escape the reality I was in. I needed to just switch off. Sign out. Leave mentally, since I couldn't physically. The irony didn't escape me that I was just like one of Joe's victims trapped in that glass box, with a psychopath forcing me to stay with him.

At 3 a.m., when he finally trusted that I was calm enough not to walk out on him and it was too late to get anywhere, he kept my phone as I went and sat on the balcony looking out at the river. Staring into the dark sky, and the reflection of the moon in the water, I started to think of all the times we'd spoken about loyalty. All the times he'd declared that he wasn't a liar. How he swore on his mother's grave that he'd never cheat on me. How he told me, 'You were there when Mum died, I would never cheat on you.'

I thought back to all those times he'd accused me, all the crazy lengths I'd had to go to in order to prove my innocence. Then I started to think about how it was all over, how the fairy tale I was living in, a fairy tale of true ignorance, had come to an end. He *actually cheated on me*. Yes, he was abusive. He was awful, the worst man at the best of times, but a part of me really believed in the unbreakable loyalty we had between us when it came to sex. That that was something just for us. That he still *did* love me regardless of all the pain he put me through.

After enough staring into the skyline, I began to feel tears roll down my cheeks. The numbness wore off as I started to process the truth. The truth I fought so hard to not believe.

He came out and picked me up in his arms. After trying to fight him off, I let him carry me back to bed and lay me down.

'Why am I not enough for you?' I asked. 'What am I missing? Is it my body, is it my face, is it my sex, is it not good enough . . . ?' I sobbed over and over, *my* demons whispering in my ears.

They whispered sweet lullabies about my insecurities. They sang me poetry of my pain.

'I knew it. You lied to me, you made me feel crazy and I knew it. I knew it and I know you fucked Sabrina in LA, I know you did,' I protested.

But he denied it. He insisted this was the only time – that he was on so many drugs and just didn't know what he was doing. That he regretted it. He loved me and only me and it didn't mean anything.

'It's like having a wank with someone's body, I don't even remember their faces.'

I decided it was finally time to leave and he couldn't try to stop me. I told him I'd need a few days to figure out where I was going to go and to make arrangements.

Axel's birthday was that week and, after a few days of keeping my distance and making plans to move out, he came to our house and insisted we go to Chiltern Firehouse together. I watched them talk at a hundred miles per hour, on coke, about the album as I slowly zoned out, holding Jefe in my lap. The fireplace twinkled somewhere in the corner of my vision as the DJ played some blues music. I sat there, melancholy and numb, and gave periodic nods and forced smiles.

When we got home, I got into bed and rolled over to go to sleep. Nero tried to spoon me like he always did but I just wasn't there. I was well and truly cold.

Being cheated on changes a woman. Nothing felt special anymore. That sacred feeling, that thing that was only meant to be between us – our promises, our future – it was all gone. It was all worthless. Everything I'd endured. All that I'd suffered. All that I'd lost.

All I could think of was the text he sent me at 3 a.m. that night saying he loved me. Was that guilt?

He kept pestering me to cuddle, and then he started pulling my nightie down by the straps.

'What the fuck are you doing?' I turned around, actually disgusted.

He pulled down my nightie, revealing my boobs, and tried to put them in his mouth. I pushed him off. 'Nero, no!' I shouted.

He started to beg, almost crying. 'Livi, come on. You're my wife . . .'

'Your wife?!' I said. 'You fucking had a foursome! I'm not your wife anymore. We are over. You think I want to ever have sex with *you* again?'

He kept insisting, kissing my neck and pulling at my nightie, begging 'please'. His coke demon had a massive boner that was growing bigger and bigger the more I resisted. I got so frustrated that I got out of bed and went to the living room to sleep on the sofa. He followed me like a lost puppy.

'No, Livia, please just come back to bed,' he cried.

'Only if you stop trying to fuck!' I told him, and even then he disagreed, saying again and again that I was his 'wife'. That we *needed* to.

I got even more frustrated, telling him I was going someplace else – I don't know where I thought I was going. He got down on his knees and grabbed my leg, sobbing uncontrollably. With snot coming out of his nose and his eyes bloodshot, he looked up at me and pleaded with his hands together.

'Please, Livi. I need you, I need you. I'm a drug addict and

I have no one and you were there when Mum died. Please, I have no one. Please.' He cried harder and louder, pulling on my night dress. 'I'm a mess, you're right. You're right I need help. I don't know who I am anymore. You're the only person I have. Livi, please.' He tugged at my leg.

'Nero, stop. You're full of shit.' I told him. 'You have all those girls in Berlin! Message them and ask them to come and take care of you.'

'I swear to God, let God strike me down right now, let God take away everything I love, let my career go to shit. I need help, I know I do. I'm fucking depressed, Livia, can't you see? I'm suicidal, Livia. I don't know if I'm going to make it. Without you I'd rather die. Please, Livia,' he sobbed loudly.

From that moment, I'd emotionally checked out. The love was just never the same for me again. So, when I chose to stay, I stayed for him. For that boy who was naked, crying his eyes out on the cold floor, begging for me to stay. I felt bad for him. I genuinely pitied him. I thought that as a friend, I needed to see this through. I needed to help him, at least get him sober. Because he was right. He had nobody.

He was right, he needed me.

He needed me because I was his supply.

That's it: nothing but his narcissistic supply.

28

Welcome to wits' end

The love bombing didn't last much longer after I caught him cheating.

I couldn't tell anyone. Not even Ruby. It was honestly too painful to talk about. I felt embarrassed and deeply ashamed.

On New Year's Eve, after celebrating at the Pack, we headed back to our place for the afterparty.

Blake sat on the sofa in our living room. Since Nero had disallowed him being rude to me, he just outright ignored me, with this awful passive aggressive energy. *He just did not like me.* He wanted a Nero single, and that was that.

So when Blake began making conversation with me at the afterparty, I didn't play it super sweet, avoiding conflict at any cost like I usually did. The alcohol mixed with the newfound awareness that I had been cheated on, and the realisation that everyone probably knew, had awakened a new spirit in me – a spirit that didn't give a fuck.

I'd started making YouTube videos about spirituality and

astrology, and Blake was telling me how he thought they were cool (I'm unsure to this day if he was trying to take the piss). Somehow, it escalated to a very heated discussion.

'Well guess what, Blake. I know Nero cheated. Are you fucking happy now? And guess what too, I never! I've never cheated. That shocks you, huh? You were soooo suspicious of me, like *I* was going to break *his* heart, right? As a matter of fact, why do you just not *like* me? What is it? Am I not good enough for your boy? Not attractive enough? Huh? Huh?' I snapped at him.

I was hurt. Everyone knew what he'd been doing behind my back. Everyone looked at me like I was stupid. Crazy. And most of all, I *felt* stupid and I felt crazy. I felt it all the time.

In the morning, when I woke up, Nero was still up from the night before, and he accused me of *flirting* with Blake.

Yes, he *actually* accused me of that.

'You asked him if he thought you were attractive. He told me, I even heard it,' he kept saying.

'Blake?! You think I'd *ever* flirt with *Blake?!'*

It didn't matter how many times I explained the context, how many times I explained how much that boy disgusts me, how many times other people confirmed it was a rhetorical question or how many witnesses saw that it was an argument, he just wouldn't let go. And in the midst of me desperately trying to prove myself, we went straight back into the cycle of abuse.

He had caught (made up) me in a 'wrong' so he could return back into his position of power. I fell right into his trap. Hell, I had no choice – he placed me in it.

Nero's birthday was fast approaching by the end of January,

so I started to arrange a surprise birthday dinner with all his friends and Traza at his favourite restaurant. Axel Dupont also booked us a nice hotel to stay in.

The night before we left for the hotel, Nero and I were watching a movie called *Casino*. Whenever we watched films, if a woman ever did anything wrong – lied, cheated, acted unhinged – Nero would comment, 'See, all women are like this', 'Trusss' or simply, 'That's you'. It's like he really wanted me to be that. He wanted me to be insane or vindictive.

I always had anxiety watching, worried what the female role might do next, say next, how she might dress or act.

This time, the woman in the film was having a breakdown while leaving her husband. He laughed and said, 'That's you'. I just had enough.

I stormed out of the room and he followed me into the bedroom. The argument escalated, and I started calling him a cheat, a liar. After he cheated, I just couldn't let it go. I'd always revert back to the pain and deceit of what he'd done. I didn't trust him anymore.

At some point in that argument I began packing my things as rage filled my entire body. I told him, 'You know one day, one day I'll meet someone who won't do this to me. A real man wouldn't do the things you do.'

He lunged forward. I quickly crouched over the bed and shielded my face, as he punched my back and shoulders over and over and over again. It felt never-ending. I can still feel the places he punched me as I write this.

When he left to go to the living room, I lay on the bed for a few minutes, crying in pain until I'd had enough of crying. I picked up my phone and stormed into the room. There were so many times Nero recorded me when I would be having a breakdown, so many times I felt like a clown on show at a circus.

And in that state of sheer trauma and fight-or-flight mode, being continuously abused, gaslit and tortured, with my vision blurry, my face covered in tears, my voice shaky and my body aching, I walked in and pulled out my phone.

'You beat me up,' I said over and over in response to the speech he taunted me with from across the room.

It was as if I almost didn't believe it had happened again, as if I wanted him to just admit it on camera so at least when he returned to begging me, I could show him, look – look what you are! I genuinely felt like I'd lost my mind reasoning with him and all his personalities. I thought, *If I record this, I'm not crazy. He has to believe me; someone has to believe me.*

There was a moment of silence after my statement ...

The camera recording him ...

He just sat there on the sofa, chowing down a bag of crisps, body language unintimidated and open, shouting back at me that, yes, yes he does beat me up because I'm a 'cunt and I won't leave *his* house' ... As if he wasn't the one holding me hostage, mentally, emotionally and quite literally physically.

I put the camera down as we argued back and forth. Mid-argument my body told me to get out of that house. I felt flighty as a sense of urgency took over me to get out, just get out and go, and as I stopped arguing and turned around, I realised he knew I was going to try and leave. That sparked him to come charging towards me into the kitchen. I quickly got my phone back out, thinking he'd stop if he knew he was being recorded, that he'd think twice before hurting me.

But he didn't stop.

Nero grabbed one of my arms and twisted it backwards, shoving me into the corner of the kitchen. The camera slipped as I fell onto the floor, but it kept on recording.

'Nero, please stop. Please stop, you're hurting me. Nero, get off me. Nero, get away,' I cried loudly over and over as he twisted my arm so hard I waited to hear the sound of my wrist snap.

He kicked my legs over and over at the same time as twisting my arm, taunting me 'get up then, get up' in an almost sociopathic, patronising and monotone voice. He knew that I was completely unable to move as I squirmed beneath him in agony.

'I can't believe you just disrespected the shit out of me,' he said, twisting and kicking even harder.

'STOP STOP STOP, PLEASE STOP!!!" I sobbed uncontrollably.

My body must have moved on top of my phone as it stopped recording.

He eventually let go of my arm and jerked me back down onto the floor where I lay crying. He began to pack Jefe's things into a bag.

I crawled towards Jefe, grabbing him with my sore wrist, breathing heavily. I remember just crying into him, holding him tight.

Nero tried to wrestle him out from under me as I begged him to stop. Jefe was all I had.

'You don't deserve him. You'll never see him again,' he said again in his calm and stern tone. Like a father disciplining a child.

I cried and screamed, holding Jefe as tightly as I could. 'Please, no! Nero, please don't take him. I'll do anything.'

The thought of my baby being ripped from me made me feel like I was dying, like someone was sticking hundreds of pins all over my body. I couldn't *bear* the idea of having my only bit of happiness taken from me. It was more painful than any time Nero had ever hit me.

Eventually Nero released a big sigh and pulled us apart by yanking my hair.

'You'll never see him again. Say goodbye to Mummy, Jefe,' he said, even calmer than before.

He took Jefe and walked out, slamming the door shut on my already sore wrist, and walked away.

I sat in the living room on my own, in the middle of our grey sofa. The house was silent all of a sudden. But if you listened carefully, you could hear the echoing of the shouting and screaming of just moments ago.

Sometimes, after the war, I could hear a ringing in my ears, as my hands were shaking in front of me.

Nero would isolate me after some of his worst attacks, confuse me and traumatise me enough that I didn't even have any energy left to think. I had no energy left to make a plan or gather my things. Call anyone. Seek help.

I'd just sit there, feeling pathetic. My face felt numb. My throat closed. I'd quiver as my hormones bathed in cortisol. My muscles tensing up into new knots. My lungs filled with grief. Despair. Misery. Sometimes, an hour could pass and

I'd still be there, frozen, staring blankly at the wall. I would hyperfocus, wondering why I'd never noticed that the canvas was slanted, or the candle needed replacing.

I'd feel this emptiness deep inside me, my brain stuck in a loop, asking myself over and over why this kept happening. *Why does he keep doing this to me?*

Sometimes, I'd think about dying.

I'd wonder if the only way he'd realise how bad he'd ruined me was if I died.

I'd wonder how nice it would feel to set myself free.

I'd look out the window onto the balcony and imagine my body falling from it, heavily impacting onto the concrete beneath. Where it would land. The reaction of the pedestrian who'd find me. Who would contact my parents? How much they'd hurt. How in the long run it would make life easier for them. Sometimes I'd begin to sob as I realised just how badly I no longer wanted to be alive. How I was so damaged I couldn't do this life shit anymore. I'd had enough.

The sounds of my crying filled the empty house around me. I would cry so hard that my body would hurt.

'I just can't do it anymore, I just can't,' I'd weep out loud, pulling on my hair as I held my face

So when Nero eventually called me in the middle of my sorry state and told me to come to the Four Seasons hotel, I obeyed like a zombie. I stared out of the window on the car journey, disassociating the whole way.

I was greeted by the regular cheery receptionist who gave me my room key. 'Welcome back, Mrs Kouassi.'

I was too zoned out to show her any emotion. I could barely acknowledge her. 'Thank you,' I responded.

I was greeted by my beautiful dog jumping onto me at the door, Jefe kissing me all over.

Nero took my hand and walked me over to the bed, pulling me into his lap. He held me tight as I nestled my head into his neck. He cradled me as he kissed my forehead. It felt so fucking good to be held. I felt warm vibrations releasing the tension from my muscles. I felt so sleepy and so drained.

I sighed into his chest, falling deeper into his arms until I completely collapsed through his body, down into a long dark winding tunnel. My body fell slowly but gracefully, just like I imagined it would when I could finally let go and be free, all my pain tearing off in layers with the wind as I fell deeper and deeper. Until I suddenly landed on a pile.

A pile of other bodies.

They were me, versions of me. With my old long, beautiful brown hair.

In my old stylish clothes.

Confident.

Beautiful.

Young.

But dead. All completely dead.

They were all the versions of me that had died in Nero's arms.

All the pieces of me I'd killed to be with him.

And as I lay there, I was peaceful. It was like I'd accepted my fate.

Somehow, some way, he would eventually kill me.

And honestly, that was just okay.

29

Snakes and ladders

Not long after Nero's birthday came Paris Fashion Week. It was my second year attending with Nero. It fell on a Scorpio full moon and the energy in Paris was just as sinister as you'd expect.

Sabrina would be there because she modelled for Dolce Tanger, a brand owned by Said Ali, who was like a 'big bro' that Nero obsessed over. Most of these obsessions were just older, more successful men who displayed narcissistic traits. Very toxic masculine energy. Very big egos. Even bigger voices.

We argued on the way to Paris, Nero telling me that I couldn't pull Sabrina up on the fact she'd attempted to supposedly '*rape*' my boyfriend on drugs. His only argument was that Said was his bro, Sabrina was Said's 'sis' and that he didn't want any drama that could tarnish their relationship.

So I agreed to say nothing.

People think Fashion Week is the coolest thing ever.

In reality, it's a busy, over-crowded game of snakes and ladders – clout ladders – that everyone is desperate to climb. Everyone is trying to get into the same parties, everyone is desperate and depressed, everyone's on drugs, yes *especially* the celebrities and models.

At important fashion dinners, usually held at Hotel Costes, I'd sit quietly in the beautiful Parisian courtyard restaurant with thick velvet red curtains and extravagant sofas. I'd watch the battle of egos as Nero's eyes would be wide and alert from all the cocaine, scanning his opponent's faces for signs of objection, a cigarette in hand and everyone swooning over him. He would be in his element.

They'd all have their heads tilted, large taunting smiles stretched across their faces like Cheshire Cats. They nodded and laughed at his preachings, every now and then taking turns to tell him, 'You are the next biggest superstar', 'You are a genius, a legend', and 'You can just tell by the way you talk you're going to take over the world'. I'd just sit there and wince – seriously, who even spoke like this? Who idolises and worships a human being like this?

Everyone in the industry.

I could have sworn I'd heard a sudden knock under the table from his dick becoming erect after all the compliments. Everyone was ready to stand up from their chairs, rip their clothes off and pounce at him.

Usually some random older fashion exec woman or edgy fashion director man would randomly start touching me (only after they realised I was his girlfriend), saying how beautiful and pretty I was, and 'ooh la la' and . . . *please stop touching me.* I'd fidget and slide their hands off my thighs.

Sometimes I'd be so overwhelmed by the fake energy at these functions that I'd go to the bathroom, stick my fingers down my throat and make myself sick. I don't know why, but it somehow rebooted my system. I'd look at my face in the mirror, flushed with pink, mouth covered in saliva and mascara running, and disassociate from my own reflection. It was like looking at someone else. Other times I'd take a bump of coke just to bear it. If you can't beat them, join them. It felt like selling my soul to the devil. It made me numb, allowing me to operate on their awfully low vibrating level. I didn't feel so hyper aware of all their intentions and auras anymore. I blended in better. I might have even cracked a dull joke or, better yet, laughed at one.

I mean it when I tell you, being around industry rats during Fashion Week is *unbearable* sober. I'd stopped taking cocaine a month or two after Nero and I moved into our apartment. I'd only ever dabbled in it here or there harmlessly, but after I saw what it did to Nero, I was sickened by the thought of the white powdery substance being anywhere near my nose – so to survive Fashion Week, I hated myself.

We headed one evening to meet Said at the Ritz and, of course, just as I'd anticipated – Sabrina was there.

She was sitting across from us at the grand dining table, decorated with huge candles and expensive cutlery, as I avoided eye contact so I wouldn't lose my shit. Nero was so fucked up. I was desperate for some reassurance but he couldn't even acknowledge what the situation was doing to me. I could see my fingers shaking in my lap as I used my other hand to keep them still. The anxiety was thick, polluting the air around me.

We left the Ritz and headed to a huge club called La Rouge. I was sitting next to Nero at our table, my legs over his lap, in matching Astrid Anderson fur outfits when Sabrina approached us almost out of nowhere. In a short exchange *they hugged*; then, she tried to hug me. I scowled at her and looked the other way, biting my tongue as I tried my best not to cause a scene. I wanted so badly to say something but Nero had made clear that I couldn't cause drama, and I was too scared of the repercussions. Just before she walked away, they said something to each other, and when I asked what it was, Nero told me she asked for a cig and he told her to fuck off.

I was so angry that they'd hugged but he just kept telling me, 'How am I meant to ignore her? She's Said's "people"!'

When I got up to go to the bathroom with another girl, Nero gripped my arm tightly and pulled me back into his lap. In my ear he said firmly, 'If anyone tries to flirt with you in this club do NOT fucking chat to them, you understand?'

I sighed.

When I got back from the bathroom, Nero was in the middle of the dance floor getting into some kind of confrontation with another guy. They pushed each other back and forth as they both ran outside, so I stumbled after him.

As I got outside and felt the cold air hit my face, the full moon lighting up the Parisian streets, I wandered over to Nero. He was head-to-head with the guy, another standing between them, mediating the situation.

I tilted my head to the side, staring hard at the man, trying to recognise him ... Squinting, I combined all my drunken brain cells trying to understand who was fighting my boyfriend. It was fucking Jude.

A fight broke out between the boys and I began to remove my stilettoed, knee-high sock boot. I ran towards Jude, heel in hand, as people shouted among themselves in the commotion, 'One on one! Nobody else get involved', 'Fair fight!!'

It was as if they had a lot of mutuals who saw that this was a *long* time coming.

I took my heel, charged in and whacked Jude over the head three or four times before one of Nero's friends lifted me up and carried me away from the ruckus.

Once we got back to the hotel, Nero cried. He hadn't even necessarily lost the fight – they were both far too drunk and high to really get more than a few punches in, each failing to catch their breaths in between. He lay on the sofa and cried, saying that none of his boys helped him, that nobody was there. I told him I was. I told him I jumped in. But he just wanted to be alone.

As I fell asleep, in the distance I could still hear him crying. It softly faded more and more, and eventually, if you listened carefully, you could hear those demons, just laughing at him.

The Great Shower Wall of Survival

Have you ever felt dry in a shower?

After three hours of you battering my brain, the house was covered in smashed glass and there was calm complexity after the war.

The house was a battlefield. Literally.

I carefully stepped over the broken glass and went to the bathroom, locking the door and sitting in the shower. Sometimes I'd cry and let the water wash my tears away. Most times I'd not have enough strength left to even produce any more.

The hot water would penetrate calming hormones to nourish my brain – but my brain would be numb, like it had logged off.

I would be asleep but still somehow softly awake.

So much had just happened, but my brain didn't have any juice left to think.

I'd just stare at the wall ahead of me and hug my knees against my chest, gazing vacantly ahead.

I'd reflect on the last time I stared at this wall, living in the same exact feeling.

Gratitude would trickle out from whatever receptor could feel it.

That I'm able to have this shower.

That I'm able to be in my home.

That I'm alive.

For now.

I'd step out of the shower, and in the moment between being under the water and drying my body with the towel, I'd already feel dry. Drained of all moisture

I could see my naked body in the steamy mirror.

I'd spot a new bruise forming somewhere, another from a few nights before almost disappearing.

I'd stand and stare in the mirror, feeling so dry: so depleted.

But still so grateful that this battle was over.

I'd slip on a baggy T-shirt and make my way to the living room.

And there you'd be, waiting for me.

Sitting on the sofa.

Ready to reward me for my submission.

For my return.

Ready to watch me slowly piece my brain back together.

Until you batter it again.

And again.

And again.

I grew to look forward to being reacquainted with that shower wall, water raining down on me.

It signified a desperately awaited peace. Survival, reward and another chance of love waiting for me.

30

Goodbye home

Nero's debut album was to be called *Love Spelled Backwards is Evil*. And in the lead up to finishing the album, for one last time, Nero began to pour some love into me again.

We practically lived at the Four Seasons hotel now. £900+ a night for a room was pretty ridiculous considering our home was so beautiful, but he just loved it there. We'd always ask for a specific suite. It had a dark wooden interior and an electric blind covering one enormous window that, once closed, felt like you were in a luxury spaceship floating somewhere above earth. The best part was the bathroom though. The shower head and taps were golden, with an enormous tub surrounded by little golden tiles. He'd bring his studio equipment and Jefe. We'd order him dog food from the doggy menu. What a lavish life for a little prince.

Nero and I would spend hours in the spa downstairs. He'd try to teach me how to swim and I'd record him doing laps in his funny swimming goggles that made him look like a bug.

We'd book the couple's room for massages where there would be an interactive steam room, and after the massage we'd have an hour in there alone, so we'd make love on the marble seat as the green neon lights and steam filled the space and rain poured down on us, rainforest sounds in the background. We were far away from reality, like a delicate bubble that could be popped by a pin should it not be handled with absolute care.

Afterwards, we'd lie on the soft king-size bed in our robes, hair still wet, knees and noses touching with the Bose sound speaker playing Bon Iver. We'd hum along loudly to the strange sounds throughout the track, in imperfect harmony.

I'd sit with my head leaning on his shoulder as he broke the no smoking rules over and over again, not giving a single fuck about the £500 fine, recording into his mic, frequently turning to me for my advice. Sometimes we'd even make songs together, recording my voice too, and later have sex to it.

One night at the hotel, Nero got a drunk call from Kai.

Nero, Kai and Ziggy had all officially parted ways as friends a few months ago over some business quarrels, and I heard them arguing from the toilet.

Kai was on speaker phone. I heard him say something along the lines of, 'You don't even know what you've got coming, you don't even know how many times you were about to get taken out.'

Nero glanced over to me in the tub. We just stared at each other for a moment.

Nero proceeded to tell Kai, 'Tell me what the fuck you meant by that right now or you're fucking done'.

I used my entire body weight to stand in the way of the door. Nero was so ready; he wanted to kill him.

'Please. Nero. Please, it's not worth it,' I begged him.

He finally gave way as tears started pouring out his eyes. I didn't even know how it had got to this point between them but I knew Kai was very fucking drunk and it wasn't going to end well. I had no idea why he resented him so much, or why he would say what he just said, but it was destroying Nero.

Kai revealed a horrific sequence of events to us.

So horrific that I could barely speak.

On the night of the white party at the end of last year, when we saw Jude … It wasn't a coincidence. It wasn't by chance. Jude was supposed to be there.

While we weren't due to leave so early or through the back, Jude was on his way around to the front of the venue, where he was going to be joined by a group of friends, those friends that pulled up in the black van that Jude jumped into just *moments* after our Uber sped off.

They had knives. They had knives and they were coming to attack Nero.

It was all a set up.

But it wasn't Kai who set Nero up … it was Ziggy.

Ziggy had had a war waging inside him ever since Chiara was forced into having the abortion. He had spiralled down a long, lonely road of alcoholism and addiction. Grieving for all that Nero had caused him to lose had led him to setting Nero up.

But Ziggy wasn't tactful enough. All the girls he admitted to inviting that night with the intention of winding Nero up had caused us to leave early. That saved Nero's, and maybe even my, life.

'After everything I did for him … wh-why?' Nero sighed. 'He's a master manipulator you know. He is the worst person.

I'll fucking kill him if I ever see him. Livia, I swear on my mother's—'

I hugged Nero. We held each other tight, both shaken up.

An hour or so after comforting Nero, he ran me a bath and took my hand to lead me into the bathroom. He played Jhené Aiko (one of my favourite artists) and smiled, 'Livi bath,' he said. I giggled as I held his hand and climbed into the tub.

He took a photo without me realising of me smiling in the bath from a distance. My body was covered, just my face on show, beaming and relaxing in the tub, and he posted it on his Instagram.

And then he joined me in the beautiful golden-tiled bathtub, his gorgeous dark skin glazed by the hot, steaming water, my feet carefully propped on his chest. We sang songs to each other. Kissed long and deep and rubbed our noses on each other's cheeks to the synths of the music.

Looking back, I guess he posted the picture of me to piss off Kai, proving that we didn't care, but at the time, I was just so grateful for the unexpected kindness and love, keeping the bubble intact for as long as possible.

Just a moment longer. I'd take whatever I could get.

When we got back home, I remember sitting on the sofa as we spoke about how my twenty-third birthday was approaching.

'We'll book a suite at the Four Seasons. I'll get all your friends into London, have a spa day with your girls at the hotel. We'll get a table somewhere in a club on the night and then all throw you in the air and shout, "Livi, Livi Livi!"' he exclaimed enthusiastically to me.

When he asked what I wanted as a gift, I said what I

always said on my birthday, 'Nothing, I just want a poem.'

I never wanted anything material from Nero, truly.

When we went to the shops, he'd ask if I wanted stuff from Supreme, Stüssy or Carhartt, and I'd be uninterested. He offered me gifts on birthdays and I couldn't care less about a designer bag, I was happy wearing his baggy T-shirts and my old clothes. I just wanted something sentimental. I was screaming for love, and if I could have the opportunity to choose it, I was going to, every – fucking – time. I wanted to ease that little girl inside who was still screaming with pain on the floor after being beaten. I'd walk into the empty house and lift her off the ground, show her the letters, the poems, the cards and the drawings and she'd smile and wipe away her tears. I'd convinced myself that's all she needed. Love. Love, love, love, love, love, love, love, love.

To finish the album, Nero, Jefe and I headed out to Angelic studios for a few weeks, a recording retreat in the English countryside. We were joined on and off by Axel Dupont, Traza and a few of the boys – whoever was left in the gang by this point.

My birthday was going to happen while we were out there, but we agreed we'd drive back to London afterwards to celebrate since it fell on a weekend.

The retreat came fit with cows, horses and a personal chef. Nero spent day and night in the studio. We had a no alcohol rule which quickly got broken after he felt the need to reward his hard-earned hours. But the no coke rule still stood.

I'd sit in the studio next door, looking after Jefe, playing *The Sims* and writing. I wrote poems, poems and songs about me and Nero. Nero would come into the room every few hours and check on me, leaving me with a kiss.

We'd all dance in the larger studio together, with its beautiful oak floors and walls and a huge mixing desk, and spotlights to warm up the atmosphere. We'd listen to the tracks, and Traza would swing his arms around Nero as they both bounced in excitement about collaborations. Traza was exec producing *Love Spelled Backwards is Evil*.

On the first weekend during our stay, we all headed out together to the Farmhouse, a member's club and a country retreat with a few bars for us to all celebrate the completion of the album. Nero and Traza sung in the karaoke room as we all laughed and danced along. I was mid-conversation with one of Nero's female producers when I noticed Nero and one of the boys talking to two random men, before one of them reached into their pockets and passed Nero something.

I walked over and said, 'Nero?' I didn't even need to say anything.

'Look, one bump is fine, Livi. Chill out . . .'

But it wasn't fine. It was NEVER one bump. The ESSENCE of cocaine is you NEED to keep NEEDING more as the comedown starves you of a fabricated, chemical-induced dopamine hit every fifteen minutes. And furthermore, Nero, Axel and I had agreed, we *promised*, that at least while finishing the album, there would be strictly <u>no cocaine</u>.

I walked outside to the front to get some air and calm down, looking out at the stars over the fields. I tried to call Ruby but her line was busy. I was scared. I was scared for my life once again. Scared the demons would take it, once again.

As I walked back in, I couldn't see anyone, so I checked the back smoking area. I could feel that it was bad. The bubble had popped.

Traza and Nero were arguing back and forth in the middle of the courtyard lit with fairy lights, that kind of loud laughing, passive aggressive arguing boys do, putting on a show for the rest of the crew as they stood in a circle around them.

'You're saying you want to have kids with her, but you can't have kids if you take coke every day, bro,' Traza said to Nero.

At a video shoot a few weeks earlier, Traza had told me that I'd be the coolest mum, and Nero would be the coolest dad.

'I already have one kid!' Nero shouted back in defence, talking about Jefe.

As soon as I stepped out into his vision, as soon as the coke demons smelled my scent, he switched, and venomously roared at me in front of everyone.

'*You fucking controlling bitch!*'

I can honestly say, from this moment on, Nero truly hated me. A new, potent type of hate.

It was like a fresh vengeance had formed against me because Traza, the only person he saw as '*above*' him, the only one who would dare confront him, had defended *me*.

I was Nero's property.

'Nero, you know you need to finish the album ...' I tried to contest.

But he proceeded to get angrier, shouting to all the boys, 'Do you see what I have to deal with? Always trying to control my fucking life, fuck off man. I work to pay the fucking bills, I pay for everything. I can do whatever the fuck I want. What the fuck do you do? Besides moan all day?'

He went on and on until everyone got uncomfortable and started ushering him away from me towards the car.

Traza told me to get in his car instead of the van. Inside the matte black Lamborghini, Traza assured me over and over, 'He's just doing this because you're the closest person to him, and if he ever gets too much I want you to just call me and say, "Yo T, your boy is moving mad" – but the one thing you can't do is leave him. You can never leave him,' he continued. It was like he was talking to someone else, projecting, thinking about a previous lover.

Back in the house, it got worse. We were all in the living area playing cards and Nero made snide remarks over and over. Everyone sat awkwardly around the table until Traza eventually said, 'If I win this round, Nero has to change his vibe'. He did win the round. But Nero's vibe did not change. And with the last remark he made about me, blaming me for the fact that Jefe had peed by the table, I got up from the table and ran to the bedroom to cry my sorry ass to sleep.

In the morning, I saw Traza briefly in the studio. I sat next to him as we both sipped our hot teas.

'Thank you for standing up for me,' I said softly.

He didn't know that that was genuinely the first time anyone ever had. It meant the world to me.

His energy was a little different as he softly smiled and gave me a nod. I figured he was just hungover as I left the room. But realistically, who knows what Nero said when I left that table.

Traza had once told us how we made him believe in love again. It was only earlier that week, when Nero was sat between my legs as I massaged his head on the beanbag, and Traza looked on at us, smiling . . .

Isn't it funny how nothing is ever as it seems?

31

Happy birthday, Livi, I hate you

My birthday was fast approaching. I took it upon myself to offer an olive branch to Nero as Axel, he and I sat on the kitchen countertops drinking tea before his session began

'Nero,' I said, 'we don't need to do my birthday here, the album is more important. We can just cut some cake and celebrate just like, me, you and Jefe, and then when we go back to London we can do a late birthday celebration like the one you said.'

For some reason that really annoyed him. I thought it was a kind and considerate offer but he said it was 'immature', that I should just have it here at the farm. The farm that was his album retreat. His album. His world.

In the same conversation, Axel suggested that he swap two of the tracks on the album when Nero suddenly switched on him.

'It's not your album though, is it, so don't tell me what to fucking do.'

Sometimes Axel and I exchanged looks, quietly consoling each other with our eyes. As much as I disliked how much he enabled Nero's behaviour, I could empathise with him just as much because, at the best of times, Nero also spoke to him like fucking shit.

When Nero was having yet another blowout, he'd retreat back into his difficult and cruel, very very hard-to-crack shell. I was alone all night as he barely even acknowledged me. I didn't even drink, I just sat on a bar-stool, kicking my feet and people-watching.

I watched Traza charm two older women at the bar. How their faces lit up with stars in their eyes, both throwing away any sense of dignity in competition to stand an inch closer than the other, desperate for his attention, desperate for his eyes to be locked on to theirs for just one moment longer than the other.

I thought about how women behaved around hip-hop artists. It was like hypnotism. It actually destroyed these men. Their egos become so inflated, they lose all empathy for anyone around them. They became monsters.

Nero was dying from supply starvation, so he struck for his easiest prey: a good old-fashioned Livi on the rocks.

I hummed along to a song that was playing. Nero's song.

'Oh you like that song, huh? You like it, yeah? I sing that, HAHA,' he taunted me in a patronising tone.

The boys all sniggered awkwardly as I rolled my eyes. He continued provoking me all night, until he ran upstairs to our bedroom where Jefe was. I came up the stairs behind him, excited to see my baby, but Nero was holding the door shut.

I grew more and more impatient as I banged on the door. I looked behind me and saw everyone coming up the stairs into the games room as they side-eyed me, their judgement seeping through.

I'd had enough of being bullied at this fucking farm.

He finally opened the door, and as I tried to get in, he slammed it hard on my hand. I screamed in pain.

As he opened the door, Jefe jumped on me. Tears streaming down my cheeks, I faced him.

'I hate you! You're actually evil,' I cried out loud as he grabbed me by my top and charged me backwards into the hallway. He threw me into the clothing rack when Mika, the world's least helpful person, walked into view. He saw me getting up from the floor, and to my *disbelief* he put his arm around Nero and said, 'C'mon, you don't need this'.

I got up and yelled at Mika. I was so angry. How, how in the hell could someone see *me* on the floor but proceed to check if the man who had clearly just pushed me was okay? As they walked out into the corridor together, Nero bathed in his glory, 'Look she's fucking crazy. I told you man, look at her.'

I charged behind him. A part of me knew I looked insane, but by this point I was over it. If they thought I was crazy for just acting like a human, a human who has a nervous system, a heart, a soul, a limit, a capacity, then that's exactly what I was. I was crazy. And I would show them just how crazy.

'You're an abuser!' I shouted, my voice cracking a little towards the end.

It was like all the years of agony had taken over me – I was reacting to every act put upon me. I was filled with rage. I was ready to finally stick up for myself, and I didn't care who was watching – a part of me even felt a lot safer that we weren't in private.

'You're FUCKING stupid!' he shouted at me. 'You're literally so stupid if you think anything you say right now is going to help your pathetic life.'

'A-And you're a fucking sicko who likes to fuck girls while they're asleep,' I let out.

Two of the boys were ushering him down the stairs, trying to hold him back. They just continued to drag him away. They didn't even react. Why did I think anyone would care? I could never win in an environment primed for his validation.

A few days of silent treatment later, I was so lonely and desperate to feel any kind of human connection. When the boys made misogynistic comments about women's bodies and body counts, I wished there was another female there to give the *look* to. Or a camera to stare into. Anyone to witness what I was witnessing. It felt like I was being punk'd.

I would bore myself to sleep. Walk Jefe. Try to be civil with Nero. Feel everyone's energy in the studio until I couldn't hide the anxiety anymore and leave. On repeat.

The night before my birthday, Nero asked what I wanted to do when it hit midnight. With so much yearning in my voice I said, 'Can we just watch Netflix on the laptop in bed?' It was truly all I wanted. I missed my home. I missed normality. I missed the simple pleasures I was still able to get my hands on back in London, when we'd at least make up for a day. It felt like because he had an audience, he was making the most of it, using everyone as a weapon to intimidate me. There was always someone, somewhere, listening, granting Nero an even nastier essence, an even bigger means for supply.

When the clock struck twelve, Nero told me he had to go over to the studio to do a live stream for the release of his new single. Yes, he decided to drop it bang on my birthday. 'I'll be twenty minutes,' he said.

I cleaned the room, put Jefe in his bed and got the laptop ready. I watched the live stream and when it ended, I waited. An hour passed. But nothing.

I texted Nero.

'Are you coming?'

But nothing.

'It's my birthday . . .'

Another fifteen minutes passed and we started arguing over text. Then, he blocked me.

It filled me with pure hatred. I put on my shoes and stormed over to the studio one hundred yards away.

As each step I took made loud noises in the gravel, the piercingly cold wind sweeping my hair back in the dark of the night, I knew I was about to look crazy again. But I couldn't control my steps. A fire had been ignited in me, a phoenix beginning to rise from the ashes: just slightly, moving a little every now and then, an indication that she is in fact alive – not much, but perhaps just opening her eyes from the rubble she's buried in. Eyes alight with a glint of justice. Slowly but surely. I'd had enough. I was ready to protect myself.

I had been beaten mentally, physically, sexually and emotionally that many times that I was reacting from pure trauma. He had driven me to insanity. But at the same time, I truly felt so empowered to just finally break free from his shackles and rip off the tape covering my mouth for so long. Even when I looked crazy, it was such a fucking relief, because that meant I was finally doing *something*.

It's my fucking birthday, I kept thinking as I walked into the studio. I just wanted someone to sit with. I'd been alone or bullied, bullied and alone for two weeks straight Do you know what that does to someone?

As I barged open the door to the studio, all the boys were sitting in a circle. They turned their heads. Nero stared at me intensely, as if his prey had walked right into his trap, licking his lips as he salivated, appetised by the feast that awaited him.

The room was silent. Suddenly, the phoenix closed her eyes shut again. Tightly.

'Can ... Can I speak to you, Nero ... ?' I stuttered, almost choking with anxiety. Everyone's energy was so loud. I could feel all their thoughts coating me with shame. I could feel the voice in me getting smaller and smaller. My hands were shaking. Eyes filled with fear.

'Aww, I was just about to get up, wasn't I, mandem?' he asked the boys.

I looked at the floor. I couldn't stand to look anywhere else.

He stood up and began to get his coat from behind the chair. My heart was beating frantically as I thought he might actually walk out with me – but it was like he heard my thoughts. He realised he could strike right now. He stopped, looked at me, then looked back down at the chair.

'See, thissss is why I don't want to come with you,' he groaned loudly.

He looked at the boys pathetically, as if he needed saving

from the crazy girlfriend who might take him and drink his blood.

My heartbeat was going a hundred miles per hour as I tried to string a sentence together. Everyone's eyes on me were making me so anxious that my vision was going blurry.

'Please can you just come uh, talk to me out here?' I mumbled, not wanting to cause a scene.

He slowly stomped out, looking back at the boys saying, 'Fuck sake man,' over and over. I was so embarrassed that it was painful.

When we got to the hallway, he continued telling me that he hated me. I just couldn't believe this was happening because I wanted my boyfriend to keep me company on my birthday instead of sitting around doing nothing with his boys.

He walked back into the studio so I ended up running back to the residency alone. I got into bed and honestly, this was the hardest I have ever cried in my life. And I cried *a lot*.

I remember the silhouette of the four-poster bed towering above me turning into one wet blur as I sobbed loudly. You'd think I'd just taken a bullet. I had. I remember thinking over and over, how did I get here? How did my life end up like this? I was so full of pain.

I ached for what felt like forever, drowning in a sea of sadness until Nero joined me. Was he here to rescue me? Throw out a life float? Or had he come to dunk my head under until I simply ceased to exist?

He walked in and saw my swollen eyes. He just shut the door and went to the bathroom.

When he came back in, I had wiped my tears and was facing the other way.

He grabbed my shoulder and turned me onto my back. Then he got on top of me with all his weight and held me down by both my wrists. I tried to wriggle out, saying 'get off me', but his impression remained cold and unbothered. He stared deeply at me, his eyes fixating from my left eye to my right as he scanned me.

I stopped wriggling and stared back in angst, tears trickling down the sides of my face.

He brought his right hand up to my cheek and slapped it once as I scrunched up my face in pain. Then twice more, firm and fast, before clenching my face in his hand.

'You're twenty-three now, it's time to grow the fuck up,' he told me sternly.

I began to panic and attempted to get him off me, but the more I tried the harder he gripped me.

He shook my face in his hand and raised his voice slightly. 'Are you fucking listening? It's time to grow up! You need to listen to everything I say, you need to do everything I tell you to do. From now on, just fucking listen. It's time, Livi.' He shouted in my ear so loudly it was as if he believed there was little Livi sleeping inside, all wrapped up in my cochlea. He used one hand to continually slap my face faster and harder, trying to wake little Livi up, while the other hand held it tight in place with his fingers on either side of my chin.

'I hate you, I hate you so much, Nero,' I cried.

He sighed. 'If you hate me, then leave,' he said softly, the corner of his mouth lifting a little, still holding my face in place. He slapped me again. 'But you CAN'T, CAN YOU? WHERE ARE YOU GOING TO GO, LIVI? YOUR LIFE

WILL BE OVER. LIVI WILL BE OVER!' he shouted louder into my ear.

'Anything would be better than this, Nero, *anything*.'

He smiled. 'Watch. If you ever leave me, watch what happens to your life, and watch what happens to mine. You're going to wish you were dead . . .'

He spread my legs apart and pulled down his tracksuit bottoms. He put his dick inside me, and he began fucking me as tears rolled down the sides of my face. I lay there, still and defeated. The girl he'd called upon showed up for him, she always did.

He stopped, and while still inside me, he said, 'You know what I'd love? I'd actually love to kill you.'

I lay beneath him, expressionless.

'You're the only one, the only one who knows everything. Oh, it would feel sooo good to kill you,' he said, moving deeper inside me.

I stared at him; he stared back.

I felt a sharp pain inside me.

I suddenly pushed him off me, and left the room.

I stood in the bathroom catching my breath, realising that my body was rejecting him.

The morning of my birthday, Nero decided he'd throw his album listening party on the very same night.

We got to the studio where Nero had invited out some of his old friends he hadn't seen in years. They were reconciling. They knew him as someone else, broke and ambitionless.

They told me how great they thought I was, how happy they were for us. While we were all super drunk and had taken some molly, I asked how he ended up how he is. And, without any context, they knew exactly what I meant. They sighed and said, 'he's always been like this'.

I thought I'd get some insight and truly understand the trauma behind it. How one man could be so wicked. They simply told me that it was just him.

My birthday was a blur. Since we'd all taken MDMA, it numbed Nero and me enough not to fight that night.

At the party, he shouted over to the producer, 'Play the song about killing Livi!'

A few days earlier, he had ushered me into the recording booth after not speaking more than a few words to me. He had asked me to scream into the mic. Assuming they needed a girl's vocals for some beat, I did it. This was before playing me the track, revealing it was about two men kidnapping and assaulting me.

This wasn't the first song he'd made about violently hurting me either; Nero also had a hit song called 'My Brain'. In the studio, he had recorded lyrics into the mic as I sat on the sofa, 'I'll grab the knife and then then I'll stick it in my wife' . . .

When asked what inspired that song in an interview, he blankly told them, 'My girlfriend, she was in the studio with me and I was just writing a song about her.'

The interviewer clarified, shocked that he was just recording lyrics like that while I was right there.

'Art!' He laughed.

32

Screw you

The time had finally come to leave that godforsaken farm. And I was happy. So very fucking happy.

I could almost smell home, feel the comfort of my bed. The dewy light flooding into the living room in the mornings. The LED lights framing our bedroom in lilacs and reds. I wanted nothing more than to be there.

As our cars departed, we all debated about this new disease spreading called Coronavirus. It was almost exciting, joking what our apocalyptic plan would be if this bizarre virus did in fact take over the world. With photos of bat soup and videos of hospitals in China overflowing with victims flooding the internet, Covid was going viral as a contagious, fast-spreading disease that could kill us all.

Nero kept mentioning to the boys how much he had enjoyed their stay on the farm, how much he wished they could all live together, how they should get a big house together and made it a permanent thing. My blood would boil. The whole trip was hell for me. But I kept my mouth shut because home was so close I could almost taste it.

In the car journey, I sat next to Nero in the back, with Mika in the front seat. He was showing me a photo that he wanted me to come up with a caption for for his Instagram when I saw he'd screenshotted a picture of him and another female artist. We'd had an argument about her a long time ago because he told me she was trying to fuck him on a night out, and then I saw a message on his phone a day later where he boasted about her whining on him at a club.

Yes – it was yet another heart-fell-out-my-ass embarrassing incident which he talked his way out of.

When I asked why he had that picture screenshotted, he grew instantly defensive and let out, 'Because she would give me clout and you wouldn't.' I felt my lungs collapse in on themselves. His friend in the front didn't even turn his head, but I could see his eyes were widened in shock.

I stared out of the window, as tears streamed down my cheeks for the rest of the journey.

I was *beyond* defeated.

The raindrops rolling down the window raced the ones on my face. Home was so close. I kept telling myself, *as soon as you get there, you can just take some space, stay in separate rooms, let him calm down. He eventually will and he will make the effort. There'll be no boys around to distract him or for him to use as a weapon against you, he will calm down and eventually come around.* That's what I was associating our home with: the fact that there, the cycle did eventually end. Kind of. For a moment at least. But at the farm, it was ongoing. It was a public torture show with no escape in the middle of nowhere. At home I had some hope. Some peace.

As we walked to the front door, I shoved the keys in the lock and Nero said, 'Is that how you're gonna be, yeah?'

I guess he didn't like how I opened the door.

With a deep sigh, I said, 'I'm so done,' shaking my head and beginning to twist the keys.

He grabbed me by my T-shirt and threw me backwards onto the suitcases behind us. He opened the door, hurried the dog in and slammed it shut, locking it behind him.

After he finally let me back in twenty-something minutes later, we began to argue.

'How can you be angry at me when you're the one who fucked up?' I asked. 'You always want me to apologise for things you did wrong. I'm done with this.'

And he told me, 'You're done, yeah? You're done? What does that mean? Done with me?'

'Done fighting, Nero. Done with whatever this energy has been. You've literally turned into a monster,' I cried back to him.

'You're fucking ungrateful. I should never have brought you to the farm in the first place. It's my biggest regret, and now you want to tell me *you're* done?' he shouted as he heaved heavier and heavier, pacing the room.

He grabbed me and charged me backwards, and the door slammed behind him, locking us out.

'Now, look what you've fucking done. You're so fucking stupid,' he said as he began rustling in the suitcases.

And then, almost as if it came from nowhere, he found a screwdriver and jabbed it into my shoulder. I let out a scream.

So he did it again.

And again.

And again.

He kept going until I pushed him away by his stomach to stop, and then became shocked when I accidentally touched his crotch because he was, in fact, erect.

I stared up at him in disbelief. I still remember exactly what he said.

'I'm not hard because of that, I'm just hard because I'm excited.'

Once we finally got the door open, the arguing continued as Nero kept circling back to me being the problem in our relationship. That I was too 'in love'. That I didn't have anything else going for me in life. That he was the best I could ever get so I should act right. That I should never talk back. Ever. I should just listen. Over and over, he shouted, 'Everyone just needs to fucking listen!'

I argued back that he was delusional, that I'd lost my best friend, that he'd taken years of my life, that the money and drugs had all got to his head. I cried and cried as my mind flooded with all the things he'd done to me.

'You literally cover me in bruises, Nero. You're supposed to love me.'

'So why don't you fucking leave?'

'You really want to play that with me?' I replied. 'You really think you'd let me leave? Even if you do at first, you know what you do, you know what you do to me, you know this is my family and I love you and Jefe. You would never let me truly go because you use it against me. You always find a way to trick me back in, or you'll always punish me until I do. You use Jefe, you know what you're doing! You've broken me and ruined who I am inside on purpose. I never used to be like this,' I told him, filled with sorrow. 'You promise you'll change, you promise me the world, and then I just end up back here ... back to you *abusing* me!'

'Abuse?' He raised his eyebrows in disgust. 'You come back because you know deep down I'm a good guy. You fucking know it, Livia.'

'I *think* you are, that's why I came back! But you never change – you promise you will and you never do. A good guy wouldn't hurt me. Look at my arm,' I shouted and showed him the marks on my shoulder.

He didn't even allow his eyes to rest on my arm before rolling them, 'It would be much worse if you were a boy,' he said.

I started to cry into my hands, standing at the living-room door. 'You're delusional! You're a coke-head! A fucking coke-head abuser!' I told him, everything pouring out of me.

The next thing I knew, he was charging towards me. He kicked me with all his might in one shin. I doubled over but didn't fall, so he kicked me twice as hard in the other.

I fell to the floor as he kicked me repeatedly in my ass and back. He got on top of me, squeezing my face and choking me. He headbutted me and let out a loud grunt. I turned over onto my side, trying to hide my face, but he moved my hands out of the way, slapping me repeatedly. He then slid me along the floor by my hair and pressed the back of my head down on the hard wooden dog bowls.

'You stupid, stupid girl,' he exclaimed as he dug his fingers into my face.

When he finally let go, he said, 'That's it. You're fucking going to wish you never did this. You're gonna be nothing without me. Your life is over, TODAY.' He started packing his things.

And just like that, he got Jefe, he got his shit, he even took the food out of the fucking cupboard, every last packet of crisps, and left. He made sure I'd be sorry. He made sure I'd need him. He made sure because I wouldn't even be able to eat.

And I didn't even try to stop him. I just lay there, each bruise in my body pulsating in pain. I could barely even stand up. This was the worst he'd ever beat me up.

Once I finally made it into the shower, stared into the wall of survival and disassociated from reality, I eventually crawled into bed.

As I lay there, the deep feelings of loneliness crept in. I felt so unworthy and hopeless. I felt ugly, used and abused. I would try and imagine life without him and my mind would just resist. With all his preaching in my mind. The cortisol from the consistent abuse over the last few weeks overdosing my mind. I had no clarity or stability, no real sense. I had truly lost my sanity. I was too traumatised and beaten to think straight. All I thought was, he was right, I won't get better than him.

I don't deserve better than him.

I believed that this was all I deserved from the world.

Things would creep back up in my mind . . .

The baby.

What if I'd kept it? What if this is my bad karma? What if I'm a murderer?

I spiralled.
And spiralled.
And spiralled.

Over the next few days, I slept most of the time. My legs hurt each time I got up to use the bathroom and it reminded me of what he'd done. I'd have flashbacks and all I'd see was the rage on his face, feel pain in the places he hit me as if he was doing it all over again.

Maybe I needed to just submit. Maybe I should have just said yes and agreed to everything. Maybe I needed to stop having emotions, stop having feelings. It would have been so much easier than this.

Eventually he called me to come to an Airbnb he was staying at with the boys – he got what he wanted. The UK had announced it was going into lockdown and I was all alone. There was no transport available for anyone; I couldn't go anywhere. I imagined myself turning into a skinny corpse, a skeleton alone in that apartment. Oh, how much easier that would be than to live.

When I got to the apartment, seeing Jefe soothed my heart. I cuddled him for a few hours and then Nero came into our room, in some comfy silk pyjamas, energised and almost radiant.

'We're not together,' he said. 'I'm doing this for you because I love you and I'm a good person so I'm not just going to leave you there.'

'You don't deserve this at all,' he reiterated.

'I'm just a great guy,' he restated.

'Nobody will ever love you as much as I do,' he remembered.

I thought of what he wanted me to say right now.

I wanted to say one million things. But I never did.

I knew I had nowhere else to go. If he chucked me out, I was truly fucked.

'Thank you, Nero,' I said, quietly looking into his eyes.

His face looked ever so slightly smug. With his chin tilted high, he walked out and slammed the door behind him.

I looked at Jefe and he looked at me. 'Daddy is fucking evil,' I told him.

33

Pandemic prison

Imagine travelling twenty-four hours to the other side of the world, with no sleep, and then doing a full day's work.

That's what it feels like to be in an abusive relationship.

There was no cycle anymore, no love bombing or fake promises to keep me going. No breadcrumbs. No hope. Just thick, hot, sweaty, juicy abuse.

This was the worst time of my entire life. So, here's a trigger warning, if it's not already too late for that.

Nero's narcissism had found its perfect playground, at the perfect time.

I could not leave. The whole nation was on lockdown.

Shops were shut.

Hotels were shut.

Transport was shut.

You weren't allowed to go out, other than to buy essentials.

He also had an audience: his beloved flying monkeys.

He had full control of the entire house; he was paying for everything.

He had me right where he wanted me. No escape. No need for him to play nice. He had caught me in the middle of his web. My arms were tucked tightly inside, legs wrapped up. I couldn't move. I couldn't fuss or fight. He even spun webs around my eyes and mouth, just leaving my ears to make sure he was heard as he'd strike time and time again for his most delicious, flavoursome supply, over and over, until I completely perished.

This was a dream come true for Nero. He could punish me every single day.

We were in an Airbnb to begin with, in Marylebone. It was beautiful: old money vibes with brick walls in the bathrooms to give it that artistic contemporary feel. Mika and his girl-friend Jenna moved in with us, with a few of the outer circle followers occupying the other rooms. Nero would ignore me the entire day. Not a single word. If I asked a question, he would act like he couldn't hear me. Even if it was just me asking where the dog lead was or if he had eaten.

The only time he responded was when he asked the group what we should order for dinner, and I suggested Chinese.

'Why the fuck would you have a say?' he scowled at me in front of the group. And, as usual, everyone just awkwardly sat in silence.

I used to sit in our bedroom, downstairs in the basement level, to try and cope alone. I'd call Ruby and even she would be surprised we hadn't 'made up' yet. Because to her, I never singled out the bad times enough. I always downplayed each event, or most times didn't even mention them at all . . . but when we'd make up and he made even the slightest kind gesture, I'd exaggerate it to her so hard. Not because I wanted to lie, but I would get so excited every time that he'd changed. I'd find so much happiness in talking about it and believing in it. It was like I liked lying to myself.

But, to my dreamy ass's surprise, sometimes *belief just isn't enough*.

I remember trying to talk to Nero when he came into the bedroom to get something.

'C'mon, Nero. Please talk to me. We're going to be in here together. We can't just be like this the whole time.'

He literally shoved me into the wall behind me and walked past.

He starved me over and over of any love, any connection, any acknowledgement, just forcing me to grieve our relationship and remain confused and delirious.

Any time I went upstairs, the thoughts the boys had about me and our relationship were too loud. I'd feel my whole body fill with anxiety and I'd quickly lock myself back in the bedroom: the only place I felt safe, the only place I felt like I could breathe. Whatever I did up there, I was scrutinised. Bullied. Made fun of by Nero in front of his friends. Whether he'd command me to make everyone food or clean, whether he'd complain because I'd talk to Jenna, whether he'd get mad because I took too long to play my card in blackjack, 'Why are you even here?' he'd say, causing everyone to go quiet.

He reduced me to nothing.

Some nights when Nero was up doing coke with the boys, I could hear them talking about me. I would lie in bed listening, unable to sleep, an anxious wreck waiting to see how he would act when he came downstairs. Scared of what he would impose on me, what demon he would be getting fucked by tonight. What demon would punish me.

Sometimes I wasn't even sure if they were talking about me. I'd hear sentences and my name in the distance, but I just didn't know anymore. I felt like I had truly gone insane.

One night, he began touching me in bed ... I instantly submitted. It felt normal for us to have sex, we'd been doing it for three years and all I wanted was some kind of normal back. But aside from that, maybe this meant we could make up? Maybe this meant he would be nicer to me? Maybe if I just fucked him good enough he would love me again, and this daily torment and shaming would stop. Maybe I'd be able to come upstairs and hold a decent conversation with everyone without having an anxiety attack and running away. I heard the others laughing and enjoying themselves – maybe I'd be able to be happy, too.

I just wanted to feel desired, and what does that more than having someone's hands all over you?

When he asked me to turn over into the doggy style position for him, I told him nervously, 'You don't want me to do that, there's a huge bruise on my ass', to which he replied, almost proudly, '*I know, I'm the one who put it there*'.

And after *he* came, I instantly lay on his chest as we always did ...

'We can't cuddle. Obviously, we're gonna fuck because we can't fuck other people, but if we cuddle it will feel like we're together.'

So I just lay there. My boyfriend of three years had had sex with me, and told me he couldn't hold me after.

That feeling was so fucking degrading.

I felt so empty as he rolled over and slept like a fucking baby.

Every fibre of my being was begging me to speak up, to tell him how wrong it was to do that to me, but I just bit my tongue. The phoenix was well and truly silenced.

You have nowhere to go, Livia.

Don't do it.

What if he starts dragging you out by your hair? Everyone will hear. Everyone will see. What if he chokes you and no one hears? No one sees?

I couldn't think straight. Each night, I could hardly sleep. My mind would run in circles until my thoughts would become half-conscious nightmares, still somehow half awake.

During the day, I'd go on Instagram and post videos about how mental health was difficult for us all during lockdown, giving people motivation, uplifting them. I encouraged them to message me if they needed to talk to someone, telling them they were not alone. It was the only thing that made me feel better sitting in that room by myself all day – helping other people was somehow a coping mechanism. It made me feel like I had purpose, if even one person said I helped them. I dreamed that I had someone to do that for me – thinking about what a blessing it is to be relieved of pain. I never wanted people to be alone, or ever as alone as I was. Helping people, it's just my thing.

Another day, we took shrooms. It was the worst thing I could've ever done. With shrooms, or any psychedelics for that matter, the rules are pretty simple – your environment and mindset are key. So what did I do? I took liquid shrooms (the most potent kind) off the back end of an argument, at the peak of a pandemic, during the height of my abuse, with my abusive boyfriend and his enabling fake-ass friends.

It started off okay as we were all doing yoga, but as the high intensified I started to feel overwhelmed. I wasn't doing the yoga poses right so Nero began yanking my arm up, shouting, 'You're not fucking doing it right' in front of everyone, and it sent me spiralling from there.

I sat on Google for hours, searching for what to do to end the trip. My thoughts were so negative and intense I felt like I was going to stop breathing. A blog I had found online said to find the person you know the most and ask them to take you into a room alone, to calm you down a little away from too many different energies. And to drink a lot of fizzy juice.

So, after much deliberation, standing in the kitchen downing cups of Pepsi, I finally plucked the courage to walk over to Nero, who was sitting at the table sketching, and said, 'Nero, I think I'm having a bad trip . . .'

He let out one great big sigh . . . 'You look fine'.

'I'm not,' I said.

'Just sit there,' he told me. So I sat down. I stared at the pens for a moment before he got up and started preaching to the room about some bullshit.

I had to see myself through that bad trip. It shifted something in me . . . as if there was some deeper reason. Maybe the universe was trying to break the trauma bond by showing me that I don't need him. Only *I got me*.

34

Meet phoenix, she's new here

We moved to three different Airbnbs with the group throughout that month, and I remember exactly when I reached breaking point.

Nero and I had an argument late one night in the kitchen. He picked up a tin of dog food and threw it at my head, but missed as I dodged it and ran upstairs.

He came and found me. He sat on the end of the bed.

'You're an abuser,' I told him.

I just didn't care anymore. The month had bled me dry. And the one before it at the farm. The entirety of those years, rather. I had nothing to lose. I didn't even feel like a human anymore. *If he chucks me out, so be it*, I thought. *Anything would be better than this*. I'd given up, past the point of caring. I was merely existing.

He told me again, 'It would be worse if you were a boy. Nobody can speak to me like that, I don't know why you think you can.'

The streetlights leaked in between the blinds as Jefe snored on the wooden floors.

'You're an abuser,' I told him again.

'Don't fucking call me that.'

'Yes, you are. You hit me all the time, you hurt me. What kind of man puts a woman in pain? You are an abuser,' I continued.

He turned around and quickly crawled up the bed towards me where I sat against the bedpost. He whacked me across the face and put both hands around my neck.

He strangled me. His eyes were psychotically wide as he pursed his lips and grunted. He was shaking, he was strangling me that hard.

I didn't know if he would let go.

I didn't think at all.

I used my feeble hands to try and remove his grip.

He wouldn't let go.

He strangled me harder.

It hurt awfully.

My vision turned blurry and my head started to experience a sharp pain as it was starved of oxygen.

He eventually let go as I gasped for air. He grabbed me by my feet, pulled me off the side of the bed and began to drag me out of the room naked. I was terrified he was going to pull me down the stairs and someone would see, but he stopped at the door, just taking me far enough to scare me.

Afterwards, I called Axel Dupont.

'He just strangled me,' I said. 'Please, Dupont. Axel, please, you're his big brother. Maybe he will listen. Please, somebody needs to tell him, just anybody needs to tell him that this is wrong. I need someone to tell him because nobody is and he doesn't think it's wrong. He genuinely doesn't. Please help me.'

But Axel did what he always did. In his calm, 'it doesn't really matter' tone, he told me that it was fine, that we always fought but we loved each other and we just needed some space. That it was normal. That this was what couples do.

He told me Nero would stay with him, that I'd get our house and I could stay there with Jefe until I got a job and enough for a deposit for my own place. In the middle of the pandemic, may I add. But I was finally determined to leave, so I did it. And strangely enough, Nero agreed. I don't know what Axel said to him to convince him.

A friend of a friend was looking for a personal assistant: £2k per month to start, and a salary review in three months. It was perfect. I remember sitting on my sofa back in the Waterlight apartment and crying from happiness. From gratitude. I felt like God had put his sights back on me again. I felt for the first time that I wasn't alone in the world, that I had something, someone watching over me.

Nero and I acted civil. At first. He'd come round to the house to walk Jefe and then go back to Axel's. We wouldn't say much to each other – there was nothing to say.

Already, I started to look better. God, when I tell you that abuse makes you look like someone has stuck a vacuum in your eye sockets and sucked you dry till you look like a raisin. My skin would be pale and dull, with huge bags under my eyes. I would look so, so ill.

I started working out and feeling remotely cute. Ruby came to visit and took some photos of me in the bedroom, surrounded by the purple LED lights. I even felt motivated to post on Instagram. To feel like a normal twenty-three-year-old.

In one of the pictures, I lifted my shirt a little to show my stomach in the tracksuit and baggy T-shirt I was in, and it revealed a bit of underboob.

Nero was so angry he texted me saying that it was 'disrespectful'. He posted on his Story, 'she's for the streets', then proceeded to send me screenshots of his little fanboys agreeing with him, shaming me.

But I'd spent a week away from him now. The cortisol levels had lessened, the love bomb wasn't love bombing, the phoenix was awake – she was awake and she was standing. And she wasn't going to put up with his shit anymore.

In anger, I posted a poll on my Instagram Story, sharing my picture and asking if it was slutty. It was a little unhinged but I couldn't have cared less. I won by a milestone very quickly and Nero asked me to take it down. He quickly deleted his Story, so I deleted mine too.

Another day Nero came by to walk Jefe ... He was being a little too friendly. We dyed my hair together, as my roots had got insane. We made a total wreck of my head, might I add, leaving it blonde, black, brassy orange and purple from toner.

He kept touching me, cuddling me in the bathroom mirror. Smiling. 'Liviiii,' he'd say, wrapping his arms around me from behind and swaying me side to side.

He could smell the scent of strength on me, of happiness. If he could just get rid of it, the supply would be so. Fucking. Good.

The next thing you know, we were in the living room. I was sitting with my back against the window, clouds floating past. He was in between my legs, his head on my lap, begging me to fuck. To kiss. Begging me to give him one more chance. Let him in just once more.

Each time he touched me, it was like an electric current being transferred from his fingers through each vessel in my body. I could feel this magnetic pull towards him. Like he was casting a spell on me. Demon hands behind me, pushing me towards him.

But still, I resisted. 'No, Nero, we can't.'

'Stop, Nero.'

'I can't do this anymore.'

I moved my head away from him as he kissed my neck and kept putting his head in that 'special place' in the centre of my chest. Each time he'd connect to it, he'd let out a groan and say, 'Ugh, but this spot right here, it just feels so good!' and hold on to me harder, letting out whimpers and begging me over and over.

'You know it's always gonna be us. You know I love you and you're the only person I'll ever love. I truly mean that. There's only one Livi. It's only you. I'll marry you, it has to be you.'

He began promising me that he'd never ever do coke again. 'On my mum's grave, I'm done. This relationship is my focus, I had it all wrong before. There's just something about you. Something I'm in love with inside you, like an energy or something. I can feel it, I need it, I need it every day. I need it all the time, Livi. My Liviii, pleasseeee.' He eventually got right on top of me. He glanced away as if a thought angered him and then let out, 'you can't trust Ruby by the way', looking deeply into my eyes.

'What?' I replied. *Literally, what did you just say?*

He didn't have much to say; he just tiptoed around it, saying that a real friend wouldn't take a photo of me like that.

I knew he couldn't stand what had happened. He hated the lack of control; it was brewing a storm deep inside him.

He was leaving because it was his friend's birthday but asked if he could come back after.

'It's your house, Nero. I can't stop you,' I told him bluntly.

It wasn't long after that when, over text, he admitted he'd taken some coke. I rolled my eyes and went to sleep. My hopes weren't crushed because I didn't have any.

At 6 a.m. he was banging on the apartment door. He came in and begged me for sex, for even a cuddle, but I was so repulsed that he'd taken coke after that big spiel, I didn't even want to touch him.

So, he fell asleep. I rolled over and fell back asleep too.

The cord between our bodies frayed a little more.

The demons let out cries from afar.

35

Jefe knows everything

The morning came and, just like old times, Nero was in a pool of sweat next to me. I quietly left the room and went to Waitrose – it was almost like it was too routine for me not to.

Later on, I cooked some homemade spicy chicken pizza with coleslaw, and handed Nero his plate as he lay on the sofa on his phone. I saw him messaging another girl – the same female singer I'd seen in the photo in his camera album.

I got so mad. 'Why the fuck are you begging me to get back with you when you are texting a whole other girl? What the *fuck*, Nero? You'll never change!' *The audacity*, I thought.

The argument went like it usually did, until it reached its typical end: Nero stood ten feet tall above me, waiting for me to bow down, telling me to 'get the fuck out'.

I paused . . . 'No.'

There was a worldwide pandemic. The city was still in

lockdown. I had nowhere to go. The deal was that I could stay until my first paycheque. It had been five days.

He was tired of trying to get me under his control again, and now that he was on a comedown, he was going to play his best cards: homelessness, abandonment, force, pain, dragging, hitting ... You already know how it goes.

'Get the fuck out my house, Livia,' he said.

'I've got nowhere to go, Nero. You and Axel said I could stay here until I get my first paycheque and I've asked for an advance. If you want me out, give me a few days to come up with a plan ...'

He hated that I was *actually* prepared to go.

Or worse, that I was being RATIONAL.

He stood up, spitting out his mouthful of pizza.

'This is some of the best fucking pizza I've ever had,' he laughed loudly, getting ready to unleash the beast. 'Either apologise or get the fuck out of my house. You're going on the fucking streets, Livi. Do you understand?' he taunted me, still grinning.

I just couldn't do it anymore. I was done.

'You can't hit me. I've told my friends; if you touch me one more time, just once more, Nero, *they* will call the police!' I told him, hesitantly, because he knew that *I* would never call the police on him.

'If you don't apologise I'll call the fucking police to get you out the house,' he said.

'So do it; I'll tell them you beat me up. Fucking do it! I'm DONE with you,' I told him.

His stare was filled with so much rage, those comedown hormones pulsating the veins in his neck, sweat glazing his forehead. He approached me, his gaze locked in mine, and suddenly forced his head forward as if he was about to give me one swift headbutt. I flinched and covered my face. But he didn't actually touch me.

He sat back down, got his phone, and called 999.

'Hi, my girlfriend has been emotionally abusing me ...' he started to say. The cheek of it.

I quickly grabbed Jefe and ran into the bedroom.

London Bridge was falling.

The *Titanic* was sinking.

The sun was setting.

The storm was reaching its peak.

The doves were being released.

There was so much uncertainty in that moment. I was so afraid of what my life would be now.

Was I really going to be the pathetic nothingness he had brainwashed me to believe?

Was I ever going to love myself?

Was I ever going to stop loving him?

Was I ever going to be happy?

Was I ever going to be okay?

Where would I go now?

Where would I sleep tonight?

Who was I?

Who the fuck was I?

But I just held Jefe tight. I held him tight because I knew that this would be the last time. On top of those silk black bed sheets, with the subtle glow of the purple LED lights still on from the night before, both my arms wrapped around him, his face nestled under my chin, I could feel his heartbeat and he could feel mine. Just me and my best friend. My baby. My only safety.

I held on to him as the walls slowly collapsed around us, the glass windows smashed, the ceiling gave way and the daylight revealed itself. All eleven stories of Waterlight Quay beneath us caved in one by one, rubble falling all around us as we fell closer and closer towards the ground, huddled on top of the bed together.

The bed splashed deep into the River Thames, our bodies floating gracefully under the water. I began to panic, I thought I would drown, but Jefe gave me a look of reassurance, blinking long and slow. I let go of all worry. I felt his protection imprint on me, as if from this moment on, no matter what, he'd still be guarding me.

Whether it was the baby.

Whether it was simply the soul God gave me to carry me through these demons, I felt something hold me in this moment.

There was an angel, the whole time, fighting those demons with me. Giving me a beam of light in my darkest times. And that was Jefe.

I kissed him long on the head as I began packing my things. Suddenly there were four or five police officers in the room with me, as if they were expecting to rock up to some violent attack, but instead found a girl crying in her bed, holding her dog.

They were really nice. They asked if I was the homeowner and I said no, so they told me I'd have to leave. I asked if there was anything protecting me at all because I did live there for a year and half. I explained that I had been told I could stay until I found somewhere to go, and that I had nowhere else to go.

The policewoman said no with a lot of remorse, but she assured me they'd help me safely get to Ruby's in Manchester.

Nero was never going to let me leave on my own terms, with any pride or dignity. Now that I'd got a job and was prepared to go, he *had* to punish me. He had to make me go out *sad*.

But still, I wouldn't.

As gracefully as possible, I packed my things and left. The police had to stop him coming into the room more than a few times. He kept shouting and trying to take pictures. They grew more and more frustrated with him, shaking their heads at each other and closing the door while I packed.

When I got in the car the policewoman turned to me and said, 'If I ever see you back at this address again, I'll be so disappointed, Livia. Because that guy right there, is a fucking prick.'

36

Rope burns

When Ruby's family first saw me, they must've thought I was batshit crazy. I mean, I know they did; they told me. They made everything light-hearted, just like Ruby – and honestly, that was exactly what I needed. But I was sick, really sick. I needed help and I was finally in a place to get it – or to at least not get any worse.

Waking up next to Ruby felt just like home. Like safety.

There was a flower that had died on Ruby's windowsill but she was determined to bring it back to life, so she watered it every day with care and made sure it had sunlight.

She was working from home because of the pandemic so she would just sit next to me and work while I slept. And I slept a lot. Since it was summer, sometimes we'd sit out on the lawn. I also worked my new job from my phone.

My body was emerging out of fight-or-flight mode for the first time in a long time, and it was very, very tired. Doing anything was difficult. My eyelids constantly felt heavy and, combined with a very low appetite, I had barely any energy.

Can you imagine how damaged my brain was, having fight-or-flight mode constantly activated? Your whole survival response, the biological defence to danger, constantly being triggered? What your body and mind would go through each time, attempting to house the extreme cortisol production, your intestines switching off because the natural fight-or-flight response was telling our stomachs to prepare for no food for days? Pupils dilated, being extremely on edge and hyper aware for danger, heart rate increasing, hearing becoming sharper, trembling from the sudden burst of energy, temperature spiking or decreasing, breathing speeding up attempting to give your body enough oxygen as your nervous system has a whole breakdown: imagine that every day, or even a few times a day.

Sometimes I'd lie in bed at Ruby's and just stare up at the ceiling, feeling the world around me. It was like my feet were landing back on earth for the first time in . . . ever. I would lie still as my brain noticed the changes in the environment. I was suddenly hyper aware of everything, like I'd just woken up from a deep slumber. The smell of summer creeping in from the window. The birds chirping outside. Her family laughing downstairs. But what I noticed the most was the lack. For the first time in years, there was no urgency. No panic. Nothing to do. Nothing to say. Nobody to explain myself to. Nobody was watching my every move and thinking, *How can I hurt you?* Every day. Every single day.

For the first time, there was nobody there, constantly draining and draining and draining me.

My mind was blissfully still. Vacant. Aware. Where had it been this whole time?

I cherished moments where I'd find myself laughing with Ruby or her hilariously nonchalant grandmother. 'You best not be on the phone to that *fucker*,' she'd tell me in her incredible thick Manc accent. The laughing happened a lot. Maybe I hadn't fully processed what had gone on yet. That's the thing about CPTSD, it doesn't kick in right away. It's very normal for there to be a large, long delay. All I knew is that I was very tired and very, very grateful.

Ruby's family are all tightknit – they all lived on the same street and regularly walked to each other's houses for BBQs and dinners. Everyone made an effort to get a smile out of me, even if my hair was a jump scare, which Ruby did correct for me. I was finally the blondest I'd ever been, an electric platinum silverish blonde. Nothing like fresh hair after a break-up, hey?

There was a dog that Ruby's uncle had rescued after being abused by her last owner, and I was so happy to see her because if I cried about anything a lot during that time, it was Jefe. But when I tried to get close to her, she would whimper and run away. They said they'd never seen her act this way. It's like she wanted to get away from my trauma after escaping her own.

Ruby would constantly tell me to stop apologising because I found myself saying sorry over *every* little thing. We spoke a lot about the parts of my story I'd purposely left out over the years. Things I'd hidden from her. And when I told her, revisiting the truth now that I was out of it, I felt myself grow resentful. It sounded so bad trying to finish some of the sentences, trying to describe to her what I'd been experiencing. Seeing her facial expressions change would stop me in my tracks, making me wonder about just how normalised it was to me.

That resentment grew larger each day.

And with each night, the feelings of being violated totally drowned me.

Eventually, I could not fucking breathe whenever I was struck by memories of Nero and me.

One thought circled my mind continuously:

Nero had called the police on *me*.

After everything I did for him. After I was there for him, *the only one* there for him. Throughout his mum's passing. Through everything. After I had thrown Christmas for his nieces and nephews. Repaired their relationships. Helped him get sober many, many, many times. Helped him fight that fucking addiction. Fought it for him. Wrote his lyrics. Was his muse. His pornstar. His slut. His wife. His punching bag. After I held him while he cried, saying that everyone hurt him. After I stood firm by his side when everyone turned their backs. After he looked me in the eyes and told me that if it wasn't for me, he'd be nothing. After I forgave him and gave him chance after chance. After I killed our baby for him. *He called the police on me?*

I couldn't believe I'd let myself be treated so fucking bad. It hurt. It hurt so fucking much.

One day, Juno put me in touch with her good friend who was an activist in the London scene for women's rights. We spoke about the word 'justice' and what that would look like to me.

She put me in touch with a lawyer.

We collected all my evidence and drafted a letter to the record label.

All the texts, the arguments, every time I recorded the abuse.

The photos of bruises and cuts I'd sent friends over the years.

The video . . .

The video.

That night last year when he'd attacked me on camera and admitted he abused me, I sent it to an old friend, Joseline, in America with the message, 'Don't watch these, just keep them for me please'. Then I deleted the conversation and videos from my phone.

Ruby and I sat in shock, staring at my phone when I sent everyone a text asking if they had anything from over the years that would prove Nero's abuse. She wasn't expecting that video. *I* wasn't even expecting that. It had been so long, I'd completely forgotten about it.

Joseline didn't. God did not.

Then there was the NDA, proof of him trying to silence me.

And because I'd been given Nero's old laptop, I did some digging in there too.

I found messages between Nero, the head of his label, Axel and his ex-manager George on a group chat discussing what to do with my pregnant twenty-two-year-old self. There was a screenshot of me stating, 'I'm going to the police, you have physically, mentally and emotionally abused me.'

Their response was, 'We need to get our lawyers involved.'

And Nero's response? 'Don't worry, I'll never lose.'

These were grown-ass men. *With daughters.*

I was extremely keen to hold everyone involved accountable.

At the time, after much deliberation, I'd finally settled on a goal to walk away from the situation. I'd been left with nothing but trauma. I just wanted to move away and start my life over. It was the least I deserved.

I wasn't sure if I wanted to speak out on what happened. The day I travelled to Manchester in a rage, I posted on my Instagram Story that I'd no longer be abused or silenced, and that the music industry protects too many people.

It was shared on the gossip blogs and even though I'd not stated his name, it wasn't hard for people to start making assumptions. Most wrote me off as sour, not believing the accusations held any weight.

I wasn't sure what justice I wanted. I felt like if I made it public, I wouldn't be able to live with knowing I destroyed his career. I still loved him a lot, no matter what he'd done. I somehow still cared. His career was everything to him and I knew how much damage those videos would do. How much damage *his* actions would do.

So, I thought the easier route would be to let him move on with his life, and I would move on with mine. Maybe I'd take some kind of pay off? The letter also stated all the work I'd never been paid for, for my voice on his songs. It seemed fair enough. It was justice because he was being held accountable, I guess?

In all honesty, I didn't know. I was in a constant state of confusion.

The activist lady mentioned to me that her friend, a singer by the name of Cherry Monroe, had asked that we be connected.

I knew who she was. Cherry and Nero had made a song together a few months back, and had been practising dance routines together for the music video until lockdown had begun.

The song they made was beautiful. Truly.

Aside from that, Cherry was a very powerful and talented woman. I wasn't sure why she wanted to speak and I was actually nervous. I'd never had much communication with anyone in the industry before without Nero chaperoning me.

That day seemed like such a normal miserable day. I had no idea that I was about to meet someone who would change the trajectory of my entire life. That's the thing about the universe: even at its dullest, it's still working its magic. That's what's precisely so beautiful about it – maybe one of the *only* beautiful things about it.

The first thing Cherry made clear to me on our first phone call was that she would be dropping her song with him, and my heart almost fell out my ass.

Why? Literally, why would anybody do that for me?

'Are you sure? You don't need to do that,' I said, instantly feeling like a burden. The song was so good. It surely mattered more. It was too much to ask.

But she reassured me that it didn't matter; she wouldn't be making a song with an abuser regardless. For the first time in years, I felt that I wasn't invisible.

The curtains of the Nero show were officially drawn shut.

My brain just could not fathom that something was happening that was *not* in his favour.

This industry had belittled and invalidated my abuse for years. I had lost all hope that anyone cared, that it was even important when there was money to be made.

I had watched grown men chuck all their dignity out the window just to co-sign his abuse. I had watched grown women enable him and turn a blind eye to keep the bank-rolling going.

But now, someone as incredible, successful and talented as Cherry Monroe was going against the Nero grain.

He suddenly felt as tiny as a grain.

Because Cherry was also healing from abuse. She too was looking for her justice after suffering at the hands of a man she once was manipulated into loving.

Somehow, we were finishing each other's sentences as we detailed our experiences. Behaviours and patterns that were so specific to Nero mirrored her experience with her abuser.

And whenever the words, 'It just makes me feel so ...' began to leave my lips, she would sigh and describe to me what I couldn't yet articulate followed with a, 'That's because they ...'

I burst with energy. 'Oh my God! You know what I mean?'

How the hell did she know what I meant?

And she'd repeat continuously, 'He did that too ...' followed by her example.

They were the same. We were the same.

When I struggled to explain why I kept going back, she simply said, 'It's okay, I did too.'

It was a feeling I just can't describe.

Followed by another, 'That's because we ...'

She just got it. She had all the answers. Every single

emotion, every single reason, every pain in my body, she felt in hers too. It was beyond comprehension and the connection instantly struck like lightning between us.

The only time I had briefly seen Cherry was in a club in Paris during Fashion Week, and she was surrounded by her posse, dancing in a big fur coat. I was so anxious in that busy environment and she seemed to have handled it so well, so aloof and guarded.

She now recounted to me how that club had given her anxiety too.

And when I told her how awful Angelic studios was, how I lay in that four-poster bed sobbing loudly on my birthday, she explained how she had coincidentally checked into Angelic studios right after us, and that the bedroom had just been deep cleaned because of Jefe. Cherry also lay in that bed and cried awfully. That exact same four-poster bed.

I was humbled by the randomness of the universe.

And, after a few hours of a very emotional back and forth, lots of advice, strength and validation, there were two things I'll never forget that she told me in that call.

'I'm about two years away from my abuser. It's still hard. I'm going to be real with you, Livia, this takes years. You're young and resilient and you will get through this, but there is no quick fix, it takes a long time to recover from abuse.'

When she asked me, 'Do you know what a narcissist is?' I told her yes, but I wasn't sure that Nero was one.

'Why not?' she asked me.

And I had no reason.

Absolutely none.

Welcome to death row

There was once a moment when Nero and I lay in bed. He had his head buried in my stomach, crying, as there was the Google definition of a narcissist open on the laptop:

Symptoms
Signs of narcissistic personality disorder may include:

- An exaggerated sense of self-importance.
- A sense of entitlement and may require consistent, excessive admiration.
- Expect to be treated as superior to others even without the achievements that credit it.
- Be obsessed with fantasies about success, power, fame, looks, perfection, etc.
- Believe they are superior and only deserve superior people around them.
- Belittle people in conversations to make them appear inferior.

- Expect favours and unquestioning obedience with their expectations.
- Take advantage of others and manipulate to get what they want.
- Have an inability to empathise or recognise the needs of others.
- Constantly envy others and have delusions that others envy them.
- Behave in an arrogant, pretentious and rude manner.
- Insist on having the best of everything – are ungrateful of what they have even when they get what they wanted.
- When faced with anything people with NPD may perceive as criticism, they may respond by,
  - Becoming impatient and angry, throwing a temper tantrum.
  - Reacting with rage.
- Have difficulty regulating emotions.
- Feel depressed and moody because they believe that they must be perfect.
- Have secret feelings of shame and vulnerability.

He asked me to read him each symptom. I did.

Then he asked me if I believed them to be true about him.

'Umm ...' I mumbled nervously as I ran my finger along each sentence on the screen next to me, my heart in my mouth.

'No, Nero, you're very generous and nice to people ...'

He stopped me halfway and began to sob harder.

'I am all of those things, Livia. I use people and to take what I want from them and then I drop them, I do it to everyone! I did it to Ziggy, Kai, I just take from people and it's never enough, but I promise ... I promise I'll never do it to you ...' he exclaimed with his big, watery eyes, cupping my hands in his as he kissed them.

I removed one hand and entered into Google 'What is a narc like in a relationship?', finding an article that said:

Narcissists are known for engaging in infidelity quite notoriously ...

'You're not a narcissist because you don't cheat ...' I told him, hesitantly, just in case he was going to suddenly confess in this strange pity place he often crawled into. It would never manifest into anything more than him dwelling in his emotions and feeling sorry for himself, only to return to his cold and calculated nature the next day.

And that was it, case closed.

Nero didn't cheat, so he wasn't a narcissist.

How naive I'd been.

37

There's no such thing as closure

I'd been staying with Ruby for a total of four weeks now. I worked from my phone for the record label I'd secured a job at, so I actually had my own money for the first time. We cooked meals together every night. Watched movies. Spent time with her family. Lay in the sun a lot. We made signs together to attend the Black Lives Matter protests in central Manchester.

'Racism isn't born, it's taught,' my placard read as we marched together, shouting with thousands in the sunshine. It was so liberating, hearing people of all colours and walks of life stand on the podium and give speeches in a bid to stand against the racism against Black lives. The energy of change was in the air, passion filling the streets. It was truly remarkable to experience the power of people fighting towards justice.

I even visited London at one point, when Juno had invited me down. Arriving in the city felt so foreign and strange, so nostalgic and bittersweet. I stared out of the window in the taxi on the way to the Airbnb, thinking about how much I loved it here. I was excited to be back.

Juno and I hugged long and hard, discussing everything. We did facemasks and got tattoos.

'I'm honoured to do this,' said Celia, the cute ginger-haired tattoo artist covered in self-done tattoos, as she filled in the banner that held Nero's name with black ink on the back of my arm.

Juno held my hand and they cheered me on. The needle was prodding deep into my flesh, every stab hurting even more since it was already going over a tattoo. I visualised the pain to be releasing him. *With each layer of the needle cutting through my skin, I am cutting the cord and releasing him*, I thought as I clenched my eyes shut and squeezed Juno's hand.

Once I got back to Manchester, one evening Ruby and I went to her uncle's house for a family BBQ. I smiled, sitting on the grass as Ruby and her mum danced in the middle, all the rest of her family laughing and looking on. There was so much joy around. Life felt slow and peaceful. *I would love to have a family like this*, I thought, sitting on a beanbag on the grass. So unproblematic and free.

Ruby's uncle's dog came over to me . . . and to my surprise, she leapt her whole body on top of me and cuddled me. She was stuck to me the whole night: she wasn't afraid anymore. She was so strong. I looked in her eyes and imagined someone abusing such a beautiful creature. In her big, brown eyes, I saw my own reflection.

I loved her so much. And she loved me.

It was like when she first met me, I still had Nero's energy within me. She was afraid of the danger I presented carrying the energy of an abuser since she too had been abused. That's why she was so frightened of me.

That same night, Ruby cuddled me in bed as I cried to her about how much I missed Jefe, saying that I didn't know whether I would ever heal from all these losses. She pointed at the flower that had been dead when I arrived at her house. It had come back to life; its frail, small stalk was just about standing on its own.

'That's you,' she said. 'That's your progress since you got here.'

I had sent the letter to Nero's label to kick off the settlement earlier that day, and just before we went to sleep, to my utter disbelief, Nero was trending on Twitter.

He had chosen, on #blackouttuesday, to post a colourful square instead of a black square. He literally told the world that all lives matter.

Tell me why that was the most Nero thing ever? He had zero interest in any cause, in any culture, in any change – just himself. Or not even *really* himself in this case.

They annihilated him on Twitter, calling for him to be cancelled, berating him. The universe was humbling me with its randomness again.

And the universe decided to do it once more because, in the morning, Ruby's phone rang and I could hear Nero's croaky voice saying, 'Please, please just let me talk to her.'

'He's just saying this now because of the case,' Ruby said. He had received the letter that morning.

Ruby stood next to me as we looked down into the deep, dark hole where Nero stood at the very bottom of the pit. We could barely hear his voice as he yelled up for help.

He'd dug it himself and now he wanted help getting out. It was nothing new. But if I were to even begin to try and help him, it was obvious that I'd tumble down there with him.

'Livi, please,' he cried up to me, where I stood safely on greener grass. 'It's not about the case, you can still sue me. I deserve it! It's about us speaking face to face, one more time, without some *white* label exec people between us, just one last time! Under *God* I need to make it right. I need to make it up to you, you deserve it.'

'You always say this,' I yelled down to him. 'You never change.'

'I know, I know I do, but I'm not going to try and convince you to drop the case. We have been together for three years – we deserve the chance to speak properly. After everything we've gone through, we need to end this properly.'

'You abused me,' I told him.

'I know I did!' he shouted back.

'You chucked me out of the house with the police,' I shouted down, my voice filling with pain.

'I know I did. It was fucked, I shouldn't have done that to you. I admit everything. You were the most perfect girlfriend. You were always by my side. You didn't deserve any of that,' he said.

He didn't need to shout anymore because the hole some-how seemed much less deep.

As hearing him confess eased some frustrations within me, I thought about how I *had* spent years with him. How this was truly the end, and that maybe I *should* finish it properly and hear what he had to say. That it only seemed right since this was someone I had spent every day with. Years. Sharing a bed, a shower, sometimes even a toothbrush. Eating together, napping together – all those memories, good and bad. Some closure and an apology would surely make this whole process easier. Maybe it would hurt a lot less too . . . Closure . . . Yes . . . that's maybe what I needed . . .

I stared down at him in hesitation. He was crawling up towards me now . . .

He was so close now that he could just whisper . . . 'Jefe . . . we can share him. Jefe misses you so much.'

Afterwards, I argued with Ruby as she sat on the bed staring at me disappointedly. 'He calls just once, and just like that, you're going to go?'

It was like my body was moving and I couldn't even stop it. I had this urge to make myself feel better. But it wasn't only the closure I'd fooled myself into thinking I was seeking, it was just another fix that my brain was addicted to, too.

Juno texted me in the car to the train station.

'Livia, I swear to God. Livia, fucking turn around!'

Ruby had obviously texted her. But it was too late: my mind was already made.

Made by Nero.

'I'm just going to go and hear what he has to say. I'm *not* going to *ever* get back with him, or drop this case. He doesn't even want to get back. Trust me. Nothing would make me drop this case. *He needs to be held accountable*,' I told her.

I was so sure of it.

I plaited the front two parts of my hair to frame my face. I wore make-up. I wore whatever *I* wanted to wear.

I sat on the picnic benches outside St Pancras station, waiting for him to come. My heart was pounding and my stomach ached as my entire body processed the immense anxiety of that moment. The wait felt like forever. With every new person that walked into my view, my heart would aggressively palpitate in the split second between my brain realising whether it was him or not. I shoved my earphones on and played 'Godspeed' by Frank Ocean as loud as I could.

I wish these fucking Apple earphones could turn up that little bit louder, I thought as I smashed the 'volume up' button repeatedly, trying to drown out the reality ahead of me.

Life didn't even feel real, as my eyes fixated on each pedestrian leaving the busy station ... *I wish my stomach would just stop,* I thought as I held it tightly in my arms. I didn't know how much longer my nervous system could take the anticipation before I'd need to explode in one way or another.

And there he was.

Just like that.

Walking that same walk, taking larger steps than a normal human, causing a ruckus moving out of the path of no one, one hand in pocket, dog on lead in the other, speeding towards me with purpose. He somehow always made a statement with his presence alone.

How could he be so chilled that he kept a casual hand in his pocket at a time like this, while I was attempting to not vomit all over the bench.

A true Aquarius visiting a true Pisces.

Like wind and water.

He was always fifty shades of cool while I was as deep and undiscovered as the ocean.

He caught my eye and let the dog lead drop as Jefe ran

towards me. As soon as I knelt down and my hands touched his furry head, I felt an enormous wave of emotion wash over me. All that anxiety was released through my tear ducts, ruining my carefully done-on-the-train make-up as Jefe licked my chin, catching some of the drops and jumping up into my lap.

I could feel Nero standing over me but I couldn't even see through all my tears. I felt him put his hand on my shoulder and say softly but firmly, 'Let's go ...'

I wiped my tears away and stood up, turning to face him. He smiled and looked in my eyes.

'What is this hair?' he laughed as he tugged on my braids.

We got in an Uber and sat in silence as Jefe excitedly jumped between our laps.

'Where are we going?' I asked him.

He paused slightly, staring out of the window at the gloomy London sky before turning and saying, 'home'.

'I thought you don't live there anymore?' I asked. On the phone Nero had told me that he'd moved into a new place. 'I cook now, I clean, I'm doing anger management, I've been making paintings to direct my anger. I need to show you them.'

'Yeah but first we need to go *there*,' he replied.

The Uber dropped us outside Waterlight. The building looked haunted as the rows of balconies towered above us.

We walked into the abandoned apartment that was still on contractual lease. Jefe made himself comfortable in the familiar surroundings. The house was cold and the dull, early evening light poured through the huge windows.

As I sat down and took my coat off, it revealed my tattoo

peeking through my mesh sleeves. He glanced at it, the banner where his name no longer was, and then nodded his head in acceptance as he looked out at the view.

I sat on the sofa facing him, waiting to hear what he had to say.

He strode over to the other side of the sofa and sat down, simply plopping his head down in shame. Hands behind his neck and elbows resting on his lap, he exhaled. He looked down and said, 'You go first.'

I felt cold and strong.

Stern and wilful.

And I began.

'You threw me out of our house. With the police. How could you do that to me? After everything ...'

I waited for him to interrupt me but he just listened quietly, so I continued to pick up the pace.

'I've done everything for you. All you've done is abuse me over and over. You never stuck to a single promise. I have never done anything wrong to you. I've been such a good girlfriend. I deserve better, I really do. I'm not dropping the case. I need to get out of London and move on with my life. I'm starting afresh, it's the *least* I deserve ...

'... And you and your weird-ass, stupid, misogynistic friends, all I ever was was nice to all of you. You made me look so crazy, you turned everything around on me, even when you were wrong. Especially when you were wrong!

'You cheated on me, covered me in bruises, and you never even said sorry. Not once! How could you say you love me? What did I ever do wrong to YOU? You beg me to come back each time and just abuse me again. You have mentally and physically abused me . . . You got hard when you attacked me with a screwdriver!

'I feel violated. Fucking violated! You have robbed me of years of my life. You have told me lie after lie to keep me here when all I did was love you. I did everything for you . . .'

I went on and on and on . . . with no tears, just a voice. With no trembles or stutters, only a few pauses of disbelief and plenty of emotion. When I finally stopped, he looked up at me, his head still angled downwards, like a dog in trouble.

'I'm sorry. On my mum's grave. On Layla's kids' lives. On our baby. On Jefe's life. If I'm lying I'm a piece of shit. I am so sorry,' he said slowly and boldly, with a face full of remorse.

His eyes pleaded with me, but I wouldn't give in. I looked away and listened without speaking.

He spoke for what could have been thirty minutes straight. Agreeing and admitting to every point – almost as if he had memorised each and every feeling he'd seen me suffer, just to make me feel validated at this very point.

How was he suddenly getting all of this? How did he suddenly speak my language? He was actually criticising himself, holding himself accountable.

I got up from my seat and walked over to stand by the window, looking out at the sky which had turned black.

'You look beautiful. You deserve to be happy, Livi. More than anyone in this world. I am an awful man. You should go ahead with the case, I will never try to stop you. But just one thing . . .'

I turned my head away from the window.

'I want to get back together.'

38

Welcome home!

We sat in the car on the way to his new apartment in Bermondsey. I'd missed the last train to Manchester so he convinced me to go and see it. 'I'll get you a hotel – you don't need to stay with me,' he pleaded.

'I can get my own,' I told him.

We walked into the rented and ready-furnished apartment on the top floor. It was beautiful.

He offered me wine.

I needed it.

There was a huge mezzanine towering above an enormous open-plan space. It was an old factory that had been converted into large loft-like apartments, with brick walls and giant mental beams. There was a glass nine-person dining table with vintage leather chairs, a massive TV on the wall, enormous white sofas that reclined into chaise-like beds. The house was stunning, decorated with unique paintings and sculptures and with two bedrooms and two bathrooms.

He showed me the mezzanine level where he'd set up a studio, office and play space, surrounded by the owner's large spread of Roche Bobois colourful cushions. In the corner of the mezzanine was a hidden set of steps leading to a little secret treehouse at the very highest point of the loft. It was lit up by fairy lights and filled with blankets and pillows.

We crawled inside and sat there together.

On the shelf behind us were small canvases he had painted, all with titles.

Anger, Jealousy, Rage, Hope, Happiness.

He gave me the *Hope* one and told me to keep it.

I was quiet as I sat on the blanket, my knees tucked into my chest, staring over the glass balcony down to the dining table that was surrounded by huge industrial windows. It was dark outside. A half moon illuminated the courtyard and fountains outside in the estate.

In the treehouse, the fairy lights radiated a warm glow. Nero sat next to me with his legs crossed.

Downstairs, soft acoustic music played ...

'You're actually so beautiful, Livi ...' Nero said, turning to face me.

'Shut up,' I told him quietly as I sighed without turning to look at him.

'No, honestly. You're the most beautiful girl I've ever seen. I always thought that about you,' he said.

I just listened to the music quietly. A memory floated through my head. I felt the pain in my chest and my bare feet touch the cold bedroom floor at Waterlight while the words came out of Nero's mouth, '*Once* I did think you were the most beautiful girl ever,' he'd told me. I'd never forgotten that.

'I had all of you ... now I have none of you ...' the song played downstairs.

'I had a girl around, yeah, at some afterparty,' he continued. 'Jefe literally got on her lap, sat there and slowly just pissed the maddest, longest, hottest piss all over her lap.'

I turned to look at him in disbelief but as we caught eyes, we burst out laughing. It felt nice to laugh with him.

We went downstairs to grab glasses of wine and we sat at the dining table together, updating each other on every part of our lives, each and every detail excitedly. It's weird how it doesn't matter how much someone has hurt you, you can get lost in the joy of catching up. I told him about Ruby's family's dog and how Nero's spooky energy inside me probably scared her away. He told me about the album and how it was almost perfect.

Time passed as we enjoyed each other's company. Both of us ignored the elephant in the room. We knew that if we brought it up, it was over. This bubble of peace and friendship we were existing in, each and every one of our demons watching us from outside.

'I know you say you don't want to get back with me, Livi ...' he said, the wine giving a little bit of extra confidence to his words. 'But I know I can make things right. I will under GOD treat you how you deserve to be treated the whole relationship. I will heal every single wound I've left. I'll never put my hands on you again. Do you think I'd EVER do that to you again?! Never. I'll do therapy every week. Anger management. I've not done yay in two weeks. I'm done with that shit. We can do therapy together, for as long as you want. I need to make things right under GOD for every time I've hurt you. I will give you the love you deserve . . . I have to.'

He stood up from his seat and further proclaimed to me, 'Just give me one chance, that's all I'm asking. Stay with me for three days – if I fuck up, you *go*! You can still sue me either way, just let me show you I am worth it one last time. If I fuck up, you can leave me forever. I will let you go, I'll never chat shit again. Because I know. I know now I'm sober. I'll make this relationship work.'

He carried on. 'I'll cook for you, I'll clean now instead, you deserve to just put your feet up and be a queen. This is your home, Livi. Welcome home!'

'We can play Bon Iver and Frank Ocean and talk about star signs all day. We can just lie on the bed and look at each other. I'll give you head every single day. We can eat a thousand curries together on this dining table,' he joked, forcing me to crack a smile.

I stared through my tipsy lens around the room. Jefe slept on the floor by our feet.

Every frustration, every betrayal, every time I was desperate for this energy, was merged together right then. I indulged in how good it felt to finally fucking feel it. Even if it was just for a moment, the relief was like medicine for the disease he'd left me with. Such fucking relief.

He took my hand and used my two fingers to turn up the knob on the speaker. Staring into my eyes, he held both my hands and pulled me up into his chest. We danced together slowly in the middle of the room. He held my hand tightly with his other behind my waist as we spun in circles, smiling, eyes filled with joy as I giggled.

We were drunk.

He spun me and fell forwards onto the sofa, landing me gently beneath him. He stared into my eyes, fixating on each, from left to right. Like always.

He smiled bashfully like a little boy looking at his favourite Lego creation.

'Livi, I love you so fucking much,' he whispered.

I looked up at him; I could see his eyes filling with tears . . .

He leaned in to kiss me . . . and I met him halfway.

Fireworks erupted all around us. Atomic bombs. Hydrogen bombs. From beneath the ocean, currents jolted throughout the entire planet.

I shut my eyes tight as I felt each and every hair stand up on my body, some kind of ecstasy pouring out from each cell of skin.

This dopamine was so. Damn. Good.

He kissed me passionately all over my neck, sucking my skin and giving me love bites. He picked me up and took me over onto the large pouffes in the middle of the living room, pulling down my trousers. He went down on me for a few moments before kissing me all the way back up, and when he put his dick inside me, we both let out the loudest moan, as if we were being given that first precious sip of water in the desert after months of drought.

I looked to my right as he fucked me, staring into the mirror against the wall. I looked into my own eyes. It felt like what I could see in the mirror wasn't actually happening to me, like I was watching a film.

Depersonalisation

Depersonalisation can feel like a detachment of yourself from your mind or body, like becoming an observer of yourself. You may feel like you are on autopilot, from the outside looking in, like in a dream or living in a movie, feeling emotionally disconnected from reality, often triggered by severe stress, prolonged depression and anxiety.

39

Everything I ever wanted

I woke up with a headache. A thick hangover.

Nero came into the bedroom with a hot cup of tea.

'Breakfast is just being made,' he said quickly before running back out to the kitchen, the aroma of fried eggs leaking in behind him.

As I stared out of the bedroom window, something caught my eye. It was a necklace on the windowsill. A girl's necklace.

I took one of his T-shirts from the cupboard and threw it on. I walked into the kitchen where he was scrambling between pots and pans, trying to put together a full English breakfast.

'You good?' he asked me.

He took a few steps forward and slipped his arms around my waist, nervously looking into my eyes.

'We're gonna eat and then we can watch whatever you want on the TV, yeah? We can go take Jefe for a walk too, there's a nice park ...' he began.

I pulled the necklace out from the palm of my hand. He took it and threw it as far across the room as he could, snapping that *cheap shit* everywhere.

Don't hate the woman, I told myself. *She's done nothing wrong. You're the one who got back with this dickhead.*

'Listen, Livi. Listen, yeah, all that shit ... Look at me.' He grabbed my shoulders and pleaded as I rolled my eyes. 'Look at me. All that shit is in the past, okay? I'm sorry, I shouldn't have left that there, I didn't actually even know that was there ... but who gives a FUCK? Fuck the past. No negativity. I'm proving to you now we can be happy.'

I stared him in the eyes, blinked hard and went and got in the shower.

I stayed with him for a few days. As he had asked.

And let me tell you, when he grovelled, he didn't leave a single area of land ungrovelled.

He was waiting on me hand and foot for anything, everything. He watered each dead flower in our garden, praying and hoping they would come back to life.

He even let me finally speak about the abortion he'd forbidden me from mentioning. He held me as I sobbed in bed and when he apologised, I sobbed even harder for the fact that he'd never let me speak about it. How could this relief be so painful?

I did that a lot. I was constantly triggered by memories of his injustices. I couldn't help it; even the movie scene in *American Psycho* where the lead character has a threesome triggered me about when he cheated on me with multiple women at once. I walked out of the room and lay face down in the bed, imagining random girls naked and giddy, each dying for him to blow his ego in their mouths, while I waited at home, staring at my phone screen for a text back from my boyfriend as the white blood cells in my body worked to heal the bruises he left on me.

The thing he did most, and what I needed him to do the most, was listen to me. That's how bad he was before: the bare minimum of *listening* seemed miraculous. He used to get so angry if I spoke about my feelings. It would sometimes overwhelm me that he was actually – for the first time – listening, that I'd start nervously speaking extra fast as if I was running out of time. He'd have to constantly tell me, very gently, to slow down.

One evening he even posted something on his Instagram Story which resembled a 'confession'. He spoke about how he had let his anger and toxic coping mechanisms of being a manipulator – which he'd apparently learned in order to 'survive' – make him an aggressive person. He said he was sorry. And when someone replied to the Story asking who it was for, he said, 'This is aimed directly at one person.'

As the days went on, I almost felt as though *I* was now being toxic. It was like no matter what he did, I just couldn't help but feel triggered or retreat back into my shell. I found myself wondering if we could ever make it back this time, or if he had just simply damaged me too fucking much. With every relief I was somehow haunted by the realisation of how little I was treated like a human, with how easy it actually was for him to just be nice to me. How easily Nero could have loved me but how he actively chose not to. He was more than capable.

With a lot of hearsay out and about in the streets and on

the scene about our relationship, stepping outside was hard. Would anybody believe this man had abused me if I forgave him? Would the things my body had borne witness to suddenly become a lie? Guilt and shame were two demons constantly sitting on either shoulder, whispering in my ear.

And of course I'd let my friends down – my family. People who wanted to help me get justice. I felt like a snake, waking up next to someone who I had been so ready to fight against, someone who represented what I hated most in this world. He felt like the enemy, and I would wake up every morning filled with remorse.

The only person who truly understood was Cherry. After I gave her some big spiel about how we were doing therapy and why it was different this time, all she asked was that I message her regularly to let her know I was safe. She was patient and understanding. When I asked her why she told me simply, 'I did it too'.

Nobody else understood.

Especially not Ruby. It was so hard for her to see me go back to him, and the distance between us filled me with even more resentment and shame.

Nero could see that I cared most about how distressing this was to Ruby, so he reached out to try and make amends. When that didn't work, he kept insisting. He even sent her perfume and begged that she didn't need to forgive him but just to give him a chance to show that he would treat her best friend right.

He often wanted to post me on social media (probably to give himself a Get Out of Jail Free card against all the rumours), but I told him I didn't want to yet because I hadn't told my sisters. My family relationships had always been sensitive, so the idea of upsetting them ... I just didn't have the capacity for it. I hadn't for years. I don't know if I ever will. I just feel that shit *too* much.

One evening, Nero was on the phone to Axel Dupont while I watched TV next to him, cuddling Jefe. He put the phone down and sat on the sofa, just smiling at me like a child waiting for their parents' reaction to their school project.

I side-eyed him before he let out, 'Let's all go to Paris! You, me, Dupont, his boyfriend ... and ... and RUBY!'

'I don't know if Ruby will want to come to Paris, Nero ...' I began.

And just like that, he got on the phone to her and practically begged her to come. 'We'll go on a road trip there, it'll all be paid for, we can all dance, party, sing songs ...' He bounced around the room excitedly.

And so we went.

Whether or not it was a part of a calculated plan, the trip was amazing. We all got along and enjoyed Paris from a tourist's perspective rather than the rush and work of Fashion Week. During the day we went around the city wearing berets and visited Montmartre. We had our caricatures drawn by a local artist – he was an old man who'd been doing it for twenty years. 'Take good care of her,' he said. 'One day I want to see you bring your own children here.' It was a picture-perfect moment. We even enjoyed some very mediocre Parisian food and almost got robbed by pickpockets. It was just perfect.

And when the nights came, we partied as a group. Aside from Axel and his boyfriend getting into arguments in every club, everyone was having a great time.

One night, Ruby, Nero and I stayed up partying till 6 a.m. We drank liquor in our hotel suite and did karaoke to old R&B songs until we all eventually fell asleep in the same bed, but not before getting the hotel breakfast sent up to our room – egg yolks all over the sheets, we passed out as soon as it hit our bellies.

That night as I danced with Ruby, jumping on the bed and singing my heart out, using a heat protectant spray as a microphone, Nero lay below us, smiling at me.

'This is just what you want, isn't it, Livi, you just want to be happy. This is the real you.' To this day I'm still not sure what he meant by that, or why it sounded somehow sorrowful.

On our last night in Paris we went to see the Eiffel Tower. Of course we'd seen it driving past on previous trips, but nothing like this. There was a full moon as we drove down around midnight. I had a bare face and tracksuit on with my beloved beret and I read everyone Eiffel Tower facts in the car on the way down.

'Did you know the Eiffel Tower has a post office, underground bunker, science lab, restaurant and apartment inside it?'

Once we arrived and the clock hit twelve, the huge skyscraper, which was once frowned upon by many Parisian architects, feared to be a 'a giant ashtray' that would destroy Paris's skyline, lit up in enormous flashing lights. It twinkled like Nero's VVS diamond teeth that he lost *all of the time*.

Nero kissed me hard under the tower and took selfies of us as it glittered in the background. Once we got back to the hotel room, we lay in bed staring into each other's eyes.

Everything just felt right.

The magic of the blissful weekend had seeped into our skin and I felt like it had finally crept up to my brain and I'd reached some kind of peace. All his hard work *had* made a difference. I felt complete joy. I felt . . . safe? Maybe this *was* the right thing to do.

He held my hand, kissing it softly. 'I can't wait to marry you, Livia,' he told me, gazing into my eyes lovingly.

I smiled.

I felt the smile in my heart too.

And then we made love on the balcony under the full moon, my beret still on, with Édith Piaf's 'Non, Je Ne Regrette Rien' blasting on the speaker.

The car journey home to London in the morning felt like a blur. I'd entered this weird, serene dream state. I just felt grateful. I lay in Nero's lap as Ruby slept in between my legs.

I looked up at his sleeping head.

This is a view I never want to forget. That is my person.

He looked so innocent sleeping above me.

Once we got home, a day or two passed before I headed to Scotland to visit family. The night I returned, Nero came home coked out of his head. I didn't panic as things felt new and I had more trust in him. He didn't become aggressive but just slept instead. I told myself that since he'd made a lot of improvements, I should focus on that.

I didn't want to leave my dream state.

Anything not to leave my dream state.

But, in some form of self-sabotage (or self-love) I woke up in the morning and reached for his phone. I didn't know what he'd done while I was in Scotland but I didn't trust him.

There was a message from an unknown number.

'Make sure you hide that canvas.'

'Trusssss,' he'd replied . . .

Canvas?

With his phone still in my hand I threw on a baggy T-shirt and quickly ran up the stairs to his studio office area. There was an easel, paintings and unused canvases, but nothing that made sense with the text.

I sat down in the office chair, staring out at the sofas in front of it.

I pictured different girls sitting there, touching his shoulders.

I pictured them sniffing cocaine, the daylight creeping through the windows as cigarette smoke filled the air.

I looked back down at his phone. 'Who's this?' I replied to the message.

But as soon as I hit send, I realised how obvious I'd made it. I sat scratching my head for a moment longer. I *had* to know if he was doing anything behind my back. *Not this time. I can't do this again.* But also, if it was innocent, I needed to learn to trust him.

So I wrote messages to a couple of the boys, convincing myself this would be the be all and end all – something along the lines of:

'Yooo, who's the last girl I had at the crib? I think she said something to Livi', acting as though I was him, a paranoid coke-head cheat.

'It was Leah.'

'Leah bro'

Leah.

I remember this Leah girl. She was someone who Nero had known back in the day. They'd slept together years ago. All I remembered was that she was very addicted to coke, and he said that was the appeal of her.

I didn't even feel my blood boil, though my veins could've popped out of my neck. I was off before I could even feel the wooden steps below my bare feet. Suddenly I was dragging my suitcase into the bedroom. I turned the light on and began swiftly emptying all my clothes from the wardrobe into the case.

Nero jumped up from his sleep and grabbed me from behind, pulling me onto the bed. He got on top and held my wrists down with all his might, panting and panicking. He tried to catch his breath but found it difficult while he was covered in comedown sweat. I struggled to get out from beneath him. Just like old times.

'I fucking hate you, I fucking hate you so fucking much. You fucked that Leah girl while I was in Scotland', I bawled my eyes out below him.

'She's just a friend, Livia. I promise you I didn't cheat. I swear on my mum's grave I was too yay'd up – there's no way I would've been able to get hard. The canvas just said "Leah" on it. I knew you would bug out so I threw it away. I swear she slept in the spare room. We were all getting "on it" together until 1 p.m., it was an afterparty – there's no way I cheated on you, I never, I swear.'

I remember getting so exhausted trying to fight him off me, I started begging him to give me some water as my throat was so dry. But he wouldn't budge.

When I finally got out from under him, I rolled over and lay for a moment catching my breath. Then I thought to myself 'no' and shot up, proceeding to pack my things.

He physically held me hostage for a few hours that day. Whether barricading the door with his body, dragging me back up the stairs by my clothing or wrestling me onto the floor, he just wouldn't let me leave.

I eventually grabbed my phone and dialled 999. That was when he finally said he'd let me go. I hung up because, as usual, I was too afraid of what might happen to him if the police ever knew what he did.

'You did all this to bring me back, to just hurt me again? I DROPPED MY COURT CASE FOR YOU, I WENT AGAINST EVERYONE'S WISHES,' I screamed at him.

'I never cheated on you, Livia ... But maybe we don't work... Maybe you're just too nuts.'

I stopped. My pupils dilated. My heavy breathing stopped. All the voices in the House of Commons that were shouting the injustices he'd triggered were silenced.

'What did you just say?' I whispered. I could barely get the words out.

'I've done everything I can to make you happy, it still doesn't work. I love you but I think we need to separate just for a little while ... I didn't cheat on you but I just need to focus on my album now. I don't even hit you and look how you still act ...'

His voice faded into an echo in my head as he spoke. I remembered how this same voice, just a month ago, had all the determination in the world to prove to me he was a sober, good man who would walk to the ends of the earth to make it up to me that he had abused me. In his righteous tone he'd pleaded and sworn to the Creator himself that he would be granted the space to repent for his sins. He was so desperate for a chance he could barely even string his sentences together, like the whole world might fall apart if I didn't give him one moment of my time.

I stayed silent before making my way into the bedroom. I packed my things back into my suitcase after they had fallen all over the floor from him snatching it from me over and over. I could see my smashed-up foundation on one side, my eyeshadow palette on the other.

I felt numb, completely dissociated, as I wondered, *Why did he suddenly just decide to give up again?* Something just didn't make sense.

My eyelids were heavy and my throat felt tight. *What the hell was I thinking when I came back here?*

I heard Nero on the phone to Axel in the living room.

'I tried to make it work but she won't stay. Dupont man, I don't know what else to do anymore,' he mumbled, moving upstairs for more privacy ...

I saw my lipstick on the floor. I picked it up and stepped onto the bed. In the mirror above the bed, I saw my reflection: I looked tired. *I was so tired.*

I took the lid off the Ruby Woo Mac lipstick and began to write on the wall, directly above his pillow with an arrow pointing down to where he slept, 'ABUSER'.

I wheeled my suitcase out behind me and caught more of the conversation upstairs.

I can remember the exact words. Dupont's voice came through the phone, 'Now that she's dropped the case, it's safe to put the album out.'

Nero laughed.

I walked up the stairs as he hung up, tears streaming down my face.

'You guys only brought me back so I'd drop the case? You sold me a dream and put me through all of this again just so you could put your album out?'

Nero looked at me up and down. He sighed.

'What do you want, Livia?'

'I want you to admit it, admit that you abused me, admit that all you ever did was abuse me and all I ever did was love you.'

'I'm not an abuser, Livia.'

'What?' I grew angrier. 'Just a month ago you were apologising for abusing me. Now you're not an abuser?!'

He sighed again and lit a cigarette.

'Speak! SAY SOMETHING?! What about the therapy you promised? Why didn't it happen? Anger management? Making things right under GOD? Now all of a sudden you're on coke again, you most definitely cheated on me, and I have lost any chance to get justice against you because I fucking trusted you were *changing.*' The words were spewing out of me. 'And all this just to save a fucking album? Oh God, please no, please, why can't any of you treat me like a human? I carried your baby! How can I be a part of a ploy? I'm a human! A real human! I have a life too! I feel pain too! You used me. You tricked me.'

All the hate poured out of my mouth in disbelief as I realised I'd been had.

And the worst part was, he just couldn't be bothered to *have* me anymore.

I wasn't even good enough to *use* anymore.

He stayed silent.

'You are an abuser, Nero. You are nothing but a fucking abuser. You are a sick fuck and you get off on abusing women. You fucking perverted, abusive—'

Before I could finish, he stood up and kicked me hard in my chest, launching me backwards down the stairs behind me.

My elbows grazed the brick walls as I tumbled down onto the landing.

And then I finally lay there.

Dead.

Through the narc's eyes

I often thought of myself from Nero's point of view.

What he saw. What he felt. What he thought.

When she would walk into a room and smile, the genuine glaze in those big eyes, filled with hope, I would respond well to her presence, the undying willingness to be whatever I needed her to be in that moment and on that day.

The hesitation as her thumb would scratch at the side of her fingers, the pacing of her eyes trying to read my facial expressions to see what she should do or how she should act next. The destination, where she was trying to get to, was clear every time: the desperate journey to my love. Any time I felt like she was getting close to perfect, I'd find something wrong *just* to see her blindly confused at the very thing she'd taken so much time to master.

I saw the disappointment in her eyes when I would criticise her, the shame when I would reject her. When I wouldn't touch her or embrace her, especially in public. The embarrassment when she'd freeze and not know what to do with herself next. It was funny to me because she was so confident in her choices just a moment ago, and now I'd made her think twice.

The instant regret when she'd finally react and say something out of sheer anger after I'd insulted her and berated her enough. How her brain would scramble, searching for a way to calm the storm she knew was coming. The fear in her eyes would charge me up to louden my body language and move closer to her, at its most potent hit when I'd begin to raise my voice. It's like the very tone I spoke in raised her blood pressure.

She was terrified.

She was terrified I'd hit her again.

Where I'd hit her. How much it would hurt this time. If I'd stop.

But most of all she was terrified that the person I'd made her believe existed for the last few days, the person she was in love with, was about to disappear again.

She was terrified that all that work she'd put into me was for nothing.

Of course it was for nothing. I let her believe she had behaved correctly just for this very moment, so she could see all her dreams be crushed when she finally thought she could be loved.

I saw her helpless, countless times, just helpless. There was no war left in her, no agenda, no intent, no idea, not a fucking clue. She would be just below me, on that white tiled floor, half naked, begging me with every fibre left in her body to stop, to *please* stop hurting her.

She would say 'please' extra hard as if it was going to get through to me. As if it was going to make me snap out of it and stop. Like she really believed a good person lived inside of me and she was just knocking hard on the door, waiting for him to come out and save her.

When she was at her most traumatised, I'd think of ways to get a bigger hit. I'd get her to admit things that aren't real, accuse her of things she hadn't done, just to feel how good it felt to get her to agree. If I could only make her believe that this was all actually *her* fault.

Oh, the hate she'd have for herself in those moments, wallowing in remorse that she'd caused this. Sometimes, most times, it looked like she wanted to die. I made her want to kill herself because it was *her* I convinced could never do anything right. It was Livia who kept putting herself in this pain.

And after I'd completely severed any desire she had left to be here anymore, I'd pour back into her all those delusions she'd created to survive me, the ones painted for her. Like finally giving a child a toy I was holding too far in the sky for them to reach, just a touch, a hug, even just softening my tone a little, would be enough to slightly ease her mind from all the demons that I'd unleashed on her, and those demons of her own they'd pulled out too. And when I *really* wanted to establish how much control I had left of her, I'd just pick her off the floor, carry her to the bedroom and fuck her.

Then she would look confused, numb, something that resembled relief.

She looked like she'd given up.

But I needed her to find that will again, that determination.

So, I'd breadcrumb her. I'd make her think she'd worked for it, let her feel like she was in control.

She'd carefully respond to all my requests. She would pay attention to everything I wanted. I'd see the instant motivation in her eyes whenever I had any problem, hoping to prove her worth by removing it entirely from my life, the quickness at which her brain would solve it. She'd swallow it, inhale it, make it her own, anything to show me she loved me. That she genuinely loved me. Her words, her demeanour, her patience, her willpower – she responded to everything with love as if I'd never done a damn thing wrong to the girl. As if I was the victim who needed tending to. She would sacrifice herself, her needs, her wants, her boundaries, her *rights* just for me. Just for love. With so much love. The complete opposite of what I'd shown her.

And that's why I hated her so much.

It didn't matter what I did to her, her beating heart never lost its warm fleshy colour. Her intentions never changed, she just wanted to be loved. In her morals she was fair, she thought the only way to get love is to give love. She believed love would conquer all. She remained operating from this pure, child-like place, a place I just couldn't understand or reach. It was like a blind spot in my brain, this place I had no control over. The only fucking place.

Just the sight of her face reminded me every single time of how strong her love was. The fact that she could radiate love even when she was so broken disgusted me, because it made me feel ashamed. When I made her angry, crazy, shouting, insulting, mean or rude, I felt good because I knew, *hey look, she's crazy just like me!*

But her love is what reminded me that she's nothing like me.

And that made me feel weak.

So I tortured her for it.

I wanted her to die for being that way. I wanted that way of hers to just die.

A way I couldn't relate to.

She was only supposed to be an extension of me. When she vibrated love, she was her own entity.

I couldn't control her.

And I had to control her.

Because I couldn't control myself, or this empty, bottomless pit of hunger inside me.

40

You know what? I'm great

The version of me I'd given him for all those years, she was finally dead.

After Nero kicked me down the stairs I left for good.

Of course he didn't give up there. He tried to make amends, he panicked, worried (about his album), called, texted, tried keeping me sweet.

But sinking me in all the honey in the world could not sweeten me for I was truly 'sour', that thing men like to call women after we react explicitly to the pain they put upon us. I was scorned.

Burned to dust.

Unhinged.

Emotional.

Vengeful.

Sour.

There was a darkness inside me. Not one that I'd been

born with, but one that had birthed at the hands of Nero. He created who I became over the next few months.

The little mercy I had for him had diminished, the facts were clear.

He put on the biggest show, mastered the art of manipulation just to bring me back for one more fucking ride. Just so that I'd never talk about things he'd done. So long as his album could succeed.

Is that art? Art is more like when the broken becomes the alchemist, turning that pain into something *other* than pain.

I learned a lot about darkness from Nero, lesson one being the long game.

'You need to play the long game with revenge. Keep your enemies close, pretend to like them so they don't know what's coming,' he'd tell me.

The difference between Nero and me was that, although he'd put a darkness inside me, I was not evil.

I was in pain.

I didn't *actually* have a plan. Yet.

I didn't know where things would end or how. We were still in contact so my trauma was being activated every time we spoke. Clear thinking *wouldn't* come until his poison was completely drained from my lungs. I would never be able to know what justice I wanted or needed while he still had access to the trauma he'd installed in me. You can't heal a wound if you keep touching it. *That is the importance of no contact.*

The pain that I was in wasn't about to go away any time soon. In fact, the full effect hadn't even hit.

I stayed in London for work since the pandemic was cooling down and I had to show up to a lot more in-person tasks and meetings. Nero insisted I stay in our Waterlight apartment because it was empty and the lease hadn't ended there yet. I agreed on the condition that Ruby stayed with me.

But before Ruby arrived in London, one night I was there all by myself. I received a message on Instagram from what seemed like a fake account, called Healthygaga6969 – it had no display picture, no real name or followers.

> Hi I hope this message finds you well, I first want to say I'm so sorry about what you've gone through with Nero. I know first-hand what a nasty piece of work he is. There's a group of girls who have also been abused by him. He's spat in people faces, smashed up their property, used them for sex and embarrassed and shamed them in front of groups of people. We'd love to take him down and support you – he truly is the spawn of Satan . . .

I felt sceptical. I just didn't buy it . . . not entirely. Was I delusional?

I asked the account owner of 'Healthygaga6969' to call me, and after they messaged saying they'd only call on an unknown number because they were afraid of revealing their identity, I agreed. I sent them my number and they rang just moments later.

'H-hi, sorry,' they said, 'first I just want to say like, I'm such a fan of you. I'm literally so nervous to be on the phone to you right now.'

I felt awkward. A fan? What?

The voice didn't sound familiar at all. It was quite high pitched, but sounded male. I couldn't make out much else.

'Okay, sorry,' they said. 'I don't want to overwhelm you with information but I'm just going to come with cold hard facts until you believe me. I imagine this probably seems crazy and wow, I'm also scared – so are all the girls. They're scared of Nero and some of them don't even want to speak out about it, afraid of what he'd do . . .'

The rest of the conversation was brief. Whoever this person was, they didn't have much to share besides hearsay and any time I asked for details they told me that they would need to dig deeper or get permission to share first. They said they would send me any evidence and we agreed we'd talk again when that time came.

I got emotional after that call. It was being alone in that house that did it. So cold and abandoned, nothing but the bad memories haunting the home we once created. Nobody lived there, but so much had died here. And there was a stench of it.

I felt like I could hear the screams in the house. Every. Single. Corner. Of every. Single. Room had a bad memory.

The door frames that had bashed my nose as he dragged me out by my hair. The bedroom wardrobe he'd slammed my head into and concussed me.

The balcony door he'd thrown me into before threatening to kill me with a hammer.

The sofa we'd cuddle on, hungover with Jefe.

The kitchen I learned to make food in for him.

The studio we'd made love in in between making songs together.

The front door he'd walk through, both alarming and easing me at the very sight of him.

I suddenly became extremely light-headed. My ears felt like they were beginning to bleed. My heart rate was getting faster and faster, louder and louder, as the memories began to torpedo around me like a tornado of ghosts. I couldn't catch my breath. I fell to the floor and started crying hysterically, digging my fingernails into my face as I covered my eyes.

I was haunted by what I can only describe as an energy that was attempting to possess me once more, but I denied it entry. I wouldn't call Nero for answers or revelations this time. I couldn't do it. So, in my despair, I picked up my phone and rang Ruby instead.

I remember her asking over and over what was wrong as I couldn't get the words out. I couldn't think straight nor string together a sentence – all I could do was *feel*. I just sobbed into the phone, hyperventilating.

My body was covered in sweat as I held my heart in my hands. I lay down on the cold floor to try and cool myself down but it only reminded me of all the times I'd been thrown down there previously, all the times my cheek rested against those white tiles. From the corner of my wet eyes, a Vogue cigarette tucked beneath the kitchen corner caught my eye (left behind by lord knows who at whichever afterparty). I reached for it and stepped out onto the balcony, wrapping myself in the blanket from the sofa.

I lit the cigarette with a lighter that had been left out there and inhaled that nicotine long and deep, as if it was the last breath I'd ever take.

I stood out there for a while, staring out over the balcony at that same enchanting skyline I'd only dreamed of living next to when I first moved to London.

The same skyline Nero had pointed out in pure joy, 'That's the Thames, my don!'

My heart rate eventually slowed down as I looked out at all the tiny buildings. Each window housed a different heart, with a different story. I wondered what it looked like when Nero saw our story in his head. All I felt was sadness.

Repeated thoughts danced in my mind. I kept seeing myself from his point of view; the immense lack of danger I presented to him at all times. How could you do that to someone who loves you so much?

He knew what he was doing. He fucking knew. That's what hurt most, he was so conscious of it. And just because I couldn't fathom *why* or *how* someone would do such a thing, and just because *I* wouldn't do it to them, I still had to accept it: accept that people do bad things for reasons we can't comprehend, and that not accepting that fact is exactly what will destroy you.

Cherry invited me to join her for lunch. We met at a posh restaurant in Soho, with white tablecloths and real leather armchairs. She was on a call as I was brought over to her table. She mouthed 'sorry, just give me a sec' to me as she finished what sounded like a business meeting. I tried not to stare at her too much, but it was difficult not to – she was utterly beautiful, ethereal even. I counted all the different piercings in her ears clad with unique vintage jewellery. Her face was so ... symmetrical, and though she was ten years my senior, honestly, she could've been younger than me.

I was in awe of her, she was a light in my life.

'Sorry about that. It's so good to see you, Livia!' she said when she finished her call. She rose from her seat, urging me to immediately follow, and we hugged a tight and warm embrace. 'You look great, really.' She smiled, her face turning serious just seconds later. She didn't waste any time getting into it.

'He could have killed you. What if you had hit your head when he kicked you down the stairs?' she asked.

'I know ... I should never have gone back. I bet you think I'm so stupid.'

'No,' she replied, 'because I did the exact same thing. I get it. Of course I wasn't happy but this is your journey and I really understand how hard it is ...'

I sighed and nodded my head as I listened to her. She was so empowered, so in control of her emotions ...

The waiter came over and we ordered: she had sea bass and I asked for a steak. It was one of those really small but plump steaks, the kind that only run in a fancy spot.

I decided I wanted to pay the bill as a thank you, though steak and sea bass didn't quite equal what she did for me. I don't think anything could.

'How are you so calm and level-headed about all this?' I asked her.

'Educate yourself on Narcissistic Personality Disorder. It's *everything* ... giving logic to these emotions, knowledge, it will save you.'

And she was right.

The more I could pin Nero's actions to NPD, the more relief I felt. I had so many 'whys' in my head, and all the information available online on TikTok, Google and YouTube ed those for me. The explanations resonated and made sense. They did not stutter once.

Reading the stories of hundreds and thousands of people having gone through the exact same series of events spun my head. It wasn't just *me and Cherry*. It was a whole epidemic of these zombies who live among us. *They are actually zombies*. The very essence of NPD is to get supply, and that is at the direct cost of the livelihood of others.

'They suck on you like leeches to remain functioning.' Cherry's words from dinner whirled in my head that evening before bed.

I stayed up later reading stories of women who have narc husbands, messy divorces, having to co-parent, and I felt lucky. I felt so lucky I didn't have to be bonded to this demon for the rest of my life.

The hardest pill of all to swallow was the fact that they will not change. Yeah, there's a few, and I mean a few, people who insist they can ... I might have read two whole *supposed* success stories from the entire internet through weeks of research until four in the morning each night, when my eyes would be stinging and red.

And that was normal too. Trying to obsessively understand what had happened to me, what I'd gone through – the closest thing to the answers I'd wanted for so long. It's expected to fixate on understanding narcissism. It helps us understand who we have become as a result of it. Of *them*. It doesn't just help us to understand them, it helps us understand ourselves.

Once I learned that narcs can't change, I had one question left: how could I be sure, really sure, that Nero was a narcissist?

All I wanted so badly was for him to change, to show me he was sorry for all the wrong he'd done to me and my spirit. If he was a narcissist, I knew he'd never be sorry. In fact, he might never even admit it to himself. He would always intentionally gaslight me, mock me and feed off the fact that he did this to me. Even if I ran a hundred miles away, he would do it to someone else. Another girl would have to live in the constant torment I felt every moment with and without him. And I couldn't let that happen.

Nobody deserves to live in the mental prison a narc will trap you in.

And then at 3 a.m., there I was, waiting for him in our regular suite at the Four Seasons hotel.

I couldn't sleep that night. I needed to see him. I needed to know if he was a narcissist.

This was the final deciding factor. The last supper.

I had to know if he was sorry, if there was any remorse at all in him. If he was, in fact, a zombie, or just a human.

Nero knocked on the door and, as I let him in, I didn't even look at him. Instead, I knelt down and kissed Jefe. Why wasn't I looking at him? *This is what you came for, Livia. You wanted your answer, look in those eyes. Look and see who he really is.*

'You look beautiful, Livia,' he said, standing over me.

As I looked up at him, he put his arm out, asking for a hug . . .

'No,' I said, rejecting him and sitting on the bed.

'Oh, we're not cool, nah?' he said. 'So why'd you invite me here? You obviously realise I'm a good guy. You can't deny it after everything I do for you.' He lit a cigarette.

I noticed that when he lit his cigarette, he stared down at it, firmly placed between his thumb and index finger, and then he'd scrunch up his face and inhale as if there was *such* great difficulty to get the smoke out from it. When he blew out, he tilted his head at an upward angle, raising one eyebrow and crossing his legs. Much like a lord or someone of the upper echelons, whose very presence demanded respect, his body language was relaxed and firm. Intimidating and inviting. 'Enter if you dare.'

But instead of just seeing him, it's like I could see *through* him.

And the colour of see-through is so fucking blinding.

The way he scrunched up his face looked so unnatural, as if he was consciously trying to be someone he was not. The over-the-top exhalation of smoke. *What effort must that take?*

He turned to face me. He eyed me up and down, blowing smoke in my face. He was yearning for a reaction, it was so blatant – like a stupid little child seeking attention. None of it was hidden. It was all a performance.

Then he stood, forcing me up to slow dance with him.

His compliments always had to be back-handed, 'How are you so pale and pretty?'

'I probably need a fucking holiday, Nero . . .'

'Shut up, you're just wearing too much make-up,' he said, releasing his grip on my arm with the covered tattoo before heading to the bathroom and loudly peeing with the door open. I could see he felt annoyed I'd been taking care of myself.

He always peed with the door open, anywhere he went. He was so blissfully unaware of how he came across to people. See, Nero's act wasn't actually for other people – he really momentarily believed himself to be this character he played.

That's why he got so upset when everyone else didn't stick to the script.

He sat down on the bed next to me, flamboyantly swinging an arm around me, tilting his head as if a cue had just told him to do so in an earpiece. As though he heard 'action', he said, 'You know I'll always love you, right, Livia?'

When I remained emotionless, gazing through his big show, he slowly lifted a hand onto my cheek and rubbed it. I almost flinched, and he added an ounce more intensity into his stare – unaware he had already added fifty ounces too many and the whole façade was corny and false as fuck.

As the night lingered on, I began to feel more and more agitated. It was like no matter what, the veil had been lifted. I couldn't feel anything when I looked at him. He was a narcissistic robot. Every move he made was so predictable because of everything I'd studied about narcs … All I kept thinking about was everything I'd now uncovered. He fit the script of each piece of knowledge I'd learned. He was insufferable.

'Let's fuck,' I said, interrupting a spiel about how his album was better than the hip-hop artist who'd played moments earlier through the speaker.

I was just so desperate to feel something, to see the man I'd been blindly serving my energy to on a silver platter for so many years. Right as he got on top of me, he looked at me, and as if in some low-budget action film – or better yet, a sleazy home porn video – said, in a frisky tone, 'You ready?' It was said with as much romanticism as the catchphrase across a cereal box. As if I was one of his fans and I should have been excited for what was about to take place.

Everything felt so fucking fake. After a few minutes of

awfully numb sex on the bed, he moved us in front of the mirror. Like it couldn't get any worse, Nero lifted my arm up mid-intercourse to reveal my covered-up tattoo, cackled to himself like a witch and said, 'this used to say my name', before dropping it back down and continuing to fuck me with the most sinister look on his face. I wonder if he even noticed I wasn't making a sound. I was just staring at his reflection in the mirror, realising what I was witnessing, as if I wasn't even experiencing it myself.

After sex he slept soundly while I lay awake, contemplating if I could even bear to share a bed with him. I was so disgusted. How did I love a zombie? I felt like I had been under a spell for nearly three years.

In the morning, as we packed our things separately, I asked Nero, one last time, 'Are you sorry for *any* of what you put me through?'

To which he simply replied, 'I don't think you understand how lucky you've been to have somebody like me as your boyfriend. I'll always have love for you.'

So I pulled out my phone, and tried to play him the video. The video of him attacking me. I tried to show him how lucky I was. I tried to let him see something he couldn't deny with his own two God-given eyes. I tried to say, *'LOOK! IS THIS LUCKY? YOU SEE IT? YOU HEAR IT? THIS IS US! THIS IS YOU AND THIS IS ME AND THIS IS ME BEGGING YOU TO STOP HURTING ME.'*

But instead of internalising even a moment of it, it was just the usual nonchalant response of, 'That could ruin my career'. The screams of pain didn't even make him blink. He just *didn't* care.

The conclusion was made. I knew what I had to do. I looked Nero dead in the eye and told him, 'I'm going to tell everyone what you did to me so you can never do this to anybody ever again'.

His eyes spouted a venomous glare but, just as the anxiety hit my chest, I grabbed my bag and ran out of the room. I chose flight mode. He grabbed Jefe and chased me down the stairs as I took the lift. He began shouting my name as I sped out the front entrance of the hotel.

'Goodbye, Mrs Godji!' the doorman said as I whisked by.

Nero caught up with me as I turned onto the main street, trying to find a cab.

'Livia, just listen. Livia, we need to talk about this,' he pleaded as I remained facing forward, ignoring him. I panicked, looking from left to right, hoping to see a cab with its light on while doing my very best not to slow down.

He dropped the dog lead onto the ground, knowing how dangerous it was to do that on a busy main road, and turned into a corner shop behind me. 'I need to get cigs,' he said.

I let out a deep grunt in distress and ran towards the lead, adjusting it on my wrists. *What do I do now? Do I just take him? Where the hell am I gonna take him?*

A man approached me from behind, holding a child. 'HEY! Pick up your dog's shit!' – Jefe must've pooed at some point as Nero was chasing after me.

Nero saw the man yelling at me and ran outside. 'OI! DON'T SPEAK TO MY FUCKING GIRL.'

The traffic around me was getting louder and louder, every passer-by's curious eyes on the busy street left me feeling more and more embarrassed.

Nero proceeded to tell the man how he was a rockstar, how he was lucky that he was holding his child in his arms or he would knock him out.

'Do you know who the fuck I am? Fucking PUSSIO!' Nero yelled.

The man recorded him on his phone camera, laughing, 'Yeah you're a fucking loser.'

I wondered what would happen if anybody who knew us could see us right now.

I suddenly saw a black cab with its light on and hauled it over to the side of the road, opened the door and ushered Jefe in. Nero jumped in beside me and asked the driver to take us to his place.

'Please, Livia, I just have to talk to you properly,' he begged.

I stared out of the window in silence, green trees whisking past me, unsure what to do or where to go.

Nero began to cry. He began to cry because crying always made me feel bad for him. But instead, I just felt further repulsed. He was so fucking predictable.

I realised I was still trapped by his energy. Something inside of me was telling me to get out of that taxi, to go no contact. I paid such a price every time I had contact. The pattern was so clear now.

'I'm sorry but I need to get out here. I need to get a different cab to the train station,' I said to the driver, opening my door quickly as he slowed down.

Nero followed right behind me, quickly paying the driver and shouting my name. I sped off.

'Please leave me the fuck alone, Nero!'

I didn't know where I was going. I couldn't even think

straight. I walked down the path of a park somewhere in south London.

'Livia, please. Livia I beg you. You were right, you were always right, you're the only good person in my life. Please, I need you. Everyone is fake and everyone are yes men and nobody actually cares about me besides you. I deserve everything that's coming because I'm an awful man, here – take my phone.' He cried, handing me his phone and unlocking it.

'Post it on my Instagram, tell the world what I did to you. I don't care anymore, I just need you in my life. I'll admit to everyone that I abused you, tell them everything,' he sobbed.

I paused for a second, looking at the phone in my hand. Then I looked back at him and said starkly, 'You're pathetic,' before handing it back and walking away.

He grabbed my arm and spun me around. 'Let go, Nero!' I roared at him.

I stared at him in disgust, my heart pumping loudly.

He got down on one knee.

'I'll marry you right now. Be my wife. Let's fucking do this right now. I'll do anything for you.'

He actually thought that was the last card left to play.

I looked down at him, his big, forceful eyes gazing up at me, with his hand out, using every inch of his energy to try and convince me to stay.

'Please, Livia ... we're a family ...' He winced.

I looked at Jefe, and then back at him.

'We were a family ...' I replied. 'But *you* ruined that.'

I knelt down and kissed Jefe hard on his head, knowing that would be the last time.

I ran off and jumped in a cab.

I could hear Nero still shouting my name in the distance.

And I never looked back.

I burst out crying in relief.

'To Euston station please,' I told the driver as he watched me through the mirror with slight concern in his eyes.

'Are you all right?' he asked me.

'Yeah, you know what ... I'm great,' I smiled, tears still rolling down my face.

A memory of you

I spotted someone in my message requests on Instagram. It was a name I recognised; Mary Mckormick, otherwise known as Joshua Alexander's new girlfriend. Honestly, I was so happy for him. To know that he was in a new relationship filled me with so much hope, realising that this could mean that he was perhaps getting better at least.

Josh and I hadn't spoken too much over the years since I moved to London. Over the last six years, we had just the odd and very brief catch up over Instagram, ending each message with the koala and frog emoji because that was us: I was the koala because I wrapped around him like one and he was the frog because we agreed he looked like one in some strange way. That was our thing when we were together.

'Hi, I'm so sorry to message you like this, but I wanted to tell you something about Joshua that you wouldn't know otherwise,' the message from Mary read.

Before I could reply asking her what it was, I already knew.

The room turned cold as Ruby's head peeked over my shoulder in anticipation.

'Joshua had been struggling mentally for a while. He ended his own life this week. I am so sorry to break this news to you. He spoke highly of you. I am devastated.'

Ruby gasped as she held me tight, 'I am so fucking sorry, Livia'.

I'd been grieving Josh for six years, but the way this broke my heart, I wasn't sure if I'd ever even be *capable* of feeling okay again. It was like in that moment, I accepted that life was totally fucked. This was an irreversible mistake that somehow *I* had caused. The guilt decayed my heart like a flesh-eating disease.

What hit me was a different kind of depression. Every time I blinked, I imagined his face, his head lying on the pillow in front of me, his deep, silky brown eyes, so innocent and pure. Each and every memory with him replayed in my mind as though it happened just yesterday, the sound of his voice echoing in the chambers of my mind, his Scottish accent saying the syllables of my name over and over.

The funeral was just two weeks later, and as I sat on the train with my head leaning against the window, staring out at the golden fields connecting England to Scotland, I reminisced about my life there. My old life.

I hadn't been home in a long time because it was mentally draining enough pretending to be someone I wasn't around my family, never mind the idea of masking the fact I was being abused.

Returning to the small rainy city of Edinburgh reminded me of the little girl who was so desperate to escape – and when she finally did, she ended up back where she started: trapped and longing for life, for love.

I saw Shay pull up outside the funeral in his Mercedes GLC. I hadn't seen him in years. Of course Nero didn't allow me to have any male friends, and just about the only thing I was looking forward to on this trip was the big, warm hug I knew was on the other side of the shiny black car door.

I had met Shay when I was fourteen, way before I met Josh, and Shay was the one who had 'put in a good word for me'.

'Yeahhh, I told him, she's cool as fuck!' Shay said to me at the wake. 'The way you smoked me out under the table that time.' We laughed as we reminisced.

'We always end up back in each other's lives. First it was because of Josh . . . and now I guess Josh again,' I replied as the laughter faded from my expression.

'Yeah, that's mad . . .'

'So if Josh keeps bringing us back together, now he's gone, now what? What does he want now? Because trust me, I'll do whatever he wants,' I said, not making much sense between my drunken slurs.

'I think he'd just want us to live, stay out of this shitty little city and see the world,' Shay said. 'Where's one place you've always wanted to go?'

'Hmmm . . . Los Angeles,' I said.

'Me too,' he replied.

41

Exhale

I stepped out of LAX airport and into our truck. With the windows down and the breeze blowing on my face, the brightest of clear blue skies and palm trees lining each street, LA felt like London when I first got there. Just like that first ecstasy tablet again, those thousands of tiny orbs soaked into your skin, vibrating love all through you.

Each street corner looked exactly like the *GTA* map. I was convinced I drove past Trevor's house. I wondered if there actually was a military laser plane at Fort Zancudo, just north of Hollywood on the map.

I'd planned on coming to LA with Nero so many times. It was his favourite place in the world. I had put the Hollywood sign at the top of the vision board I created for him. I'd imagined so many amazing things, seeing it through his eyes, that it almost felt surreal seeing it through my own.

And how did I afford it?

Karma.

A week or two before, while in Manchester, shortly after returning from London, I was in bed with Ruby as she slept next to me. I opened my message requests on Instagram to some guy who had been messaging me over and over. His latest message read:

ANSWER THIS MESSAGE, SEND ME
YOUR PAYPAL AND GOD'S GONNA
BLESS YOU I PROMISE

With absolutely no expectation and out of pure curiosity, I responded with Ruby's PayPal as I didn't even have one. I woke Ruby up as the notification lit up her phone on the bedside drawer next to me. 'Ruby! Ruby! This random guy just sent me £1000!'

'That's nothing, I'm gonna send you ten,' he told me. And he did. He *actually* did. *Ten thousand pounds*. Not all at once. I wasn't sure if he would ever send any more at all, but little by little, without ever asking anything of me, he did.

I know ten thousand pounds may not go very far, and yes, over recent years I'd *seen* a lot more than £10k, but I'd never *had* money like that in my life. Like most young adults my age, I lived life month to month, and right now I was barely managing that. I was homeless, and almost hopeless, but not quite.

When I asked him why, or what he wanted, he just thanked me. He said he could tell that I was a good person, he loved reading my captions, and he'd be honoured to be my friend.

To this day, I've never met this dude in the flesh. Even when I tried to say thank you, to see who this person was, he was too busy. I don't even know where he disappeared to after that. Every time I think about it, I just can't wrap my head around it . . .

I am fully convinced he didn't exist in the physical realm, and that he was a cyber-angel.

It was like God wanted to reward me for saying no to Nero. God wanted to tell me, *keep fucking going, you're doing great.* How the fuck else did a stranger send me £10k in the wake of my great awakening? It was good karma. I'm sure of it.

The universe had asked me over and over and over again to leave this situation, and when you don't listen, the universe will say, 'Oh, you want to learn the hard way?'

The things that are the hardest to let go of come with the biggest reward, you just need to trust in something bigger.

Shay and I had booked to stay in a gorgeous, vine-covered Spanish house in West Hollywood; a two bedroom fit with a cute garden. We had originally booked a much smaller spot since Los Angeles was so extortionate for renting, but the agency had mixed something up and double booked it, offering us this much bigger and better place as a gesture of good will. *That was also good karma.*

Shay was the first man to truly make me begin to trust masculine energy again. At first, when he returned home drunk, I'd feel anxious, but the new memories quietly painted over the old ones as I learned to trust that intoxication no longer equalled chaos.

We rode around LA in the drop-top Benz Shay had rented, blasting music we'd listened to growing up as teens, singing along to the Black Eyed Peas. We tried out each and every little café in Beverly Hills, looking for the best breakfast eggs in town. We went to the gun range and shot guns together, explored all the tourist sites in Hollywood, and did great big grocery shops together where he was super unhelpful the whole time and just pushed the trolley, having full faith it would end up in another delicious home-cooked South Asian meal by me. It was honestly all Shay needed in life; he just *loved* home food.

One evening I was on my period and my emotions were eating me up more than usual. When he asked what was up and I told him I just felt sad, he said, 'You wanna go on a drive and get ice cream?' I couldn't have got dressed quicker.

We drove up to the Hollywood sign with the top down and parked at the highest point we were allowed to go. There you could see a spectacular view of the entirety of Los Angeles; a flat surface below us with billions of little lights flickering in the distance, a scenic orange night-time haze contrasting with the stark black sky. It was like looking at the whole world, like we were on top of the whole world.

I dug my spoon into my pot of ice cream, searching for cookie-dough chunks, as Shay enjoyed his chocolate brownie one, then we swapped and tried each other's.

'Mine is sooo much better, man,' he said, screwing his face up after his bite of mine.

'Nah not a chance, everyone knows cookie dough is elite. Here, gimme that back.' I laughed as I snatched my pot out of his ungrateful hands.

We both continued to look out at the breathtaking view.

'Wow ...' Shay said as he sighed.

'Just mad, isn't it,' I replied. 'I was sad because I was

thinking of him a lot today … of Josh … it's like, he never got to see none of this stuff, how much was out in the world. Imagine what he would say if he was with us here, at the fucking Hollywood sign at the top of LA!' I said, swallowing hard and smiling softly to pull back any tears.

'He can see us now. I bet he's laughing at us right now, saying, look at these two fucking idiots all the way in America together,' replied Shay.

I smiled deeper, both of us looking up at the twinkling stars above us.

'It's just so crazy what types of consequences can bring people back together in life, eh? Look at us, we wouldn't even be here otherwise … That's something I keep realising, everything that happens causes so many … happenings,' I said.

'Don't go all bestselling author on me now,' he laughed.

I looked at him and grinned, rolling my eyes.

'Thank you, Shay, I really needed this.'

'It's cool man, I got you. Always,' he said, smiling back.

'Not just this. You're always so nice to me, you've, you showed me that men aren't all actually … evil.' I laughed.

'Nah, you just need to stay away from them dickheads. Know that you are the prize, and that prize can't be won by just anyone. Not all men are winners!' he exclaimed.

I nodded my head in appreciation. 'You sound more like an author than me now!'

42

Guess who?

Just two weeks into Los Angeles living, Ruby flew out to join our escape from reality in our WeHo abode.

That next month felt like a movie. It was peak season, the whole of LA had just opened up after the pandemic and it felt like, resident or tourist, we were all on the same holiday, like one big school trip. We spent our days tanning by our apartment pool, arguing with Shay over whether to play grime or Lana Del Ray on the JBL speaker and partying on boats in Malibu. Our nights were spent at house parties in the Hills, afterparties at after-hours clubs, shisha lounges, dinners and drunken taxi trips to Bossa Nova at 4 a.m. on the way home.

It was like I was making up for lost time.

I was making up for the years I *should* have spent having fun and being young and puking my guts out due to too much alcohol in my system. I wore what I wanted, I experimented with my make-up and I started to feel comfortable in my own skin. I felt confident.

I felt *fucking* free.

In between all the empowering escapism and unhealthy coping mechanisms, Nero and I rarely stayed in touch.

He had sent me heaps of abuse, berating me for being in LA, slut-shaming me for my outfits, for partying, for drinking, for smiling. For purely existing.

One morning, I lay in bed with a headache, hungover from the night before.

I scrolled onto Nero's Instagram page to find a 'confession' posted on his page.

'. . . *I participated in abuse provoked, I hate myself for what I've done . . .*' the end of it read.

Provoked. As if it's justified.

You've just got to laugh. Or you will truly, truly, cry.

He really thought he could quit his own fate by jumping the gun, but instead he shot himself in the foot by literally admitting to it. Abuse is a crime and not something that's taken lightly, especially not in this day and age, but Nero didn't think so.

Some of the UK gossip blogs picked up on it and the speculation around our story grew. While there was a huge percentage of people who jumped on the bandwagon and started raving on about how, 'his ex has been trying to tell us this for a long time' – there were still many *men* who insisted it simply couldn't be true.

Source? 'Women lie.'

Credible source? 'Just trust me, bro.'

On 30 October, Ruby and I rushed to get ready for a Halloween party in a mansion in the suburbs of Santa Monica. It was one of those parties that everybody wanted to be at, with loads of security and a very exclusive guest list. We'd been in Los Angeles for around a month now, and Shay had made friends with a local DJ who had invited us.

I dressed up as Harley Quinn, with my blonde hair in two messy ponytails, a tight crop top and hotpants with some big-ass heeled boots. Shay chose the cop-out option and just wore a nice fit, carrying a scream mask in his hand. He headed out without us because, as he always said, 'I'll be old and grey waiting for you two to be ready to leave.'

Ruby was a dead tennis player, in a sexy white tennis skirt with blood dripping out of a neck wound. She swung her bat around in the air as I took photos of her for Instagram.

'Let me spray some of this red and blue on the ends of your hair,' she said.

'Won't it stain?' I replied.

'Hmmm, maybe, but it's Halloween. If you're gonna do Harley, you need to do *Harley*.'

So, we sprayed my hair and then switched positions as she took some photos of me posing against the wall.

'You look fiiiiiiiiire, girl, this one *has* to go on my Story now,' Ruby said as she posted it.

We arrived at the party around 1.30 a.m., which for LA was kinda early. Nowhere really got busy until 2 a.m.; everything just moved slower and started later.

But the party was already *heaving*.

Any time I found myself particularly overwhelmed in crowded places, my first answer was always alcohol. It numbed me out in social situations so that I could actually have fun. Isn't it so crazy that that's the case for *most* people in the same vicinity? All nervous, for the same reason – because of each other.

I don't know if it was the energy that comes with Halloween, the busy-ass mansion or what exactly, but something felt off that night. Something felt like it was impending ... something dark.

I had grown used to feeling pretty comfortable in LA. I knew Nero wasn't there; I knew he was thousands of miles away from me. He couldn't get to me.

But why did I feel so nervous tonight?

I lost Ruby on the dance floor somewhere in the living room and I hadn't seen Shay since we arrived. As I headed for the bathroom upstairs, I kept looking behind me, around me, just waiting to see Nero.

It's impossible, Livia, you're in America.

He's not here.

He's not here.

I waited outside the bathroom as the bass vibrated the floor beneath me, sipping on my drink. I couldn't help but feel *watched*. My stomach turned as I looked around once more.

The bathroom was finally free as three girls walked out. I quickly entered, locking the door behind me.

I peed, washed my hands, and stared into the mirror like every good drunk in a film giving themselves a pep talk.

Someone knocked on the door.

'One sec!' I shouted, flustered.

I looked in the mirror, giving myself a shake.

Breathe, Livia, and enjoy yourself. Stop letting this man live in your head – you are safe.

There was a knock on the door again and I rolled my eyes

as I walked over to it, unlocking it, ready to give whoever it was a piece of my mind—

I flung open the door. A man stood in front of me, wearing a totally unoriginal Patrick Bateman, *American Psycho*-style see-through coat over a suit. His dark skin was covered in fake splattered blood.

'Can't you *wait*!?' I scowled as I opened the door.

He smiled. Even his smile was like Patrick Bateman's, except fifty times more attractive.

'You've got even more attitude than when you hit me with your shoe.'

Just as that sentence left his lips, I realised exactly who I was staring at.

'Jude? The rapist? Well, the one your ex *told you* is a rapist, remember?' he said.

I froze, then tried to shove past him.

'Livia, I can help you ...'

I looked down at his hand, which he'd softly placed on my elbow to stop me from walking away. He moved it away instantly.

'You fucking weirdo fuck. Don't ever touch me again,' I shouted at him as the bass downstairs drained out the sound of my voice.

'Just hear me out,' he said, his eyes intensified. He moved his head forward without moving his body an inch closer, like a cobra preparing to strike.

'Nero is going to get Jefe put down.'

The bass paused for a second. The music stopped. The entire house went silent. All I heard was my heartbeat. I swallowed hard.

'You're lying,' I told him, as the audio returned around me.

'I have proof of everything, everything. You know your ex is a bad man, you know he's lied about everything. I know what he's done to you, and there's more women like you. I can prove everything to you. I'll come to you with hard facts and that's it. Don't you think, with everything else he's lied about, you deserve to hear the truth about what happened that night in LA?'

A couple came up the stairs arguing, screaming back and forth.

'I fucking love you,' he shouted at her while she cried. 'Why do you want him?'

'He actually treats me with respect!' she yelled back in her American accent.

Jude held open the bathroom door, 'Come, let's talk in here?' He looked hopeful, desperate, but sure.

There was a large Jacuzzi tub in the bathroom, and I sat on the furthest corner with my arms crossed, lighting a cigarette.

'You shouldn't smoke, you know. It's bad for you,' Jude said in his dense London accent.

'I *don't* smoke, only when I'm drunk or super stressed,' I said. I sighed and then blinked hard at him. 'Well, go on then!'

He perched on the opposite side of the stone tub as he pulled out his phone and scrolled through.

I couldn't help but wonder what Nero would think if he could see us together right now. He wouldn't have even be-lieved it. Despite everything, I felt some kind of guilt. Some seriously *misplaced* guilt. Like I owed him loyalty, not to be sitting opposite his arch nemesis right now, not to be engaging with him, or letting him even have his eyes on me for longer than just a few seconds.

Our eyes met just briefly as he passed me his phone.

'I just want you to know, I have brothers, friends in London. We can do everything we can to make sure you're safe, that your dog doesn't get hurt, because that's his plan, to make you suffer ...'

His voice faded into the distance as I stared at the screen in front of me. It was a screenshot of some messages from the victim of the rape. She was apologising to Jude, alleging that Nero had brainwashed her.

I was hesitant to react too much ... I didn't trust him.

'Tell me what happened in LA then? Actually, wait, I'll tell you what *I know* first,' I said. I didn't want to give him too much of a chance to explain himself as if I was ready to believe him.

'There was that girl, and she was denying having slept with you previously to Nero, right?'

Jude nodded.

'And then you guys were all on shrooms at the afterparty at his crib, and her and Nero went upstairs and almost started having sex and just then you came in and—'

'Oh, they had sex,' he interrupted me.

I went silent.

'We all had sex; we had a full-blown threesome. It was kinda rough, yes, but that's how she wanted it. She was fully on it and consented to both of us fucking her ...'

His voice was bold. Unfiltered.

I remained silent.

They all had a threesome? What?

I thought back to when Nero was back home, panicking after the trip, telling me how Jude had interrupted them as they were *just kissing* and started joining in. He said it had freaked him out since he was on mushrooms, so he left the room as he suspected that, since they'd been intimate before, they'd planned this – and then moments later she had come downstairs crying, saying he'd raped her.

That Jude had raped her.

That's what Nero told me.

Jude had supposedly left for the airport nine hours early, the girl called the LAPD and everyone was handcuffed . . .

'So why would you leave nine hours early to go to the airport?' I asked.

'What?' he replied. 'I didn't leave early. I had a flight, yes, but I was there through the whole shit. When Nero smashed her phone and—'

'Huh?' I started feeling very empty.

'You don't know about that? After we all finished fucking, Nero turned to her while doing up his trousers and said 'You fucking BITCH' loud in her face before walking out of the room. She ran after him, in her underwear, crying. They went downstairs to the living room where everyone was . . .'

Everyone? Ziggy. Kai. I started imagining all the different witnesses that could back up Jude's version of events.

'. . . and then she was crying, saying, "Why would you say that to me?" He was arguing, saying she'd lied to him about sleeping with me previously. He was just trying to make a point.'

I cannot deny that that was completely Nero's style. I can't imagine how much it would rile up his narcissistic ass that a girl had lied to him about another guy. How that would greatly disrespect his superiority. How he would want the ultimate revenge. The *ultimate bazz*.

'Then he called her a slag, smashed up her phone and chucked her out of the house in her underwear ... so she had to go to a neighbour and call the police ...' Jude continued.

I was completely speechless.

'I know you're not stupid, you know it's in my best interests to help you because I hate Nero, but you genuinely deserve all the justice in the world. He can't hurt you anymore. People *will* believe you'.

'Help me how?'

'In any way that you need, Livia, anything you could possibly need, I'm here.'

I stared back down at the messages, scanning each word from the girl. Jude's story checked out in some ways from what I could see, but I wasn't there, and I honestly didn't need to come to any kind of conclusion in the bathroom of this party. In fact, I didn't need to be speaking to Jude at all ... why was I speaking to Jude again?

And then I remembered.

I sighed as I carefully lifted my legs out of the tub and typed my number into Jude's phone. A contact name appeared ... He already had my number saved.

'Livia Nero,' it read.

I stared at the screen and passed it to him.

'If you have any evidence that he's going to hurt Jefe, send it to me ... please.'

I walked out without saying a word or even looking at him to register his reaction.

I wasn't sure why Jude already had my number, but something told me if I asked, he was never going to be honest anyway, and I had given him enough of a chance to toy with my brain.

When I got home that evening, I lay in bed staring at my ceiling all night, wondering who the FUCK I had been sleeping next to for the last few years.

How I'd helped him so much through that time with the rape allegations. How I genuinely believed in his story.

In who? In who!? I'd repeat, banging my head against a metaphorical brick wall, and almost a physical one too.

There's this era that comes after leaving a narcissist. I don't know what we should call it, maybe 'the grand awakening' ... That doesn't even credit its power enough; perhaps it should be called 'the greatest rebirth' or 'the ultimate baptism'.

But the information that flowed to me effortlessly over the next few weeks was exactly like someone was dunking my head in holy water and cleansing me. So much truth was being revealed to me, so many secrets ...

Even if my heart wanted to believe there was any chance of forgiveness left for Nero, or any chance that our love was real, it didn't stand a chance.

Ziggy and Chiara were next to reach out, full of apologies.

'I had to lie to you, Livia,' said Chiara. 'If I didn't, Nero would have made Ziggy lose his job, and Ziggy was my only priority. I'm so sorry ... I tried to tell you with my eyes that day at the hotel when you said, "I think my boyfriend is cheating on me."'

She filled me in on the exact sequence of events. How Nero's Instagram was logged in on her phone for some work shit and a German girl had messaged him one morning. Being her usual nosey self, Chiara looked at her Story and saw her naked, wearing just Nero's hoodie in a hotel room. She had called him and went crazy, and he begged Chiara to tell the girl to take it down as he was getting on his flight.

'He was terrified,' she said.

'Even I was like, cheating is one thing ... but a foursome ...' Ziggy chimed in, sitting next to her on speaker phone.

'And then when we saw you post a few weeks later, wearing that hoodie, hugging him ... We felt bad for you, Livia. I'm so, so sorry for not telling you,' Chiara said.

'It's fine,' I replied lifelessly, completely overwhelmed by everything. Completely numb.

'No, it's not fine. You were a good friend to me; you were real. Nero made out to all of us that you were the problem, that you were crazy, but we had no idea what he'd been doing to you. I know how fucked that boy is. I've known Nero for six years; I know more than *anyone* the lengths he will drive you. He destroys people, Livia, and we are so sorry we didn't do anything about it. We all just cared too much about keeping our jobs and money. He was so good at manipulating everyone,' Chiara said, getting emotional. 'He's put me through hell. I remember being too afraid to even speak around him because if it wasn't funny or good enough or Nero didn't like it, he'd make me leave the room. He stopped me from seeing my own boyfriend. We had an abortion just because he made us.'

I felt her. We felt each other. Most survivors connect, but specifically us, the survivors of a very specific demon.

I felt bad for them. I especially felt bad for Ziggy. He'd been emotionally abused by Nero for years. He actually loved him. He loved him close to how I loved him. Chiara could understand my hate for him, but Ziggy ... Ziggy could understand my love. He let Nero walk all over him time and time again because he was so confused by the friend he loved who kept switching on him. He knew what it was to lose him every time you thought he was back.

'It was like, one day he was so funny and the best guy ever, but the next ...' he said.

'I know ...' I replied. 'You're just left wondering, why are you doing this to me right now?'

We both found a lot of peace in that conversation. Ziggy needed to grieve that friendship, his best mate for seven or eight years. He had watched Nero become a monster.

I asked Ziggy about the LA trip.

'All I can say is that I saw Nero smashing up her phone and chucking her out with my own eyes,' he said. 'We all agreed to pretend that we never saw that, that *that* never happened because, well ... we had to protect Nero, and the girl wasn't necessarily accusing him of anything exactly so ... argh, I don't know. It was a mess,' he said nervously.

When they asked me, 'What are you going to do? Are you going to go to the police? Are you going to tell anyone about him?' I simply replied, 'I just don't know'.

And I didn't.

I spent those nights lying awake in disbelief, trying to process the reality that had been served up to me on a platter. I was having nightmares, really vivid ones, ones where I'd finally forgive him and he'd just shame me again in front of everyone. When I was awake, all I felt was betrayal. When I was asleep, all I felt was betrayal. Somehow, against the odds, I was barely alive, with a dagger sliced through my chest.

I was in so much pain. The revelations were so bright that they were blinding.

And it didn't stop there.

Ruby could see that all the information was burning me out and told me, 'Maybe just tell everyone ... no more Nero news for now ...' I agreed.

Until Jude called me the following day.

'There's someone you need to talk to.'

'Who?' I asked.

'Sabrina.'

Comics

The relationship between the Joker and Harley Quinn is something that is sought after too often. When we think of them, we think of passion, we think of obsession, we think of that us-against-the-world, undying, once-in-a-lifetime type of love. What's worse is that we all have our Joker, or we all have our Harley Quinn, to some degree or another.

There is a twin-flame soul tie that feels unbreakable, connecting you to that one person who no matter the tears, betrayal and attempts to leave, you always end up back in each other's lives, at each other's throats, in each other's arms.

After being abused, after learning the signs, the cycles, I began looking at them a little differently. I wanted to learn the true story of the Joker and Harley Quinn. I wanted to know the truth behind one of the most romanticised and related-to fictional relationships.

I read through articles, the original comics and different forums for hours, and what did I find?

The Joker used Harley as a plaything that he could drop and pick up whenever he wished, abusing her for years while she thought of him as her partner.

When she finally decided to leave, he'd always find a way to manipulate her and weasel his way back in, each time filling her with empty promises and playing sinister tricks on her, crushing her spirit and belief in their love.

In one of their darker scenes, the Joker kidnaps Harley and takes her to a dark location. He insists that he created her, that she is nothing without him. He threatens to mutilate her by cutting off her face. 'All you'll see is red,' he tells her. He plays a prank on her, knocking her unconscious and making her wake up to a red cloak wrapped around her head, so she believes he harmed her.

In another, the Joker drags Harley down to a cellar. When she asks if he's going to kill her, he says, 'I'm going to lock you down here with the others.'

'What others?' she asks.

43

The other woman can also be a friend

I sat in front of the large mirror in our Los Angeles living room, beneath the chandelier, while Ruby scrubbed shampoo into my hair, trying to relieve it from the spray colour damage.

I sat there, listening to Sabrina's voice notes after Jude had put us in touch. The first thing I noticed was how sweet and attractive her ultra-feminine high voice and French accent was. I thought about how that would be such a turn-on for Nero. What a perfect escape it would be from all the screaming and shouting with me at home: a sweet, younger, beautiful Parisian girl to escape into from all the stress wifey was giving him at home. Aww.

'No, that's a total lie. We slept together maybe five or six times in LA. I was with him the whole time. He told me you weren't his girlfriend. I asked him this many times.' Sabrina's voice note played in her broken English.

As the phone was raised to my ear in one hand, I stared into my reflection in the mirror, deep into my own eyes. I looked dead behind them. With one deep breath, I raised my other fist and punched the mirror hard, shattering glass everywhere. Shards of it stuck into my knuckles. It felt so good because I could finally feel *something*. After such a heavy period of numbing myself and dissociating to deal with all these truths, I could finally feel again. Pain! Oh, how I loved the feeling of home, and pain was home to me.

Isn't it crazy how it's proven that humans just want to feel at home? How we just want what we're used to, even if it's bad for us? Even if it hurts? We're habitual, us humans. And I think *that's* the worst curse that God put in our biological nature.

Maybe that's why I was willingly sat there sending voice notes back and forth to the girl my ex cheated on me with, with a cut-up hand bleeding out and a shattered mirror all around me.

I returned to reality as the shattered mirror returned to being intact, my reflection put back together once more.

I played the next voice note.

'I dare myself to lie to you. Women are the most important, beautiful things in the world to me and I am so sorry you had to deal with this disgusting perverted narcissist,' she continued.

When I humoured her with the story about how Nero had said she'd forced herself on him, she laughed in disbelief. 'Oh my God!' she cried.

She told me about the time she was in *our* house. The planetarium projector was on was because he took her in there, onto our bed, and was pleading with her to stay with him. She said she could see my shoes and clothes everywhere, and it just felt wrong. He could no longer deny we were together.

So that time I'd arrived home early in the morning and I randomly let out to him, 'Has Sabrina been here?', despite the fact that she didn't even live in the same city … she had. He must've thought I was a fucking witch.

Everything was starting to add up. Everything.

'He never told you he had a girlfriend?' I asked her.

'Not at first, but then I would figure it out from Instagram and sometimes he would message me from some weird accounts. When I would ask him about you he would tell me some sad story about how you are crazy. Actually, when I saw him in Paris, he spent the whole night talking about you. Now that I *really* think about it … he always talked about you until he would fall asleep. It's funny because he would talk about how crazy you are and I would feel bad for him, and then he would talk the same amount about how much he loved you. He would be on so many drugs, I thought he was just some poor confused boy in some toxic relationship.'

I sighed a lot.

She sighed a lot.

Sabrina told me how on the night she'd ended up at our apartment, just hours before I walked in the door, he was telling the whole room how I 'hit myself and then threatened to call the police' if he tried to leave. Just as I went silent with shock, computing in my brain what she was telling me, I could see that very morning in my head.

I remember feeling so weird when I walked through the door that day. I remember making fucking pizza for everyone, like a stupid idiot trying to reason with the energy in the room and figure out why there was so much intensity directed at me. I helped clean Nero and his vomit up, and put him to bed . . . No wonder nobody ever stood up for me. He convinced them all I was *fucking* insane. Dangerously insane. Scary insane. Hits herself insane and threatens to frame him insane. Needs to be sectioned insane. Something out of *Shutter Island* insane. Not even just insane, evil.

He was creating a *smear campaign* against me *this entire time.*

Smear campaign

A smear campaign is a technique a narcissist implements against their victim by hijacking the narrative about their relationship, creating embellishments and lies to discredit the victim and destroy their reputation.

Do I think they believed it? To an extent. I don't think it's possible they would have bought that this dominant rockstar, who was travelling the world and having coke blowouts every night, was being held hostage by some girl *he* always begged and whined for back into his life. Everyone individually had their own selfish gain in turning a blind eye. It was easier to convince even themselves that they fell for his story. It made them feel like victims too, like they weren't bad people. That they were nothing like him.

And the icing on the cake? At Paris Fashion Week, the same night I took my heel and clawed at Jude's back in the drunken brawl to defend Nero, we saw Sabrina. When she departed from our awkward run-in, and I asked what Nero had said to her, he'd told me, 'She asked me for a cig and I said no.' Turns out that was lie.

'Ignore her, she's a weirdo! That's what he said,' Sabrina told me.

My heart really sank at that one. I was literally sitting with my legs over his lap, in matching outfits. But it really didn't matter what I looked like on the outside, I was still a clown.

She sent me some heartfelt messages after applauding my strength and sending me love, and to be honest, she was as genuine and honest as she could have been. I thanked her for the truth. I wanted that for years – I just so badly wanted to know the truth.

After that, I had to block her. I just couldn't manage seeing her name or face anywhere whenever I opened my phone.

I told Ruby I had to make more one call.

I had to call Nero.

Trust me, I knew there was no point. I was well past the point of thinking I'd achieve anything besides further hurting and frustrating myself – but I still had to do it.

I needed him to know that I knew.

I needed him to know that despite that time, all the effort he put into covering up the affair, that I knew.

Why?

I guess I just wanted him to be scared. I wanted him to revel in that very fear he had inside him, knowing what I would turn into if I knew the truth. What the love I had for him would turn into. Only he and I knew how big this betrayal was, only he had looked into my eyes as they were big and watery, pleading with him to tell me the truth time and time again over these past *years*.

I wanted him to know that I finally knew who he really was. So I clicked on his name.

And as the phone rang on speaker, lying on the table in front of me, I braced myself for impact.

He answered. He didn't speak.

A few moments of silence passed. We were both trying to gauge the danger of the situation.

I was certain he would be recording the call, considering all the abuse speculations online and his recent failed attempt at damage control.

But I didn't care.

I didn't have the time or energy to be tactful or smart.

This moment was too real for me.

I inhaled a deep breath. 'Nero.'

'Livia . . .'

There was more silence and then I just let it out. 'You fucked Sabrina.'

And after one last pause . . . he laughed.

He laughed.

'Why are you calling me, Livia? We're broken up, remember?' he began to taunt me, but I could hear the fear in his tone. He was performing. There were people there.

The more he continued, I realised, *he was terrified.*

I hung up the phone.

I looked up at Ruby just as she walked over and put her arm around my back. She gave me a half hug as my ass sat firmly in the seat where I'd just spun through a hundred different emotions.

'Do you feel better?' she said as she rubbed my shoulder, resting her head on top of my wet blonde hair.

I took a moment to check with my body, and for some reason ... I did.

The morning after, while staring at the picture of Nero dressed up as the Joker on social media – a clear attempt to taunt me after having seen my outfit on Ruby's Story – I finally filed my police report.

I had been reluctant to do so for so long. I'd convinced myself that I didn't want to put an ethnic minority through the system. As a woman of colour myself, it just felt wrong. I still had some strange sense of loyalty to the man I was once with. The man I had loved.

But it was all just excuses because what he did to me was wrong. The loyalty I was holding on to was a fucking illusion.

Protecting Nero had made me delusional. Now I had to accept that there was never even a single thing between us that was genuine or sacred. It was the hardest pill to swallow.

I had to start grieving the person he'd made me believe existed. Do you know how hard it is to grieve someone you're in love with? Someone who's still alive, but the version you loved has died?

Waking up from the Nero coma was severe. Untangling myself from his web felt never-ending, a perpetual unwinding.

I felt like a newborn baby. Naked and vulnerable, born into this world again, crying for something to believe in.

44

You can be free, really free

Jude, who was based in New York, continued to stay in touch with me. In fact, he insisted on helping me in one way or another while I figured out what I wanted to do next. I decided to take a break from alcohol, which meant I had drifted slightly from Ruby and Shay. As much as they sympathised with me through and through, they could not *empathise* with what I'd endured. Nobody could.

Ruby was still my rock and biggest supporter, but I couldn't make other people who hadn't endured a narcissist understand what I was going through. After some advice from my mentor and guardian angel – Cherry – I agreed that it wasn't fair to expect anyone who hasn't *actually* been through it to get it.

'That's fine. It's completely fine if they don't get it. They still love you,' she'd told me.

Speaking to Cherry was always like time travel, as if I was speaking to a more healed version of myself a few more years into her journey, and vice versa for her.

So while I spent a lot of my time feeling lonely because Ruby was tipsy at a party somewhere in the Hills, or Shay was getting high with some of his guys, Jude was somebody who I naturally gravitated towards.

It felt weird being supported. I almost felt undeserving of it, like it was too good to be true. Even though I knew that was just the voice that Nero had instilled into my head, I'd be lying if I said it wasn't hard to feel worthy of much right then.

I wasn't wary of Cherry because our friendship wasn't for her own gain.

But Jude . . . Jude kind of scared me, in a way that was all too familiar.

His dark, masculine energy was incredibly alluring for a woman who had just been occupied by one just like it – someone who she was still cleansing herself of . . . As I always say, we *like* what we *know*.

When he spoke to me over FaceTime, his charisma and magnetism made it impossible not to warm to him. He was genuinely beautiful. He wore a curious look on his face, dark skin over chiselled cheekbones and a strong jawline matched with a bright, childish smile. A mischievous smile, the contagious kind, decorated by a perfect set of plump lips.

Though he was tall and muscular with a fair bit of facial hair, he had this youthful look about him, almost like an air of innocence – the butter-wouldn't-melt type. The sort of face that could get you in all kinds of trouble, while simultaneously preventing him from getting in any.

As November began, the leaves covered the pavements in shades of orange and brown as what Americans call 'fall' was very much living up to its name.

Everyone was having the same conversations with me, asking the same question: What did I want to do?

By this point, we were all convinced that I *needed* to put my story out there.

Out to the world, to his fans, to everyone.

The pictures.

The videos.

The messages.

The confession.

The NDA.

Hospital records.

Police reports.

The full picture.

Nobody pushed me. Everyone told me to take my time, that it was my decision, but deep down I knew it would always have to go that way.

The decision didn't come to me at any significant moment. Rather, it was always there, a seed at the back of my mind, growing slowly. It had been planted the first time Nero laid hands on me, that first slap in the summer when I had just found out I was pregnant.

Sometimes I would compare that incident to one of the last times he laid hands on me. The fateful first slap instantly followed him crying into my stomach, begging me, kissing me all over for forgiveness.

On the last day in the Airbnb during lockdown, I lay there with my face stinging from the aftermath of him slapping the same exact cheek. Instead of crying and explaining himself, he was weighing down on top of me. Instead of apologising, he was digging his fingers into either side of my neck so hard that it left literal finger marks.

Puts a lot into perspective, doesn't it.

That same perspective rang through my ears over and over again. I could picture both the events and everything that happened in between *so* vividly, replaying beneath my eyelids like a film before I slept at night. I could feel the touch of his lips against the skin of my stomach; the impact of his hand as it met my face. I could hear the sound of him sobbing, apologising in disbelief; the look of rage on his face while he ruptured my throat with his bare thumbs.

I was in a constant state of dissociation. It felt like time travel. While living out these haunting memories, if someone so much as closed a door with a slight slam or let out a laugh from another room, I'd feel panicked and agitated. Ready to fight. Or flee. Or freeze.

I will never forget my first real panic attack. I'd experienced some form of panic attacks with Nero, when I'd break down and couldn't find my way back to reality after one of his outbursts.

But this was different. My brain had entered a new phase since leaving him. If I wasn't always on edge or hyper aware of everyone and everything around me, I was zoned out and unavailable. Neither felt good. Both exhausted me and made me want to sleep. I slept *a lot*.

It happened at a party, with Ruby and a group of friends. The house music blared throughout the squeaky-clean minimalist beach club as everyone danced in their bikinis, heels and trunks. People spilled champagne as they shouted drunk nothings over the music into each other's ears. I sat on a chair in my bikini and shorts, talking with some random Scouse guy who was telling me something about my eyes. I wasn't listening. I was focusing on Ruby, who stood opposite me by the Jacuzzi. She was talking back and forth with one of the guys we were with. I could tell they were drunk from their body language. I noticed her expression get less friendly, as if she was offended. She began using her hands more, and all I could imagine was him hitting her.

I began to feel light-headed as my diaphragm tightened up. I was confused as to why I suddenly felt so uncomfortable, so I turned to the Scouse guy who was still talking and asked for a cigarette. I tried to inhale it deeply to shake the anxiety running through me, but it only began to intensify.

When I looked back over at Ruby, they were having a full-blown argument. I took a few steps over to ask her if she was okay, but she was too engaged and intoxicated to even acknowledge me. Everyone else was oblivious; nobody even noticed there was an issue.

Until everyone started noticing me.

'Are you okay?' said one of the girls in the Jacuzzi.

I just nodded and scurried back over to my seat. I must have been visibly upset.

'Are you good, Livia? the Scouse guy asked.

I picked up a can of Coca-Cola and tried to dampen my increasingly dry mouth before someone walked past the back of me, slightly brushing my hair.

I jumped up as I got a fright. Suddenly everyone within three metres of us looked at me.

I grabbed my purse and ran towards the front door. I felt like I was hallucinating, as if I was being chased by someone with a knife. This feeling of impending doom. I moved faster and faster until I booked an Uber.

By the time I got in the ride I was heaving and holding my head. I couldn't take a full deep breath – it was like something was stopping me every time I tried, and that in turn filled me with more panic.

I called Cherry and she explained to me that I was having a panic attack. She was calm and that made me feel calm, as she told me it was all going to be okay. She encouraged me to go home and relax. It relieved me that I wasn't dying – because it honestly felt like I might have been.

My eyelids felt heavy. My brain was *exhausted* from the ordeal. I lay down in the taxi and dozed off for the rest of the journey.

Once I got home, I jumped straight into bed. When I woke up, I remembered what Cherry told me in the call. Panic attacks are a symptom of CPTSD – Complex Post Traumatic stress disorder. It's similar to PTSD, except the traumatic event was a repeated trauma.

I knew I needed help. I wasn't coping. The whole reason I stopped drinking was because the hangxiety wasn't bearable. I needed all the dopamine I could get, quite frankly. I didn't really go out much anymore and when I did, I felt too sensitive for the environment because I was sober. I was constantly struggling to feel normal like everyone around me.

As the days went on, I couldn't even get out of bed. I was depressed. Another symptom of CPTSD. I slept no earlier than 6 a.m. Most nights I'd be up on the phone to Jude for hours. Although he was meant to be this guy who hated my ex and wanted to help me seek justice for his own benefit, we clicked on an emotional level. He was a Cancer – as water signs, we always do.

He grew to care for me more every day, and it made me feel more and more safe to open up to him. Making sure I ate, staying sober or just checking in at random times, there wasn't a day he'd forget about me. Sometimes he'd stay on the phone to me for hours into the morning while I'd shed a tear or two, sharing my most painful memories with him.

'You're fucking amazing, Livia—' he'd say. I'd laugh and interrupt him, saying thank you from the nervousness that would gather in my heart from the unfamiliarity of being complimented. The feeling made me feel a bit sick.

But he'd insist. 'No, you listen to me. I see all the healing shit you post on your Instagram and I'm not just saying this – you are one of the most amazing, strong and resilient women I have ever witnessed in my life. You are beautiful inside and out – you are powerful. I swear, Livia, you are so powerful. Who else could go through all of this and still be so gentle and uplifting to others? A blessing to this world . . .'

I smiled deep and long.

I hadn't thought about that . . . ever.

Jude did that a lot: *he empowered me.*

I had made an all-girls' Instagram for women to share their trauma with each other, offer advice and comment without feeling unsafe or judged. I even asked every girl to send me a video explaining why they wanted to join the page, to protect everyone else in there. I would endlessly share all the resources I found about narcissism and trauma. It gave me purpose. It helped me just as much as it helped them, each with their own heartache, looking for someone to relate to.

When I wasn't up all night talking to Jude, I was obsessively researching more and more about NPD. One night I came across a Narcissistic Abuse Recovery Coach. I booked in for a Zoom therapy session with him right away.

Ishaan was amazing. He'd been in a relationship with two narc partners and was raised by a narc. He'd attempted to take his own life twice as a result of CPTSD.

In our first session, I sobbed over the camera, sharing every detail of what I'd suffered.

'I feel broken. I feel like he has damaged me ... Like I am damaged goods. I pee really frequently. When I eat, I get a stomach ache because I have IBS now. I can't sleep on time and then I sleep through the whole day. The nightmares are never ending. I'm growing distant from my best friend because I'm sober and she's always partying, and for some reason that triggers me. I have a really bad neck and shoulder ache. I can't even leave the house most days, it overwhelms me so much to be outside ... and I'm constantly exhausted ... Oh wait ... did I mention I've started getting migraines? I literally never had them before and now I get them so bad, I can't even move. I have to lie in the silence and in the dark and—'

'Livia, slow down ...' he said. 'It's okay. I'm listening and I'm not going anywhere.'

I snapped out of my emotional rant and looked back into the camera.

'You are strong and you can choose to get justice any way you wish. You are free now,' Ishaan told me.

Right after my first session I already felt so much lighter.

I was talking to someone who could do more than just sympathise with me. I zoned out, staring out of the window to soak just a little longer in the peace of mind I'd been granted.

I excitedly picked up my phone to call Jude, but he'd already texted me four minutes ago.

'PAKISTANI PRINCESS, WAS ISHAAN EVERYTHING WE HOPED FOR?'

I smiled, realising he'd remembered to text me at the exact time my call ended. The little things felt so inflated. The bar was so low, it was in hell.

I picked up the phone and called him right away.

'Miss Dalia!' he answered happily, 'Asalamalaikoum,' he attempted to greet me in Arabic. 'You know my grandparents would be so happy if I married a Pakistani girl? They're Indian you know.'

His jokes had got increasingly flirty, but I didn't mind. I just brushed it off with an eye roll and giggle. 'Shut up, Jude.'

'So tell me everything. Wait – let me go somewhere I can hear you better and give you all my attention.' I heard him leave a busy space for a quieter environment and he exhaled as he sat down. 'Okay, my favourite part of the day: tell me all about what's happening inside Livia's beautiful brain,' he said eagerly.

So, I lay back on the bed and did exactly that. He challenged a few of the things Ishaan had said, making sure he was the right fit to become my therapist.

'Send me this guy's page again, I just wanna check him out,' he said. He was almost protective of me – but not overbearing. I guess he really wanted the best for me. He would always give me advice on how to detach, how to ground myself, how to have healthier habits, even sharing his own traumas.

Jude had been through a lot, just like me. He understood what it is to have darkness inflicted upon you by another, with love being the avenue used.

After I told him all about the session, he asked me how I felt.

'I feel free,' I told him.

'You are free,' he repeated back to me.

'I . . . want to speak my truth . . . I'm ready,' I told him.

'You *are* free!' he said once more.

45

Freedom day

My days were filled with a rotation of calls between Cherry, myself and Jude, until we eventually created a group chat for pure convenience. Everything felt hectic and exciting. I had a team and they were all brilliant.

There was a lot of deliberation on the best way to share my story of abuse with the world. We knew there were a lot of *wrong* ways. We didn't want it to go over anyone's heads or get brushed off as social media messiness. We wanted to do it justice.

In terms of narcissistic abuse, a lot of women's stories are brushed under the rug, or they are accused of attention seeking. That was simply terrifying – disgusting.

'You will be a guinea pig for so many women,' Cherry told me. 'It will have such a ripple effect, so many women will have the courage to speak out because of you. There's someone I'd like to share those videos with, Livia . . . If you'd give me permission, I could even have him drive over to my home to watch them if that would be more comfortable.'

Cherry wanted to share the video of the attack with her head of PR. They had worked together for ten years. She told me that her relationship with him was special and she knew he would do the right thing because he also happened to be in charge of Nero's PR. He was overseeing the entire album campaign.

He dropped him right away.

He actually dropped him.

Shortly after that, Axel Dupont did too. Side-eye.

Dupont, big showbiz Axel Dupont who gave his life to desperately make Nero a star, Dupont who knew the entire time what he was – he dropped him. After all that … he dropped him.

I believed in my story. I believed in my evidence.

Most importantly, I believed in the truth.

Jude asked me to send him my initial statement that I was planning to present on social media, giving a short timeline of events of what happened. It turned out to be eight pages long. I couldn't help but trauma dump everywhere. I simply didn't know how to tell the shortened version of the story. It was too real and raw for me.

'It's okay, don't worry. I'm going to work on this with some people I know.'

He gathered more people to help, reaching out to women's charities and organisations around London, specifically ones that were culturally relevant and involved in the music scene. He introduced me to these great women and with each introduction I had an overwhelming sense of appreciation for the amount of time and kindness each had to offer me.

He had a few female writers and friends in journalism and PR, carefully contacting each for advice. One evening he jumped on a call with three of them for four hours. After they introduced themselves to me, Jude said, 'Livia, I'm going to work on shortening your statement with them. You can jump back in whenever you want.'

And the few times I silently re-entered, Jude was carefully crafting the statement.

'Guys, she really needs this,' he said. 'We need to make sure we don't miss a single detail. We need her to be heard – it needs to be executed perfectly. Livia deserves to be believed.'

There was only one thing I cut after reading the final version of the initial statement: the bit about the sexual nature of the abuse. I had referenced the screwdriver incident when he became aroused but, I guess at that time, I just didn't feel like that was something I wanted to share with the world. I also knew that his life would be over if people knew that he was more than a woman beater, that he is, in fact, a deeply twisted and perverted man who got turned on by it.

I knew the abuse allegations could jeopardise a lot for him, but that was his own fault. I simply brought what went on behind closed doors into the light.

'He can say what he did to me with chest to the whole world!' I said to Jude when I explained how Nero thought the abuse was justified.

But I didn't know if I'd be able to handle the whole world knowing the depth of just how far that wicked mind could travel into the demonic abyss. I didn't know if my conscience could cope. I was worried that someone might hurt him real bad.

At the end of the day, I did actually love him.

The next step after perfecting the statement was perfecting the roll-out.

I made a private Instagram page with Jude, Cherry, Ruby and a few other girlfriends to give their opinions. We did a trial launch there first.

First, I posted a shorter statement on my main page, with the summary that I was finally ready to speak out on the mental, physical and psychological abuse I'd experienced in my relationship. The slide had a few of the more graphic pieces of evidence and directed viewers to my Instagram Story for the full account and the rest of the evidence.

I wanted to make it as educational as possible. I was passionate about spreading not just my truth but also knowledge for other women out there to recognise similar themes in their own relationships and protect themselves. I highlighted screenshots of texts, ones where he was controlling me, threatening me and berating me, with references to terms like 'gaslighting' or 'manipulation and control'. Next was a series of photos of my injuries, the videos of the attack and then some examples of his behaviour towards me on social media since I'd left him. Again, I wanted people to see the patterns. The delusion. The grandiosity. The revoked confessions. The mocking.

The fact that his entire Instagram had eighteen pictures of just him and the dog.

And the fact that his beloved album that was titled *Love Spelled Backwards is Evil*, the album name he'd got a tattoo of and a whole custom chain made by a bespoke artist for, he changed at the last minute to taunt me.

He changed the fucking album name to Jefe.

He knew that the only way he could hurt me was through the purest thing ever: my love for that fucking dog. So he rubbed it in my face in each and every way possible. He even covered the entire diameter of his back with an enormous tattoo of Jefe's name.

After a few tweaks to the order of importance of things, we were ready. Next, we just had to choose *when*.

'I think it needs to be before the album drops,' Jude explained. 'Like you said, there's yet another song about you being killed on there.'

'I don't want all the young female fans to listen and sing along with that shit. Oh, the thought of it makes me sick, Jude,' I told him.

But the album release was tomorrow.

Which meant the story would have to come out *today*.

'If you're ready, do it, Livia! You've got this!'

I remember counting the exact number of posts, making sure I didn't miss any from the sequence as I stood opposite Ruby in a baggy T-shirt. She was sitting on the edge of the bed pouring two cups of champagne. My heartbeat was so loud, I could have sworn that with each pump, the floor shook. My hands were shaking so much I could barely piece it all together, but I held my phone tight as I counted the last of the posts, breathing deep and heavy.

'17, 18 ...'

This was it.

This was the moment I'd been waiting for. In some ways I felt like I had been waiting for this moment my entire life. For every time I didn't stand up for myself. For every time I was walked all over, covered and trodden in dirt. This was more than just speaking out against Nero. This was more than just justice. This was my freedom day.

'19, 20 . . .'

This was me reclaiming my identity. This was me choosing me. This was the inner child, the lost little girl who so desperately needed tending to, finally being found after years of being locked in a dark, forgotten cupboard, leaping into my arms as I rescued her.

'21, 22 . . .'

This was really it. The phoenix was flying high above all the ashes below, in those ashes that scattered out all the demons, and oh, did she breathe fire and fucking burn each and every last one of them. She did it all by herself. She always could.

She always knew, eventually, she would.

And she did.

Lighting the skies up with violent tones of orange, blazing reds, violets, mixed with indigo blue, she breathed fire into the sunset as she broke free and screamed wildly, her wings lifting her into the very skies she created herself.

'I DID IT!!!!!!!!!!!!!' I screamed to Ruby.

She shot up off the bed and we both danced on the spot, hugging with one arm.

'Oh my God, babes, you did it!!!!! Here, you are allowed just a sip!!'

I took a baby sip of champagne as a FaceTime from Jude came in on my phone. He was back in New York, holding a glass of wine and we cheersed through the camera, all three of us.

'You should be so fucking proud of yourself, baby girl. *This* is your freedom day!'

'Yes! Today marks freedom day! Today the ...' I looked down at my phone.

I hadn't even realised that the date was 11/11.

1111

1111 is regarded as a message from your angels or the universe that you're on the right path. It's a sign to keep going, to trust the direction you're moving in, that everything is falling into place.

46

Impact

More than 1 million views on my post in twelve hours.

Dropped by his record label.

Dropped by his PR.

Dropped by his management.

Album cancelled.

Blocked by over seventy-five per cent of his monthly listeners on Spotify.

Thousands of news articles, podcasts, videos, blog posts, debates, tweets, messages, comments, likes, reshares and reposts.

Tears were streaming down my face as I scrolled through the thousands of messages, but I couldn't feel them.

I was overwhelmed by the level of support I was receiving. I couldn't even get through all the messages before I refreshed and twenty more came in. Everyone was outraged. Everyone cared so fucking much.

People really cared. About me. They cared about what

I'd gone through. They didn't try to silence me, gaslight me, pay me off or cover it up. It confirmed that all the pain couldn't be processed until this very moment, until this many people processed it with me. Yes, it was wrong. It was all so wrong.

What I had suffered was wrong.

All my love and all my pain was all wrong.

I was a victim, yes, but finally, I was a survivor.

Life did not feel real.

Celebrities from all over the world reached out. People who even Nero was a fan of. People who had backed him. Other hip-hop artists. Males who wanted to show their support. Some of the biggest pop stars on the planet. Then followed an unimaginable avalanche of women *and men* sharing their stories with me: what they'd endured, what they'd survived, them recognising the same behaviours and patterns.

What hit me most was the victims who sent me photographs of their abuse with long messages stating that, because of me, they had found the courage to finally leave.

Those messages would make me blubber like a baby. I'd sob from disbelief.

The fact that my story had the power to save another victim in theirs.

That was truly the biggest blessing; the best feeling I've ever felt.

I felt like a true alchemist, transforming pain into power.

The beauty of karma was breathtaking. She was such a vision to see. A sight for sore eyes indeed.

Of course, Nero reacted. In a video looking worse for wear, he recorded himself the following morning saying that he'd been set up. In fact, he even called it the 'biggest defamation in history' (pause to laugh). He claimed I was simply obsessed with ruining his album; that none of it was true.

Nobody paid it any attention; my evidence was simply irrefutable. And if the video wasn't enough there was a video of *his* confession. If the confession wasn't enough, there were the pictures of burst lips, cuts, bruises all over my body. If the pictures weren't enough, there were texts, texts where he laughs at the fact he kicked me in my stomach, texts of him admitting he abused me for years. If even that wasn't enough, there was the NDA sent by his lawyer offering me money to stay hush. If still that was not enough, there were hospital records of my injuries matching a police report.

But the wicked thing about this earth is, sometimes, for women, it just isn't enough. Nothing is enough.

We live in a society where women were nothing but baby-making machines less than a couple of hundred years ago. No rights. Nothing. We have come a long way, but boy do we have so far to go.

When was the last time women felt safe to go outside alone late at night? Could you imagine feeling safe enough to walk in the street at 3 a.m.? What if I asked you, as a woman, what would you do if men didn't exist for twenty-four hours? I bet you'd wear what you want. Stay out as long as you want. Act how you want.

I don't think I know more than two women in my life who haven't been sexually assaulted at some point. Whether groped, taken advantage of drunk, raped or coerced, the violence against women comes from men. Male-on-female violence. In fact, it's an epidemic. A war.

Two women a week are killed by a current or former partner in England and Wales.

An average of seventy women in the US are shot and killed by an intimate partner every month.

One in three women experience domestic violence at some point in their lives.

Six women are killed by a man every hour around the world.

And with generations of fatherless men, and women with little self love or empowerment as a result of trauma being passed down, men and boys rarely ever care about women and what we suffer at the hands of them. There's a dire need for accountability.

And the silence among men is deafening.

We create them in our bodies.

There were maybe just three per cent of people who took Nero's side, and they were just misogynists, men who have a deep hate for women because they have a deep hate for themselves, and they couldn't stand to see a woman be empowered. Or they were seventeen-year-old fans who were trolling for fun and didn't care about either of us.

A lot of weirdos exist on the internet.

I had to quickly learn to grow a thick skin since so many people suddenly felt entitled to give me an opinion on my private life, but that experience in itself was rewarding. A true sense of detachment overtook me in regard to being judged – especially because of how little the fraction of hate was in comparison to the passion displayed online to support me. It gave me hope that the majority of people who have half a brain are the only ones with opinions that mattered.

It hurt me to think of the women who don't have a video.

The women who don't have anything but the sorrow, memories and CPTSD to last them a lifetime.

'*It shouldn't take a fucking video to be believed,*' I repeated to *everyone* I spoke about it to.

In my disbelief of the fortunate turn of events, all I could think about was karma. Nothing else made sense. How could I be so fortunate to receive this much love and validation in my deepest and most vulnerable moment?

It was like Nero had a bank that had been filled with all his karma, from each intention with each action to match, gaining him coins and coins of bad karma, while my bank was filled with the genuine care and intention I poured into that relationship. And now we were living directly off that. I was a millionaire in good karma and he was bankrupt, in debt to bad karma.

I got karma tattooed on my middle finger. I learned that, in life, you may be able to delay karma, but you can never escape it. I learned that your karma will protect you at the end of the day, even if the day is really long. And no matter fucking what, *every* dog has their day. *Karma does not miss.* That was so comforting to me; it made me feel connected to the universe and the realisation that we are in fact never alone, especially not in our biggest grievances.

And though I felt proud and enamoured by the cards fate had dealt, psychologically I still had a big debt myself to pay for what I'd endured over the last three years.

After my story was put out, I agreed to celebrate with the girls and actually enjoy LA again. I was bombarded everywhere I went by people showing warmth and coming over to share the strength they witnessed in me, or their own personal stories of abuse. It was like I was famous. But it was better than fame. Fuck fame. I had *actually* made a positive difference to real people's lives.

I was inspiring.

The girls and I headed out to celebrate at a house party in Laguna Beach. It was much needed and I finally wanted to have a drink and let my hair down. I finally felt safe to. We entered the party down some stairs, leading to a beautiful outdoor pool. The humid Californian air was complemented by a night-time breeze, with gorgeous palm trees towering over us, wrapped in thousands of fairy lights.

I was carefully walking down each step in my black mule heels and a white sparkly mini dress when my phone began to ring.

Nero was calling me.

'Ruby, go down, I'm just gonna be one sec!' I shouted over as she nodded, excited to get in because she really missed us having fun together.

I still hadn't blocked him and I had a few reasons. A part of me knew that in a public and criminal battle, it was better to keep evidence of everything to protect myself. I wanted as many receipts as possible.

But deep down, secretly, a part of me was still . . .

Still hoping for an apology. Or something that resembled it. I don't know if it was hope or if it was the soreness of my heart *still* longing to be healed . . .

Grief-stricken mermaids were swimming in the aortic valves of my heart, singing songs of agony as they bathed in the blood of a love once alive, seeking some kind of resolution that could relieve them, so that they wouldn't need to do things the long and painful way – suicide. They had to be killed so they could rebirth into who they really needed to be. I needed to sharpen my heart.

So I grabbed that blade and I did exactly that.

I declined the call.

I wish I could tell you that I then took my ass downstairs to boogie, but this story is too real. Instead, I started having a panic attack. I sat on the bench by the beachfront pool as the ocean waves crashed in the distance, stars embellishing the sky above me.

'What if he's going to kill himself or something? I'm scared. I feel so bad, I feel so, so bad – I've ruined his life,' I cried down the phone to Cherry.

She quickly and firmly snapped me out of it.

'Livia, you are a victim of domestic violence, you have been gaslit. This is what gaslighting does to you. Nero isn't going to kill himself because he's a narcissist, and he loves himself *way* too much to ever do that. *He* ruined his life!'

'But his career was everything to him, I just feel really bad—'

'Do you think he felt bad? Did he ever feel bad? When he almost killed you, he never felt bad, not a single day. Even now he's denying it like he never abused you,' she interrupted me.

And she was right. I could see it again. The vision of me through his eyes. How helpless and innocent I was to him, lying on the ground in front of him as he *chose* to inflict more and more pain on me, my body, my heart and my soul.

He knew what he was doing.

If I was going to do this, I had to know what I was doing too.

Our intentions create our karma, and our karma creates the world around us. And my bank was very full.

I decided to be kind to myself and headed back home. After a long journey back, I entered to find Shay asleep on the sofa. I quietly removed my heels and covered him with a furry blanket.

He opened his eyes and smiled. 'Thanks, Mum,' he groaned.

I tried to hold in my giggle as his eyes widened and he started laughing with me.

'How was your night? Where's Rubes?' he quizzed me as he yawned, re-entering reality.

'It's still early! I just wanted to come home. I did try to enjoy it but—'

'What happened? Something happened, right?' he asked as he moved over, making room for me.

'Is it that obvious?' I sat down, my eyes welling up with tears.

'Aww, Livia. What's happened, man?' He put his arm around me and rubbed my shoulder.

'Nero called. No, I didn't answer, but it just made me feel guilty and I couldn't even enjoy my night or celebrate. I don't know what he wanted to say and I don't know why I even felt bad. I just hate that he's controlling my life still.'

'Yo, freedom day was *today*, babe. Relax! You didn't answer and that's what you should be proud of, right? Everything just happened, give yourself a wee chance to process it all.'

I nodded my head.

'It's okay, man, you're good. Look at me . . .' He studied my face for a second, lifting his sleeve and wiping under my nose.

'Sorry.' I laughed pathetically.

God, that was something straight out of a cringe rom-com.

'You still look beautiful,' he said quietly. Not even a second passed before he quickly interrupted himself. 'Yeah, okay where're those make-up wipes? One of your drawers?' he asked as he walked over to mine and Ruby's room.

'Yeah, or maybe just out in our bathroom!' I yelled back.

He sat back down, rubbing my face with the wipe as I undid my updo, pulling out the pins in my hair. I'd never quite realised how nurturing Shay was; he had an almost feminine side that he wasn't afraid to embrace.

He listened to me rant on about all my feelings as I cried on and off until I fell asleep on the sofa. I woke up the next morning with the fur blanket over me as he lay bare, and a glass of water by my head.

47

You feel like home

Two weeks after freedom day, I had just got out of the shower. It was around 10 p.m. and I was home alone. As I dried my wet hair with a towel and slipped on a baggy T-shirt, I went into the kitchen to switch the kettle on and make some peppermint tea. From the corner of my eye, I saw a shadow appear in the gap beneath the front door. The door had an electric lock with a code, so I knew it wasn't Ruby or Shay because they'd just let themselves straight in.

The person stood there for a moment, almost as if they were hesitant.

Or bracing themselves. But for what?

I was frozen in confusion, but for some reason I didn't feel unsafe.

Rather, just curious.

They knocked and I shot forward immediately. *Who could it even be at this time?*

I opened the door. Almost like it was CGI, in cargos and

a vest, with a suitcase and backpack on either side of him, a huge grin painted across his face, Jude was stood before me.

My jaw dropped open. We didn't do anything besides stare at each other for an entire second. It's like we forgot how to compute.

I leapt forward and hugged him.

'What the fuck, Jude!' I let out as he wrapped his strong arms around my waist, in a firm warm embrace.

He laughed as he picked me up, walking me backwards into the apartment. When he picked me up, it completely revealed my ass, since I was only in a T-shirt, and as he put me back down, his hands gently grazed it by accident. We both pretended like nothing happened.

'How are you? Oh my God, you're in my home!?' I expressed to him joyfully, still in disbelief that he was really back in LA.

'I knew how much you needed me this week, so I hit up Ruby and got your address and made it happen.'

It had been about two weeks since I shared my story. I'd been asked to take part in an incredible documentary series regarding abuse and the music industry. The documentary was a great cause and Nero was only one person who had been held accountable in a series of grown men who had participated in silencing me. The music industry was a *joke* and there were hundreds and thousands of women *just like me* who needed someone to stand up for them, especially those tied in NDAs. I wanted to be the voice to fight for them. Someone *had* to fight for us.

But in prepping for the interviews, I was beginning to crack. Paired with the enormous amount of social media coverage I'd already been inundated with, my mental health was withering away.

'You need to take a break from social media, Livia,' Jude told me earlier that week over the phone. 'There's a never-ending stream of content about you available online right now and all these opinions and conspiracies aren't healthy for you to be delving into all the time.'

'Yeah,' I replied, 'but you don't understand. Nero's saying that in the video he was just trying to reach for his phone to book a taxi—'

'No one believes him. Nero is finished,' he replied bluntly.

'No, but Jude, listen. How can that be possible? How could I have both my phone and his phone when he was twisting my arm! It doesn't even make sense – where would he even get a taxi *to*? He doesn't even have Uber. I book his taxis . . .' I continued on, explaining manically.

'Livia, why are you explaining this to me like you want me to believe you? Why wouldn't I believe you? Nobody cares what this guy has to say . . .'

And the saddest part was, he was right. I was just so used to everyone believing him. I still fell into these states of survival mode where I was so scared that at any moment things would return to their natural order.

'How many hours did you sleep last night?' he asked me.

'I don't know . . . like three or four,' I said.

There was a pause.

'You don't get it. It's impossible not to read what's going on when it's about you, and the most vulnerable parts of you,' I explained. 'There's a conspiracy theory I read somewhere where people are saying we got back together. Would you believe that?' I asked. 'And another person who's pretending they know us and giving their side of the story. That's like the third one now,' I continued. 'Oh, and would you believe the landlord from Waterlight even reached out! A huge paragraph about how she found blood on the mattress and holes in the walls. Wait, and I already told you about the landlords from his new place saying he owes them like £12k in damages and that he destroyed all their designer furniture, right? Or was that Cherry I told . . .?'

I was speaking about it so much that I didn't even know what I told who anymore.

'Livia,' said Jude, 'you're keeping your trauma bond to him alive by reading and obsessing over this. It's keeping the connection to him alive. This is the addiction. You need to stop because he can still feel that shit.'

He was right. I knew that no contact meant more than just no contact with him. It meant not being exposed to him and my trauma in any and every way. *But boy it was so hard to let go.*

'Is there anything I can do for you?' he asked. 'I'm worried about you.'

A tear dropped onto my pillow.

'I just wish you were here, Jude,' I said softly.

And now, here he was. He made my wish come true.

'Are you hungry? Oh my God please, sit down and make yourself at home! I actually made some dhall earlier if you want me to heat you up a plate?'

'I would love some dhall, you gorgeous Pakistani woman,' he said as he sat down on the sofa.

As I added some raita salad to the side of his hot plate

of dhall and rice, I could feel his eyes on me, watching my every move.

I sat down on the sofa next to him and watched him tuck in with plenty of 'mmms'.

'This shit is so good. Thank you, Livia'.

I offered him the sofa for the night but he said he'd already booked a hotel downtown just around the corner. We jumped in a cab that way as we agreed I'd take him over to check in.

In the cab, we stared at each other, with some soft smiles and giggles. I lay sideways across the seat with my sandals off and my feet touching his knees. He took my sock off my foot and placed them in his lap and then began massaging my feet.

'Yo, why do you have the prettiest feet ever? Like this is notttt real!' he shouted excitedly.

His energy was completely different from all the times we'd ran into each other. He was so full of life: hyperactive but blissful. I felt like I'd known him for years. I mean, the amount of stuff we'd gone through together in such a short space of time, it was more than what people go through in ten years of friendship.

I couldn't believe I'd seen this guy as a villain.

As we arrived at the hotel and checked in, he picked me up and playfully lunged me onto the bed – a huge super-king-size bed in the gorgeous old Hollywood Art Deco room.

He got up and ran a bath. 'I have one of these every day, I literally *have* to make sure my hotel rooms have a bathtub,' he shouted from the bathroom.

As I sat on the bed looking around the room, it suddenly hit me. *Wait ... Are we going to fuck?*

By the time he came out of the bath, I'd removed my jacket

and was just in my baggy T-shirt, sitting against the frame of the bed.

He sat down in front of me crossed legged and smiled. We both locked eyes; suddenly things felt very serious.

'We can't have sex,' he let out.

I stayed silent, raising my eyebrows. I smiled, pursing my lips a little and then awkwardly looked away.

What do I even say to that? Do I even want to have sex with him?

'Nah, it's just . . . I'm not taking advantage of you, Livia,' he said, rubbing his hands on my knees gently.

'Taking advantage of me? How?' I asked.

'When I first reached out to you, yeah, I wanted revenge. That was the only thing on my mind. I actually thought to myself, all I need to do is somehow, some way, fuck this girl, and I'll have it over Nero. But Livia . . . I couldn't help but start to care about you, and now you mean a lot to me, so I promised myself before I came here that I wouldn't have sex with you. It's wrong, you don't need that right now. You need me as your friend . . . You need to heal.'

I looked down, nervously picking my lips with my teeth. I listened to every word carefully and then nodded.

I stared up at him, straight into his eyes and told him, 'What you did for me . . . You actually saved me . . . and I just want you to know that I could not have done it without you. Thank you. I'll always love you for that, Jude.'

He stared deep into my emotional eyes with just as much feeling reflecting in his. He removed his big hands from my knees and placed them firmly behind the back of my neck and head. Leaning in, he kissed my lips.

The kiss was long and soft. I savoured every second of it. As we pulled apart, we rested our foreheads together, breathing each other in.

'Would ... you even want to have sex?' he asked, leaning back to see the response on my face.

I rested my back against the headboard and just looked at him for a second.

I spread my legs apart, revealing my purple lacy thong, and then plucked it to the side with one finger to answer him.

He grinned and lunged back in, kissing me again.

The sex was every bit empowering.

It was passionate, not desolate. There was no vacancy; it was over-filled with raw emotion, the most potent of passions. It had purpose. It told a story and it was a part of one too. It felt like gratitude for each other's bodies but it also felt dangerous and hypnotic at the same time.

Most of all, it felt emotional, for both of us.

I felt my eyes tear up a little each time I stared into his too long. The intensity was completely mesmerising, so I'd close my eyes tight as I'd feel them roll just a little, him deepening his pace and keeping his eyes wide open, staring right through my eyelids.

He kissed me hard. He kissed me like the kiss oxygenated him, like he'd die without this.

I couldn't believe I was doing this. I was doing something that was completely against the will of Nero.

It felt so fucking good to do something against the will of Nero. To break free of his control.

I'd spent so many fucking years being conditioned to please him that doing what I wanted to do and going against his wishes, after all the pain he'd put on me, was simply exhil-arating. Euphoric, even.

After we lay in bed together, both equal parts speechless and breathless, we cuddled into each other and beamed. I knew he was just as every bit overwhelmed as I was because he fell asleep on top of my arm just moments after.

Suddenly, I had a flashback to when Nero would do that right after sex when he was coked up. The taste of the chem-icals right under his nose. The stench of Jack Daniels on his tongue. The dampness forming on the sheets from the drugs being sweated out of his system. If I closed my eyes, I was right back there with him.

I got up and washed my face with some cold water, taking a few moments just to breathe.

I couldn't sleep. I was tired but my brain was wide awake while Jude snoozed peacefully next to me. I was scrolling on Instagram when something suddenly came back to me ... That weird account that had reached out to me at one point, the one with all the victims against Nero. The one who had initially refused to speak over the phone.

I racked my brains desperately, trying to remember the name of the account. I scrolled through months of messages – thousands and thousands of them – and, finally, found it. 'Healthygaga6969'.

'Hey!' I sent, pausing while I thought of the right thing to say.

Jude's phone pinged as his screen lit up next to him.

'I just wanted to know if you were okay?' I tapped out. 'Maybe at the time I wasn't ready to hear it fully, but did you ever speak to any of the other girls involved and how are they?'

Jude's phone lit up again.

I froze.

My eyes scanned the room for a second. Jude's light snores indicated he was very much asleep.

I stared back at my screen, selected a red love heart emoji and clicked send.

His phone lit up a third time.

My heart thudding, I carefully stretched my arm over his head and grabbed his phone off the side cabinet. The phone was locked of course, but there were three Instagram notifications.

They weren't Instagram notifications addressed to his usual profile, the account I followed.

They were for Healthygaga6969.

I put his phone back down and lay down flat, staring up at the ceiling.

That's why he already had me saved in his phone.

Jude and I had already spoken.

Jude knew what he was doing.

Jude always knew.

48

Victimhood OR womanhood?

They say that the perfect victim is dead.

A woman killed in a homicide, a deadly rape, trafficked or slaughtered by her male counterpart.

People mourn the tragedy; they say her life was taken too soon.

But if she lives?

There are certain *rules* society has put in place in order to still be a victim, rules that are impossible to obey.

Why is she dressing like that? She must've asked for it.

Why is she smiling? Can't have been that hard.

Why is she having sex? She's a slut.

Some people cannot fathom that a victim is a human being nonetheless. That having a life filled with the experiences of every human being can co-exist with being a *victim*.

They expect us to just be a shells of women, to remain afraid, tortured, sad, alone, confused, broken, modest, timid, voiceless. A picture of victimhood forever.

But what does a victim look like?

Sometimes a victim looks like the happiest, most confident, charismatic and switched-on person in the room. It's not that lack of trauma that made her that way, but rather the experience as a whole helped her find her way there.

Sometimes a victim fluctuates between all of the above because she is just a regular human, going through the motions of life, on her own independent journey that nobody can ever truly comment on, because they didn't witness what she had been through – and they never will.

What's worse is often, whether you are a victim of something or not, you're more likely to end up in similar patterns. It's human nature; people expect the perfect victim to also be the perfect human, without the mistakes, lessons and experiences that we all have from birth to death.

So fuck the perfect-victim narrative, because the perfect victim is dead.

49

Back in the palm of his hands

One thing about narcissists that is really quite remarkable is their will, fuelled by sheer delusion.

Nero texted me once more while I was eating my dinner one night. I had just finished a steak and as soon as I saw his name appear on my phone, I knew that the steak was not going to digest well.

He'd sent a photo. Him, his sister, Jefe, his nieces and nephews all sitting on the memorial bench I'd had made for his late mother.

Today is Mum's birthday. Regardless of everything that's going on, you were there for me when Mum died and I'll always love you for that. This bench is the most thoughtful thing anyone has ever done for this family. Thank you.

After the initial response of my nervous system flaring up, which I'd pretty much got used to by now since it had been six whole months since freedom day, I knew what Nero was doing.

The bottom line was, Nero knew me better than most people, at some points more than anyone. He knew what made me tick, how to get through to me, and he knew my heart – a heart that is filled with empathy for anyone who should need it.

But that was the Livia Nero knew. *His* Livia.

Not the Livia I am now.

The Livia who is confident.

The Livia who is fearless.

The Livia who surpassed all the expectations he'd put on me in every way.

Though naturally the text made me feel some kind of guilt, I'd learned that everything Nero made me feel initially is exactly what he intended. That was the old Livia responding, but the new Livia, she had the power to prevent him from controlling her emotions.

He couldn't get in my head.

I screenshotted the text and then ignored it.

I found a lot of comfort in being the girl he couldn't get through to. Being the girl who once was trapped in the palm of his hand, making that her whole entire world. Imagine how dull that was? Plunged into darkness, surrounded by the thousands of complex lines within his fingerprints, his DNA embedded into everything she knew and saw, until she bit into his hand hard, so hard that she almost lost her teeth. But she still made it out. She still saw that there was so much more to the world outside the palm of a man's hand.

Sometimes I could picture the disbelief on his face when I wouldn't answer him. I could hear the sound of his voice in fits of rage when I posted all those sun-kissed bikini photos in LA, the jealousy in his tone when I'd buy myself something new, how he'd scratch his head and wonder how I could afford it. His eyeballs red and bloodshot while he'd scroll on his phone at night, awake on the cocaine, checking my following lists and trying desperately to figure out who I was giving my love to now. Who was resting their head on that special part of my chest. How *I*, me, Livi could not just survive, but thrive without him. The confusion in the momentarily emotional part of his brain, fighting the feelings as the narcissistic part would take over and he'd convince himself that I wasn't actually thriving, I was suffering. That narcissistic will is so damn wilful.

That's why, at the end of the day, it's no use trying to carefully adjust your narrative online to 'seem' like you're happy – because a narcissist's very means of survival is convincing themselves that still, somehow, some way, you simply are not. Even if you were standing in front of the Burj Al Arab in Dubai with a cheque for a million pounds, the most money-obsessed narc will suddenly preach that money is the root of all evil, that wealth is meaningless and our greatest downfall as humans.

On the other hand, the *only* way to 'win', 'hurt' or 'overcome' your narc is to live in your fucking truth. To *actually* be free of any care of what they think.

Yes, they might delude themselves that you're not really coping without them at first, but trust me – they *know* when it's really curtains. They can *feel* when you have really let go. They know when you stop checking their social media or assessing how you will be perceived by them.

And nothing fucking kills a narcissist more than being locked out your head.

The stench of true growth genuinely melts their insides like a poisonous gas.

Truly doing that requires letting go of control, which is hard when you've just regained a little after being so hurt. You're terrified of being hurt again. That's normal, that's natural.

That's why I couldn't stop checking his page. Checking if there were signs, things I needed to protect myself from. Things I *needed* to know.

What does he do now?

Who is he with?

Where does he live?

What does he think?

We all do it.

I had a more public break-up and police case than the average person. All that meant was that I had to stop caring about what all those people thought about me, not just him.

I waited a long time for the police to give me any update on the case, and when they finally did, they told me it was going to be a long process because so much was out in the 'public domain', and the interview I'd done for the documentary's uncut footage had to be retrieved by the police because that now counted as evidence. Because of privacy policies, that meant there would need to be a court ruling for the tapes, and that meant there was going to be a lot of bureaucracy before he would be charged.

Nero took advantage of this and tried to trick the public numerous times. His story never stayed consistent – sometimes he'd say I hadn't gone to the police, other times he'd say that his charges were dropped, and once he even thanked the courts and police and jury, saying he'd won. That we'd already done the *whole* damn thing. I wasn't even in the country.

His lies never got him very far. Nobody seemed to care, the songs he'd released never got very many views, and whatever fans he had left, the number shrank more and more as the months went on. He had been truly blacklisted from the industry and nobody wanted to touch him. Each and every artist featured on *Jefe* dropped out and never returned.

After his manipulative text to me didn't give him the reaction he wanted, and after he'd spent enough time wallowing about the losses in his career, six months on, he finally decided it was time to fight back.

But was Nero going to play fair?

Never.

He wanted to make sure I suffered. He wanted to agonise me as effectively as possible. So, he did a countdown. A literal day-by-day countdown, promising to post dirt on me every day for five days.

What made it so impossible to cope was that I knew – and *he* knew – that I'd done nothing wrong. I had to accept that everything would be lies upon lies, and the scary part about that was that I didn't know how far he would take it. He was ruthless. He could *literally* say anything. The feeling of the unknown is what drove me back into the palms of his sordid hands.

I felt as though I was right back there. Five days spent in bed. Five days in his hands. I couldn't live. So I lived there instead.

Ruby would come into my bedroom at intervals and try to get me to eat but my stomach could not handle any kind of food at the best of times. I was a worry-stricken mess, catastrophising all kinds of scenarios as each day he posted on his Instagram Story which number day we were on now, followed by different 'evidence' to invalidate me as a victim and paint me as unhinged, a liar and simply insane. To top it off, he would painfully write things like, 'Day 4 tomorrow! So much more to come! Love you all.'

More? What is more?! I'd groan into my pillow.

'I never lose, Livia. Things were always going to go back to how they were,' I'd hear from a whisper in the corner of the room.

I felt so stupid to have believed I'd ever be able to defeat him. He was back in control of my emotions. His demons were with me all the way in LA.

Looking back now, the scariest part was the fact that, in those five days, Nero posted nothing of any weight AT ALL.

Nothing he posted had any relevance to him abusing me … The items he'd posted were some magnitude of nonsense. Irrelevant, pointless lies, clutching at straws to make me look crazy, posting our conversations where I'd called him an abuser and said that I hated him, the final call we had when I'd confronted him about Sabrina and he'd laughed at me (which I already sensed back then he was recording).

These things in fact further proved my story to be true. Most people commented that this was just him admitting to abusing me.

He insisted they meant I were sour, crazy, vengeful.

Honestly, though, why wouldn't I be? Who isn't crazy after being traumatised and tortured every day? Why shouldn't I be sour? Why mustn't I seek revenge?

But it didn't matter what my friends said in those five days to ground me, how many times Ruby stood at the edge of that bed, convincing me that nobody gave a *single fuck* what Nero had to say about anything anymore, how many times Jude consoled me over the phone from New York, how many times Cherry tried to help me see the reality that he could not harm me, that my evidence was simply so strong that it didn't matter what he would ever say anyway, I was simply terrified. That fear was something I hadn't shaken off yet.

A few days later, when I woke up to pee in the middle of the night, I briefly glanced at my phone. It was 4.22 a.m. and I had two notifications from Instagram.

'LYING BITCH,' one read.

'Ruined an innocent man's career, rot in hell,' said another.

With one eye open, I began to wake up from my sleep and ponder why I was randomly receiving these comments. The court date still hadn't come so there was nothing new or relevant to trigger his teeny leftover fanbase besides his blatant lies that, thus far, nobody was buying. I typed his name into Google and found that Nero was participating in a live stream on a large debate platform – talking about me.

There were seventy thousand people tuned in. It was trending as number two in the UK on Twitter.

As I watched, there were voices of outrage and disgust berating him as he stuttered over his words, backtracking and whimpering, trying to talk his way out of his lies.

'DID you ever hit your ex-girlfriend?' one man repeated over and over.

'There were physical times, b, b, but like, I didn't hit her, there were just physical altercations.'

'What about when you confessed on your Instagram

Story that you took part in "provoked abuse",' another man quoted him.

'Yeah ... yeah, abuse, like we were in an abusive relationship. It was both ways!'

His voice ran through me like cold metal in my veins. Every strand of hair stood on my body. *I felt sick.*

He hadn't changed. Not one bit.

I knew I should have switched it off, I knew I shouldn't have continued listening, but how could I? This entire live stream was about *me*.

The stream made things five hundred times worse for him and especially for his case.

He showed the world his true colours yet again. He was a laughing stock for the most part – there were just too many receipts people could pull up, and him trying to talk his way out of full-blown evidence was painful to watch.

How the hell did he think that this would be a good idea?

It had been six months. It didn't have to go this way. If he had just admitted it, taken accountability and gone into some form of rehab, experienced therapy, given money to a woman's foundation or apologised, just *something* to show that he was human, yes, people would have still hated him for being an abuser – but eventually people would start pointing at the fact that he'd said sorry and had got help.

'What more do you expect him to do?' his fans would say in order to co-sign and justify listening to his new music. He could have salvaged something, if anything. But instead, he just looked for ways to abuse me further and try to paint himself as the victim. It was genuinely embarrassing how far he had fallen from one of the greatest minds I'd ever witnessed to a self-loathing, self-deprecating, narcissistic louse whose biggest enemy was none other than himself.

Himself and his fucking demons.

Later that week, Ruby and I discussed it.

'You know,' I said, 'because I didn't react and this didn't affect me, or actually succeed in working against me in any way, he will have only one thing left to do to get back at me ... He'll have a baby just to spite me ... and God will give him a daughter, trust me.'

You can never have full control of *anything*. In attempting to do so, you will only further drive yourself, the only thing you can control, out of control.

I had to accept that it was time to stop fighting. It was over. It was time to let go and know that I'd done enough. All I was ever doing by staying engaged was giving him that power. His supply. His heroin.

I had to be happy for me and not for anyone else, and that meant living in my truth without a care or worry about what that may look like to others. *That's true liberation.*

A few days later, I received a message on Twitter from a woman named Catherine Dubinski. She was an author and some kind of whistleblower: a legend going up against the music industry regarding the injustices women have faced within it. She was a survivor herself, having been abused as the first female A&R at a huge label in her youth.

'We're taking down the record label – I can get you a fuck ton of money,' she said to me on the phone in her thick Bronx accent.

She was so fiery. Driven and ruthless, Catherine became another mirror for me to look in for inspiration. She was like

Cherry and me, but even further down the timeline since her abuse.

She explained to me how there are some lawyers who she wanted to connect me with, one being a *senator* in California. My jaw was on the floor.

'The record label needs to pay for what they've done to so many women. We're gonna help you and we're gonna win,' she continued.

'What do you mean? Like . . . sue them?' I asked.

'No, they would never let it go to trial, but you'll be paid. They will have to settle.' There was a pause. 'You'll get a lot of money, Livia, millions. I'm talking millions. We're gonna go for four million dollars.'

What the fuck am I gonna do with four million dollars? Isn't that like three-something million pounds?

I couldn't believe that this woman had found me. All these alignments in the universe were crazy. The knock-on effect of my story, a destiny that was just waiting to unravel – none of this would have happened if I hadn't been through this . . . no, none of this would've happened if I hadn't left.

Another time that we talked, I asked her all about her book. The idea of having gone through that much pain, only to become such a force to be reckoned with, fascinated me. I was so drawn to the idea of getting everything I'd been through written on the page, touching any person who reads it. Being timeless.

'I've wanted to write books for as long as I can remember,' I told her. 'I used to ask my cousin to sit next to me and type my stories on the computer before I could type them myself.' I laughed.

'Don't wait, just do it. Write three pages a day, honey, front and back – and before you know it, you'll have a book,' she responded.

I couldn't wait to get on the phone to Jude that night. Though we didn't speak every day anymore, we didn't need to. Life had returned somewhat back to normal and he was busy working in New York, managing artists and A&R'ing albums. I hadn't seen him since he came out to LA to see me.

'What's this senator's name? . . . James, you said? Okay, and why is he affiliated with these lawyers? Let's see . . .' Jude said, skimming Google and doing his typical sceptical background research.

'I think I want to write, Jude . . . like a book,' I said.

'And how much did you say they wanted to give you?' Jude asked.

'I don't know . . . She said millions, like four million or something. But did you hear what I said?'

'Yeah, yeah, I'm listening. Write about what?' he replied.

'My story, I think . . . I think this whole generation of women lack protection, and I could make it really knowledge-able but also like, super raw.'

'No, no, no, you can't just write a book like that, Livia. It's not that easy,' he sighed.

'Do you know I'm actually really good at writing? It's always been my thin—'

'I just think you need to be more realistic in your long-term plans, Livia. Like, what do you actually want to do?'

'I want to write, that's what I'm telling you!' I exclaimed.

'You should start a podcast if you really want to help women.

You could get mad sponsorships, you know. You're so inspiring when you talk. I'll help you set it up and I can manage you.'

'Yeah, I guess that could be cool . . . Thanks.'

'I mean, you don't have to. I'm just trying to help you, you know that's all I'm ever trying to do,' he said, sounding a little upset.

'No, no, sorry. That would be amazing. Yeah, thank you, I appreciate it. I appreciate you, of course.'

I hadn't found the right moment to confront Jude about the Healthygaga6969 account. The morning after I'd discovered it, we'd got up really early to go to the interview, which was totally exhausting, draining and emotionally taxing, and the day after that he had to fly back to New York.

I'd thought about it a lot. I'd accepted that regardless of how fucked up it was, one thing I couldn't ever take away from Jude was the fact that he'd empowered me. In my darkest time, when I didn't have a spine nor any direction towards justice, he helped me build one.

It was almost as if to beat a villain as awful and cruel as Nero, I needed Jude.

He understood Nero; he understood manipulation, gaslighting. He understood evil because I'm sure he recognised that same evil within himself.

It was such a beautifully twisted fate. The darkness that burned me was the same darkness to help raise me from its ashes.

But was I about to end up back in those ashes?

Hell no.

Even though there were incredibly good things Jude had done for me, he had also been calculated and had lied to me.

He had completely broken my trust during the most vulnerable time of my entire life. The two can co-exist, and it was time to start seeing the red flags, not ignoring them.

'Do me a favour Jude, yeah?'

'Yeah?'

'Don't tell me what the fuck to do.'

50

Nostalgia

Towards the end of summer, I decided it was finally time to come home. I moved in with Juno in London, while Ruby decided to stay out in LA a little longer with some friends because she could work remotely from her laptop. She just couldn't understand why I'd want to leave the eternal sunshine behind. Shay headed over to the East Coast for some business for a few weeks before returning to the UK.

There were parts of returning that simply felt beautiful. Like home. There are no other words to describe it but that feeling of home. That emotion of home. That tenderness and nostalgia wrapped in a warm blanket of memories and familiarity.

I missed the rain, the cold air hitting the back of my throat when I took a deep inhale. It felt like the hit of a menthol cigarette after the smothering LA humidity. The sound of the trees as the branches smacked the big red double-decker buses. The groups of young boys in Nike Tech tracksuits gathered outside chicken shops, even just the architecture of London's Edwardian houses. I appreciated the history and the stories of the buildings in the UK. LA was just so *different*. So new.

Of course, there were the downsides. My CPTSD was yet to face the place it was born: the motherland of my trauma.

I remember the first time going to my bank in Tottenham Court Road. I stood in line as my eyes wandered over to the red padded benches in the corner. This was the bank Nero and I came to, this very branch. I could see our bodies there like a distant mirage, in matching grey tracksuits, our hoods up as I lay with my head in his lap, while he recorded a song about me into my phone camera, laughing. I looked at those benches and I thought, *I never thought that I'd be right here two years later, alone, but good*. I was scared to death but there was never any reason to worry, because here I was, so fucking good.

As I walked out onto Oxford Street, I felt swamped by this one illusion: the possibility that I'd see Nero. I knew exactly which routes we used to walk down.

Then, in the distance, I could have sworn that I saw him, walking towards me. He was wearing all black, in his cap, with sunglasses on and the dog on a leash. Jefe had got so big.

My stomach turned as a passing taxi honked its horn loud enough to startle me out of my delirious state. I jumped in an Uber and headed to Juno's.

I often wondered what would become of me if I saw Nero; I feared it terribly. I had so many different scenarios playing out in my head. Him finding me and hurting me, simply because he was too coked up and his demons got the better of him. Or maybe he'd just kill me.

Whenever I went out, people still approached me about the situation. Girls sharing their stories, asking for advice, thanking me. Men approaching me all the time, mid-drunk cigarette on a night out, saying, 'Oh, I met your ex once by the way', before proceeding to tell me about some insignificant encounter. Other people would just whisper as I walked past, tapping their friends to point out that I was here, back in London. That I was home.

In and among crowds, I'd constantly see him, haunting me. All it took was the same style of hat, build of shoulders, brand of shoes, a Supreme hoodie or black sunglasses indoors. For the moment in between my eyes registering the similarity and me realising it wasn't him, my heart would sink 35,841 feet, down to the lowest part of the ocean.

I was paranoid. Naturally. This city was tainted by our relationship with him. Whenever I imagined myself through his eyes *now*, after all that had happened . . . I couldn't even stomach the emotions he must feel towards me.

I knew he would blame me for his own actions. Going from being the biggest prodigy London had to offer, being offered signings from superstars, to nothing. To go from travelling the world on tour to only performing once since, at some small event in *Russia*. To go from modelling for designer brands, being featured on billboards, to dressing like a ten-year-old wannabe SoundCloud rockstar. No class, no style, no relevance, culture or presence.

One evening back in the city, I was at private fashion party at a venue in west London. I was wearing a long blonde braid in my hair and dancing with Juno as she twirled it in the middle of the dance floor. Then from the corner of my eye, I spotted Sabrina.

And much as I wanted to avoid her, there she was. The party was small and filled with mutuals. Everyone was secretly nervous about the vibe between her and me. Everyone knew.

I walked onto the rooftop garden to find Sabrina and Juno having a cigarette together with a few other people scattered around. Juno quickly shifted up and invited me to sit between them.

'Livia, how have you been?' Sabrina asked, a genuine and friendly look on her face.

It was like everyone only continued their conversations just to *not* make it any more awkward. You could have cut the tension with a knife.

Minutes turned into almost an hour. Everyone had left while Sabrina and I sat next to each other at the garden table, unbinding our hearts. She was so easy to talk to. The more we spoke, the more I realised she really wasn't that different from me. She had come from a Muslim family just like mine. She had so much love and adoration for what I'd done. I could see in her overcompensation of energy towards me that each bit of her essence oozed guilt. As much as I wanted to, I simply couldn't dislike her. There was just no reason. Nero, he was in the past. As two individual human beings, we were super compatible. Besides, she was just eighteen when that happened and you know what, I probably did some really stupid shit when I was eighteen too. It was just wrong to blame *her*.

We filled up our cups with more wine. It was a beautiful night, the dark sky filled with stars, matched by the beautiful moment of two women coming together after a man had turned us against one another.

'Isn't it crazy that if it wasn't for Jude, we wouldn't have ever heard each other's truths?' I said, my eyes flushed with a drunken glaze.

'Honestly, Livia, I'm so glad we met. You are actually so special, like I can't believe anyone would ever hurt you. I fucking hate that stupid—'

'Ohhh, fuck him! Fuck him! He's so irrelevant,' I said, lighting a cigarette.

'Oh wow, I know . . . *But what happened to him?*' There was a pause and then we both burst out laughing.

And then, I don't know how or why, but we were kissing. It sort of just happened. As we pulled away, we giggled more and then I rested my head on her shoulder.

'Life is crazy,' I said softly, looking up at the sky above us, my blurry vision giving a vignette effect to my sight.

'Shall we take another shot?!' She jumped up, pulling me up with her.

51

Over my dead body

Four months later it was December, and London hadn't seen snowfall like it did that year in a long time. The strong gusts of wind blew furious inches of snow in all directions as it danced around violently in the sky before settling firmly onto the ground.

I'd been in London for just a few months but had already started to get used to being home again. Like always, time was a healer.

I remember exactly what I was doing when I received the text.

Juno was unpacking groceries in front of me as I pulled out my phone. When I saw a message from an unknown number, my brain quickly scanned the important words that stood out to me . . .

As I saw Nero's name, my entire body froze. My eyes assessed the other words, including 'Jefe', and 'dead'.

'. . . Sorry to be the bearer of bad news, Nero asked that I pass on this message,' the message ended with.

My sobs were loud. I could feel Juno wrapping her arms around me but the warmth of her hug couldn't be felt; my entire body felt numb as I tried to catch my breath, hyperventilating between my cries.

Between each sob I saw his little body, imagining his eyes closed, forever.

'*It can't be true, it can't be true, it can't be true,*' I kept repeating over and over as the sour taste in my mouth worsened with each word. My mind kept repeating back, *It is true, it is true, it is true.*

I sat down and shut my eyes tight because as long as I could see, I knew I was still in this reality, the reality where Jefe was dead.

I took a deep breath and picked the phone back up. Juno sat in the chair across from me, rubbing my knee.

I called the number. My voice was broken as I cried down the speaker, 'Hello?!'

'Hello,' Nero cried back, sniffing. He sounded just as devastated, like a child: a little boy.

'How did this happen?' I responded. I didn't even care that Nero and I were on the phone, I didn't even acknowledge it. I was in complete shock, acting on pure emotion. It was all just pouring out of me.

'I need answers, Nero. Please! How?'

'He developed IVDD,' he replied. 'It's like a dog sickness. He got critical really quickly and . . . we, we're still getting to the bottom of it. It doesn't make any sense. I can't believe it, my best friend. I'm not okay, Livi. I can't cope without him . . .'

I felt a wave of numbness wash over me.

I realised that I'd been grieving Jefe for two years and Nero had shown no remorse that entire time. I thought I'd see him again one day, and knowing that he was safe and healthy was all that gave me peace. Now, because of Nero, I never even got the chance to say goodbye.

'Thank you for telling me,' I said, and hung up.

I was thankful. Had I found out on social media, it would've broken me even worse than it broke me in that moment. But it didn't matter how broken I felt, I didn't let Nero's emotion pull me back in.

I asked Juno for some space as I watched through the thousands of videos I had of Jefe. Every single video transported me back. I cried silently, holding my phone, shaking my head. It took me right back to those days again, being so depressed after the abortion and Jefe filling that hole, feeling so lost every day, so alone and forgotten while Jefe and his emotional intelligence and clinginess to me from the day he was born was all I had. Nothing can quite describe what that dog meant to me. In the darkest times of my life, I had a companion. I was lucky enough to have him there with me. I wouldn't have made it without him.

Nero called me back moments later. He asked if I wanted to bury him together that Sunday, and I agreed.

'I'll be driven there and back, Nero,' I said. 'Somebody will come with me, and I don't want to see any of your people.'

'You can bring whoever you want, Livia, but they can wait in the car and let us bury him together, or what's the point? We are his parents, it's our dog.'

I paused for a second. Of course, I didn't trust him – he could do anything. Different scenarios played out in my head in a quick flash: a knife being removed from his pocket, him recording me, just imagining looking into those big black eyes again . . .

But I had to honour Jefe. I loved him so much; I'd do anything to feel close to him again. He was a baby we brought into this crazy world, his little furry and delicate body shaking in the car as we drove home that very first time, the fast pace of his tiny anxious heart as I comforted him against my chest with the slow pace of my big, broken heart.

'They can wait somewhere that they can *see* us from the car,' I replied eventually.

'Okay, Livi. I'm not going to do anything. This is about Jefe, our son,' he said, his voice cracking.

Sunday was just three days away. Shay drove with Juno in the passenger seat, Ruby with her arm around me in the back. I was grateful all my friends were in London for Christmas.

'We'll be watching the entire time,' Shay told me as Ruby kissed my cheek. I got out of the car, my feet crunching leaves as I headed down the path in the animal cemetery.

It was cold, wet and gloomy. I could see two men in raincoats further down the path and the grass was covered by a blanket of snowfall. I zipped up my puffer jacket further as I approached them, keeping my hands in the pockets of my baggy tracksuit bottoms for warmth.

Nero faced away from me, smoking a cigarette as the stark air cut through the smoke he blew out his mouth. Mika hugged him goodbye as he spotted me and headed in the opposite direction.

I was just a few steps away now.

I felt my pulse racing.

'Nero,' I said as I stood still behind him.

He paused for effect. Nothing had changed – he was still as dramatic as humanly possible. He turned around and faced me. My eyes felt sore as soon as they began looking at him, like the muscles behind my sockets weren't strong enough to bear eye contact with him. I blinked as I looked away, but he continued staring at me – he had hurt bleeding from his face.

He chucked his cigarette to the side. 'Come on, we're late,' he said as he headed further down the path.

My heart beat faster as I trailed behind him, completely losing sight of the car park. We kept walking without saying a word for seven minutes. I wanted to say something, anything, but I was too overwhelmed by everything happening around me.

We arrived at a small hole dug by a tree. There was little wicker casket, with two bits of ribbon tied on either side.

I broke down as soon as my heart could fathom how small the coffin was.

The cemetery worker lowered the coffin into the hole and left us with two shovels.

'I'll leave you guys to say any last words and finish the burial. We're closed now but you can exit through the way you came,' he said.

It gets dark quickly in winter – though it was only 6 p.m., there were some lamp posts decorating the yards of the crematorium, dimly lighting the snow and tombstones in an orange hue.

I didn't feel scared of Nero. I didn't feel much at all besides sadness and a numbness, both emotions somehow supporting each other.

I watched him sob into his hands, on his knees in the mud, as I stood idly by.

I felt indifferent.

'I don't know what to say, Livi. You can go.' He signalled me forward as he got up.

I took a step closer till I was beside Nero, and looked down into the grave.

'Thank you, Jefe. Thank you for being a part of my life. Thank you for choosing me to be your mummy that day you sat in my lap. Thank you so much for existing in my life. I miss you so, so much. What a wonderful thing it was to love a dog like you.'

I wiped my tears as I saw Nero lifting the shovel from the corner of my blurry eye. He handed it to me and grabbed the other. Our wet eyes locked once more.

'Livia ...'

Hearing him say my name sent shivers down my entire body. It made seeing him in the flesh far too real.

'... was it worth it?'

He looked me dead in the eye, his tears suddenly dried up, his expression withdrawn.

'What ...?' I whispered, confused.

He dropped his shovel and lunged towards me, grabbing both sides of my face with his cold hands.

'WAS IT WORTH LEAVING US?' he shouted, shaking my head as I scrunched up my eyes.

I tried to push him off me but he held on to my head

tighter. His fingers gripped my hair as he pulled my face up close until I was nose to nose with him.

'Was it worth leaving me!?!' He breathed into my face.

'Get the fuck off me,' I yelled, 'Get off!'

I lost balance fighting him off and fell backwards onto the dirt and snow. I grunted hard as I hit the ground.

Nero lifted the spade, pointed the end in my direction, right in that special place on my chest. 'You're the one who belongs in that grave, Livi,' he shouted down at me in that raspy London accent.

I looked at him.

At his big bulgy eyes.

At his familiar grimace that grew each time he saw me below him.

At his noticeably excited breathing.

At the drool that dripped from corners of his mouth while he prepared to feast.

At the demons creeping out around him.

I looked at him and took it all in.

I looked at Nero, the man I loved.

I looked at Nero, the man who abused me.

I looked at a narcissist, one who I defeated.

And in one swift movement, I grabbed the spade, pulling myself onto my feet. I positioned my right foot slightly in front of my left, closed my fist, and swung it back. I punched him with all my might *bang* in the middle of his face.

52

Love, love, love

Rain was my favourite weather, especially the mist creeping on your window as the world is cleansed by the white noise of rainfall. Whenever it rained, it felt like the world was on pause. It romanticised any bad day, not necessarily making it good, but making it beautiful.

The rain was aggressive the morning I heard the verdict from the police. Each large drop splattered off the ground and then bounced right back into the air. I held an umbrella over my head, shielding me as I scurried out of my car and towards my house. The air smelled so crisp and fresh when it rained: a perk of living in the countryside. Just before I stepped through my front door, I let my umbrella drop for a moment. I felt the rain trickle down my scalp and took a deep breath in and held it for a few seconds, before exhaling and stepping inside.

I felt the loving arms of an embrace around me, the arms in which I felt most safe – like, actually safe, not the type of safe you think might get taken away from you at any moment, so you hold on extra hard just to savour it a bit longer. The type of safe that is so sure, so secure, so forever.

'How do you feel then?' He looked down to me, smiling his perfect smile.

Just like that, the one day that had loomed over my head for years was over. It was done. I couldn't tell you the number of nights I spent lying awake at night, imagining how I'd react to whether or not the police would take Nero to trial, replaying my responses I'd given on the stand, until eventually I dreaded the very thought of it, finding it a burden and a cloud hanging over me, preventing me from fully moving on with my life, and, most importantly, my love.

'I'm relieved, babe, I couldn't think of anything worse than waiting another two-odd years for trial to have to go to see him in court one day and relive it all over again. I've had enough, my body has had enough, that isn't my story anymore. The chapter is closed, the karmic contract ended . . .' I nestled my head back into his chest as he hugged me tighter. I felt his gentle lips kiss my still slightly damp forehead.

The police had decided not to charge Nero, after a three-year investigation.

I didn't actually expect much else. Sure, at some points I felt like they would have to consider the irrefutable amounts of evidence against him, but the justice system does not support women. With three in four women never seeing criminal justice against their abuser, the system is a fucking mess.

Additionally to that, Nero moved out of the country: he fled and moved to Germany, probably half to avoid prison, and half because the United Kingdom just could not forgive him – providing grounds for no trial against him.

I had already got my justice though. I got my justice the day I spoke out. The day I claimed back my identity, that was the day I said no. I created a boundary and put an end to the cycle. I spoke out and took my power right back out of the treasure chest he kept it locked in, deep inside his rotten heart.

And nothing, nothing matters more to a narcissist than keeping their victims down, controlled, hooked and silenced. Owned by them.

Additionally, nothing mattered more to Nero than his image, his power and his fame. He lost everything in ways I don't think anyone could have imagined, and even when I thought he had finally lost it all, he lost any chance of ever getting it back.

Nero had become nothing but a desperate, empty little troll who was on his knees on a street corner, begging to be acknowledged while the whole world passed him by without noticing that he even existed.

He let out cries for attention, throwing tantrums online every now and then, harassing me, obsessively stalking me, putting all that extra time he'd gained into attempting to discredit me and my abuse. But no one would listen. No one cared. It just would not work.

He lived in his delusions, because there is never any other place a narcissist can exist: anywhere else is too painful, too real, too much of a reflection they cannot bear to look up and see the sight of. He lived in his delusions because in the real world, Nero didn't exist anymore. So, he spent years fighting his shadow, committed to nothing but making sure the last words on his deathbed were that none of it was his fault, that I was a liar, that he deserved the world.

That fact didn't necessarily give me peace. Sometimes I pitied him, other times I couldn't care less. The more I healed, the more I couldn't feel much else for him. He was like a bad smell that simply wouldn't go away. A mistake, a lesson, an important part of everything I love about myself today: not him, but how I chose to overcome him, and how I'd become a woman who'd never let that happen to her again.

So when the police didn't decide to take him to trial, sure I thought it was pathetic, but the police cannot tell me whether or not I deserve justice. Nobody can. Nobody can tell me what I saw, what I felt. What my body witnessed, and whether or not I deserve justice for it.

Later that night, my body thanked me as I stretched my back out on my bed. I let out the biggest groan, peeking over at him, realizing just how quickly and easily he'd always fallen asleep. There were some things about my life I noticed that I don't think people do until they go through the types of loss that I have, like the quiet in the home at night, not physically but mentally, no risk lingering around, no anticipation, just peace, quiet, stillness.

Like the softness of my bedsheets as they caress my chin, while my neck releases what feel like ancient tensions more and more each time.

Feeling snug, feeling safety, feeling free of any burden.

Like the priceless value of peace of mind, noticing how quickly I can fall asleep now, how I can just drift off while the sound of silence lulls me to sleep.

I had apologised to my body. As I would rub it with oils and lotion, as I'd rub my feet together at night, I thanked my body for working so hard to heal me.

I had slowly felt the beauty of healing creep into my life, and as she did, she showed me a life to live I never even knew existed before, one where I can't help but appreciate each and every fucking beautiful thing.

I opened my laptop and placed it into my lap, staring at the document in front of me. By now, I'd thought for years how I would end my book, how I'd give it the ending it deserves. It felt impossible because the story is never really over.

Healing from abuse is like waves in an ocean; no two are the same shape or size, and the magnitude of how big or small the waves are changes constantly. They never stop.

The ocean can drown you, or it can save you, so you eventually learn how to ride the waves.

But most of all you become the ocean.

I think there's a superpower inside survivors of abuse. Not one that arrives because they were abused, but one that was always there . . .

It's what attracts the narcissist in the first place. They can sniff it on us; they take it from us.

But once you take that power back, *you become the ocean. You can drown people, or you can save them.*

It takes losing every single fucking part of you, killing every part that mourns those parts, and rebirthing yourself with every new piece of courage and knowledge to realise just how grateful you were to lose it all.

I finally knew it. I finally knew how to end my book. I had to write myself a letter, a letter to Livia who was being abused. The girl who fought for justice. The Livia who wanted to find nothing but love.

Love, love, love.

And she finally did.

She fell in love with herself.

Dear Livia,

I first want to express to you how important it is for you to understand that there was never anything wrong with you. That heart of yours is fucking magnificent. You were never wrong to love how you did, with such bravery and will. Your love is something that people would be lucky to experience in this lifetime. The only thing you did wrong was to not give any of that to yourself.

I know you thought that you could love someone into loving you, but my dear, please understand that we cannot allow anyone to fill our cups – we must meet our soulmates with our cups already full, because otherwise, at any point, they could snatch that cup back and drink it and then you're far from full.

The patience, the protection, the endurance, the hope, tenderness, grace and forgiveness you gave him is just proof that you are capable of giving that same compassion to yourself.

So it's time, it's time to forgive yourself and welcome yourself back home. Hug yourself and kiss your scars. It's okay that you loved him even though he hurt you. That's just a reflection of how much good you have inside of you, and now you deserve to be the one who reaps the benefits of that goodness. You must use those magical powers of yours to direct that love right back into its source and watch it blossom and grow you into who you are meant to be. You must protect yourself by falling in love with the peace that comes from boundaries; with each you assert you will heal the broken one from before. You must discipline yourself to break toxic habits and develop new patterns that align better with that gentle heart of yours.

You don't need to try and survive in a cold world. You can choose to opt out of it.

You can create a world around you built only for people who are here to love and grow you.

You don't need to fight anymore. You can put the weapons down and just breathe. This life is whatever we choose to make it. Once you start doing the things you want to do, the things that fill you with joy and give you peace, you will look around and realise that you're now living a life of joy and peace.

It's up to you. Nobody else has the power to transform your life the way you do. It just begins with a thought, then a feeling, and then you're here, showing up for yourself and your dreams.

I truly believe that there is a superpower deep within every human who is taken advantage of by a narcissist. There's a light inside you that the demons are attracted to, and once you learn to shelter that light from them, you will only then see just how wonderful life is as a person filled with a beam as bright as yours.

You are the love of your own life, and how lucky you are to have a love like yours.

Acknowledgements

The journey to writing this book was anything but an easy one and there's a group of very special people who made it possible with their unwavering belief and support in me along the way. I actually began writing as young as I can remember, sat at my grandmother's house on her desktop with my older cousin next to me, pushing the keys to type in the stories I wanted to tell, then as soon as I learned to type myself, I would come to write many stories throughout my childhood. I wouldn't say I lost my spark for creativity in my late teens but I definitely had other, less purposeful, things that had taken my attention, and only years later, in my darkest moments when there was nothing left to do but heal, I felt there was nothing left to do but write. The inspiration first re-sparked in me when I met one of the most powerful women on this planet, Dorothy Carvello, an author and activist herself. She was the first person to tell me to just 'get writing, don't hold anything back' and I thank you for that simple advice that echoed through my mind each time I let this story become more and more vulnerable. Gratitude to Rudy Williams, my best friend and rock who sometimes was the only thing left for me to believe in in this world, thank you for keeping my faith intact. Many thanks to Mireille C. Harper for being the first person to make me realise the power in my writing and making sure this book gets out there. I was lucky enough to be connected to or what feels more like destined to meet the best agent, Oscar Janson-Smith, and to my beloved publisher and now sister for life, Christina Demosthenous. Christina, writing this book would not have been half the experience it has been without you, you're the most insanely intelligent, creative and empowering person with the aura of a real-life angel. You're understanding and deep and read between the lines other people simply cannot, quite literally just such a beautiful soul I don't know how I could have ever gone through this entire whirlwind of a journey without you; from the first communication I knew it was meant to be! Thank you for all your hours of dedication to this book and the message behind it. A special thank you to my love, Max Ross, for being the first person besides my publisher to read this book front to back even though I know it wasn't easy for you; you met me in a new way that night you finished and I love very much for it.

And lastly, to every woman, man, survivors alike reading this book, I hope you feel a warm hug and a deep understanding throughout; I hope you find the much-needed affirmation to leave, to let go, to heal; I hope you never forget the patterns and the truths this book teaches, and I want you to know you are seen and felt in every way. Thank you for picking this book up today; I know you were meant to.

Bringing a book from manuscript to what you are reading is a team effort.

Renegade Books would like to thank everyone who helped to publish *Loving with Demons* in the UK.

Editorial
Christina Demosthenous
Eleanor Gaffney

Contracts
Megan Phillips
Bryony Hall
Amy Patrick
Anne Goddard

Sales
Caitriona Row
Dominic Smith
Frances Doyle
Hannah Methuen
Lucy Hine
Toluwalope Ayo-Ajala

Design
Ella Garrett

Production
Narges Nojoumi

Publicity
Becky Hunter

Marketing
Emily Moran

Operations
Kellie Barnfield
Millie Gibson
Sameera Patel
Sanjeev Braich

Finance
Andrew Smith
Ellie Barry

Proofreader
David Bamford